DESIGN AND DETERMINATION

For their love, support and encouragement

Edgar Montague Little
1912-1992

and

Christopher John Little
1936-2001

Design and Determination

The Role of Information Technology in Redressing
Regional Inequities in the Development Process

STEPHEN E. LITTLE
Open University Business School, UK

ASHGATE

Published by
Ashgate Publishing Limited
Gower House
Croft Road
Aldershot
Hants GU11 3HR
England

Ashgate Publishing Company
Suite 420
101 Cherry Street
Burlington, VT 05401-4405
USA

Ashgate website: http://www.ashgate.com

British Library Cataloguing in Publication Data
Little, Stephen E., 1948-
    Design and determination : the role of information
    technology in redressing regional inequities in the
    development process. - (Voices in development management)
    1. Digital divide 2. Information technology - Economic
    aspects 3. Information technology - Government policy
    4. Globalization
    I. Title
    303.4'833

Library of Congress Cataloging-in-Publication Data
Little, Stephen E., 1948-
    Design and determination : the role of information technology in redressing regional
    inequities in the development process / Stephen E. Little.
        p. cm. -- (Voices in development management)
    Includes bibliographical references.
    ISBN 0-7546-1099-3
        1. Information technology--Economic aspects. 2. Information technology--Social aspects.
    3. Globalization--Economic aspects. 4. Regional economic disparities. 5. Community
    development. 6. Regional planning. I. Title: Role of information technology in redressing
    regional inequities in the development process. II. Title. III. University of North London
    voices in development management.

HC79.I55L58 2004
307.1'4--dc22

                                                                                2004046333

ISBN 0 7546 1099 3

Printed in Great Britain by Antony Rowe Ltd, Chippenham, Wiltshire

Contents

Authors and Affiliations

Dr Stephen Little is Head of the Centre for Innovation, Knowledge and Enterprise in the Open University Business School, Milton Keynes, U.K.

From 1999 to 2004 he chaired *Managing Knowledge*, an MBA elective delivered to students across the European Union and Central and Eastern Europe and by OUBS partners in Africa and Asia. Before joining the Open University Business School (OUBS) in 1999 he held posts at several British and Australian universities.

He left architectural practice in 1981 to pursue a PhD on the organisational impact of computer-aided design at the Department of Design Research, Royal College of Art, London and returned to the U.K. in 1996 following eleven years teaching and researching information systems in Australia, based at Griffith University, Brisbane, and the University of Wollongong, NSW. He has also held visiting appointments in Australia, Europe, North America and Asia.

Dr Perry Morrison is a management and I.T. consultant and Director of Morrison Associates Pty Ltd, Darwin, Australia.

Recent consultancies include projects for Centrelink, an Australian Federal Government Department providing income support and welfare services, the implementation of digital archives in ten remote communities for the Local Government Association of the Northern Territory and the evaluation of a service delivery program to three remote communities in the Northern Territory for the Darwin Community Legal Service.

He has held academic appointments with the Centre for Social Research, Northern Territory University, Darwin, Australia, the National University of Singapore, the Department of Mathematics, Statistics and Computer Science, University of New England, Armidale, NSW, and the School of Computing and Information Studies, Griffith University, Brisbane.

Dr Melih Kirlidog is an assistant professor in the Department of Computer Engineering at Marmara University, Turkey.

He holds a BSc from Middle East Technical University, Turkey, and an MBA and PhD from the University of Wollongong, Australia. He has worked as an ICT analyst and consultant for over twenty years both in Turkey and Australia. His current research interests include Decision Support Systems, intercultural ICT development and implementation, ICT in developing countries, and community informatics.

Acknowledgements

This book is concerned with new forms of adjacency and their implications for the determination of design and development. It draws on a range of research conducted across several decades and several continents with colleagues and friends. It is therefore necessary to acknowledge the complex set of networks which have supported and contributed to the ideas set out in it.

The first acknowledgement is to Perry Morrison and Melih Kirlidog, colleagues from my time in Australia, who have contributed directly to this book from the Australian Northern Territory and Turkey respectively.

My colleagues and students at the Open University (the latter spread over several continents) and from Manchester Metropolitan University in the U.K. and Wollongong and Griffith Universities in Australia will recognise many of the concerns addressed in this book. Other valuable connections date back to the Royal College of Art, London in the 1980s and Aston University in the 1960s and 1970s.

A wider set of colleagues have contributed through a range of more formal networks: the Odyssey Group of organisation researchers since the late 1990s, the Asia Pacific Researchers in Organisation Studies since the 1980s and the Design Research Society since the 1970s.

Details and links for these networks can be found at

www.design-and-determination.com

Over this period I have been engaged in research and practice dependent on the hospitality and contributions of communities from Moor Park in North East England via Musgrave Park, South Brisbane and the East End of Glasgow to Alexandra Park and Moss Side District Centre in Manchester.

More immediately the series editor, Margaret Grieco has maintained the determination needed to get the book from me. Ashgate, as publishers, have shown both determination and patience.

Four generations of my extended and blended family have tolerated various forms of absence due to work on this book.

None of the above share responsibility for the use made of their advice and input.

Stephen Little
Manchester

PART I

DESIGN AND
DEVELOPMENT:
THE WORLDS WE LIVE IN

Chapter 1

Design and Determination: Overcoming Exclusion in an Emergent Global System

Exclusion and Determination: The Need for a Direct Engagement with Design

The relationship between new information technologies, globalisation and social exclusion has become a focus for discussion amongst the major social theorists of the contemporary period (Castells, 1996, 1997, 2000; Giddens, 1999, Ohmae, 1995). Most take the shape of the technology and its social organisation within a neo-liberal economic framework as unproblematic.[1] Concern is expressed about the distributive spread of the technology and the level of access of low income groups and areas. This is typically discussed under the heading of the Digital Divide, for example the World Economic Forum's Digital Divide Initiative is aimed at international projects, while the U.S. Department of Commerce's National Telecommunications Information Agency (NTIA) coordinates information on federal government initiatives. The U.S. IT industry has sponsored the Digital Divide Network[2] to address issues of access both domestically and internationally.

The "big design" of high technology systems determines the audience and the terms of access to a global discourse. The developed economies dominate the direction of development in these technologies. However, within the new connectivities and adjacencies delivered by the same technologies, small, collective, distributed design is providing a voice from those left outside the formal hierarchy of distribution. High technology – in a literal sense in the case of satellite based communication – is providing the last crucial link in connectivity. Global access is provided by a technology originally associated with top-down surveillance and the Cold War military history of the space race and satellite development. The wired world can now be joined to the unwired world in a way which removes the significance of spatial separation, through access to the information infrastructure critical to the functioning of the emerging global economy.

This book provides examples of the use of big technology by and for those assumed to be the objects of an electronic panopticon (Foucault, 1979; Sewell and Wilkinson, 1992). It examines how "small design" has in some cases reversed that panopticon.

The digital divide has become a recognised issue of development precisely because it is bridgeable, indeed some observers claim that the appropriation of technology through imaginative improvisation by excluded players has already reduced the impact of any divide.

Issues of development policy have become aligned with issues of exclusion from the infrastructure necessary to development. However, there are issues of the design of technology and the development of a design perspective which interact with the known contours of social organisation that have fallen through the bottom of this debate.

In contrast, this book deals directly with the social nature of design and the implications for the social design of new information technology. It is particularly concerned with ensuring that both form and content of the technology is appropriate for productive material (Harasim, 1993; Lamberton, 1995) and cultural use (Little, Holmes and Grieco, 2001) in low income neighbourhoods and regions. It draws together the results of primary international research into current and prospective developments in information and communication technologies and their impacts on the continuing process of globalisation. It moves beyond the binarism which separates the design of technology from the conditions and context of its use. The over-determination of ICT within a framework of Western or northern design is directly addressed. The materials collected together in this work are the product of joint research with colleagues in both the developing and developed world: Britain and Australia, Ghana and South Africa – these are the locations for a journey into a pathway of alternative technology design.

This book is concerned with the role of information and communication technologies (ICTs) in globalisation and the global and local implications of the development inequities arising from this process. Globalisation, in the sense of the integration of production and consumption into an extensive world economy, has increased the significance of intellectual capital leveraged by information and communication technology. Historically the bulk of this intellectual capital has been located outside the developing countries. The distinction between products and services has been blurred by new forms of locational and functional differentiation which operate across a globalised network· of invention, innovation and implementation. In the closing decades of the twentieth century this blurring was evidenced by the shift in focus of companies such as IBM from capital equipment manufacturers to an information service and support provider (Delamarter, 1988; Klingbiel, 2002). This transformation continues and is richly characterised by Dicken (1998, 2003). It will be discussed in the next chapter.

A number of authors (Perrow, 1984; Vaughn, 1996) have drawn attention to the problems created by the over integration of technical systems and the associated intellectual resources of design, scheduling and distribution. This discussion can be thought of in terms of the tight coupling of global systems. The routine integration of previously distinct and separate national and regional resources into self-evidently global resources has produced a precariously tight coupling of the global system of material production. The argument has been made that this results in the loss of the necessary buffers or slackness of resources to protect regions against global impulses emerging elsewhere. The stresses inherent in the emerging global system have been highlighted by the recent difficulties of the East Asian economies (e.g. Ernst, Ganiatsos and Mytelka, 1998). In the case of East Asia precisely this tight coupling resulted in the diverse and different problems which emerged across the range of individual Asian nation states in the 1990s. These problems generated economic difficulties for distant and not directly connected states across the globe.

The imperatives of the emerging global market have led developed economies to shift their focus towards the end of the production chain where product differentiation and customer support can maintain demand for goods and services in a global chess game of resources and capabilities. This means that smaller players require geographic leverage. This book explains why this can be delivered through new forms of adjacency inherent in the current generation of information and communication technologies (ICTs).

While there are opportunities for new entrants at various points in the production and consumption chain, segregation and exclusion are producing an unevenness of development within and between economies. The consequences can be seen in sub-nationalist responses to the consequent inequities of development. The emergent dimensions of micro (city scale) meso, (country/state scale) and macro (international) regional scales of exclusion from the core of the global economy are complexly interactive. This situation contrasts with the orderly flows of technology from the economic centres to peripheral regions assumed by earlier models of multinational development and technology transfer. Exclusion, whether socially or geographically based, threatens any prospect of achieving economic, environmental or social control and sustainability.

Three paradigms are introduced across the three parts of this book:

- a concept of "community without propinquity" from the 1960s, in effect an early formulation of virtual organisations, which foreshadows the dynamics of the "virtual adjacency" delivered by current information and communication technologies;
- a design paradigm drawn from the dynamics of high technology innovation that aids analysis of position and potential within a global production context and which demonstrates the socially and institutionally embedded nature of technical development;
- a notion of windows of opportunity through which access to the key technologies of the socio-economic paradigm might be gained on terms that can be determined by the adopters, rather than the originators of these technologies.

Taken together these paradigms can reveal how the global ICT landscape has shifted into a pattern of new adjacencies and opportunities for the less developed countries. The emerging global system does not reflect the unproblematic "end of history" posited by Fukayama a decade ago (Fukayama, 1992). It is composed of a partial and uneven set of processes which have created complex ebbs and flows of material and intellectual resources and of people around the planet. At the same time a significant proportion of humanity has been consigned to the margins of what has become an essentially neo-liberal project.

Meaningful inclusion in such a system is taken therefore to include the ability of the marginalised to determine their own destinies through the development of appropriate and localised technologies. To achieve this situation the dynamics of the emergent system, and of the technical development that drives the system must be understood. This book offers a detailed view of the interior of the technical design process, and a paradigm for the selective use of the resulting technologies beyond the context of their development. Whether such use is undertaken to join or to challenge the nature of the emergent system is the prerogative of the users.

Understanding the Dynamics of Globalisation

The first task of this book is to provide an overview of the emergent global system of design and development. The traditional view of global production and consumption has been of a developmental view of international trade as a series of flows between centre and periphery, followed by the development of multi-domestic production close to markets (e.g. Hirsch, 1967; Wells, 1972). However, the emergence of production webs and networks has blurred the distinction between centre and periphery. Information technologies have driven these changes through the reduction of transaction costs and the alteration of the relative advantages and economies of size and disparate national and regional cultures have become increasingly interlinked within networked and globalised organisations. Labour markets, both internal and external to the developed economies driving this process are increasingly interconnected, leading to complex movements of both resources and people.

The end of the Cold War and the removal of the political and economic barriers arbitrarily created at the cessation of hostilities in World War II accelerated global economic integration. It also allowed the re-emergence of geo-historical linkages suppressed for half a century or longer (Delamaide, 1994).

The current level of internationalised trade itself is no novelty. Hirst and Thompson (1996) demonstrate that on many significant measures the world economy was at least as internationalised in the period prior to the First World War. However, the application of information and communication technologies (ICTs) to the globalisation of financial markets, has been coupled with the removal of the policy constraints laid down by the Bretton Woods institutions established in the concluding stages of World War II. This shift from a Keynsian to a neo-liberal frame has internationalised private economic decision-making and transformed the volume and flow of resources. At the same time a deeper understanding of the role of knowledge and intellectual capital in the production and value chain has emerged.

Peter Dicken (1998, 2003) and Manuel Castells (1996, 1997) locate information and communication technologies at the centre of recent developments in the global economy. They also emphasise the partial nature of the emerging world system and place it in a broader historical context. Simon and Marvin (2003) demonstrate the partial nature of inclusion even within the emerging global megapolitan regions. For them the impact of Ohmae's "zebra strategies" at the urban level is a "splintered urbanism" of interpenetrated exclusion and inclusion.

Development has been far from uniform, despite the more simplistic declarations of a coherent new world order and later chapters examine the elements and implications of this present mode of globalisation. However, it is useful to look at the prevailing models of global processes at this point.

Peter Dicken uses a basic production chain to map a geographical hierarchy involving resources, manufacturers and consumers (Dicken, 2003, p.15). In common with Porter's (1990) representation of the value chain, a range of critical support activities are identified for each stage of these generic models. The models provide a thread running from primary production to quaternary post-delivery support of goods and services. A variety of service activities wrap around the core thread of the production chain. Dicken demonstrates the traditional view of the service sector as evidence of a "post-industrial" or advanced economy.

A quaternary sector is seen as the logical consequence of the ascendancy of intellectual capital over physical capital. The rapid growth of deregulated financial services and the broadly perceived shift from manufacturing to service industries supports such a view. The prestigious U.S. engineering company General Electric has moved into highly successful financial services. These now generate more income that the engineering divisions, and seem to confirm services as a replacement for primary, secondary and tertiary activities. However it can be argued that such a division of economic activities is unnecessarily simplistic.

The chain metaphor is being superseded by the idea of global production networks. Research and development, routine manufacturing, final assembly and after-market support may all be present in the same location, yet each may be contributing to different product chains and sectors. The re-distribution of these activities during the product life cycle further undermines the traditional concepts of centre and periphery. Development is not uniform, specific markets and specific technologies are at different points in their life-cycles of growth, maturity and decline. Rapid growth at locations favoured by "zebra strategies" (Ohmae, 1990) also creates serious developmental imbalances within regions and nation states. The implications for the organisations and alliances which act across the global production system are discussed at more length in the following chapters. Essentially the leading players in this game must deliver continuous innovation at the cutting edge while managing the diffusion of more mature technologies in order to maintain their position.

Mature economies are shifting focus towards the end of the production chain where product differentiation and customer support can maintain demand for goods. There is evidence of an increasing focus on the end of the "value chain" (Porter, 1990) to increase competitive advantage, for example, by ICL, a former British "national champion" computer manufacturer. This company is now a wholly owned subsidiary of a Japanese company, Fujitsu. It has moved further from its original manufacturing hardware base to position itself as an information services provider that can support the specificities of a European business environment. This end of the chain is more culturally sensitive and success requires some specific local or regional knowledge. Later in the book the impact of a value chain approach in the very different chemical industry will be described.

Hirsch (1967) describes the orderly transfer of key functions from core to periphery across the product lifecycle. As a product or a technology matures, it may be passed to a less advanced manufacturing location for routine production and reproduction. This orderly pattern has been replaced by an interpenetration of core and periphery in which market and raw materials source, production and consumption are increasingly co-located. For example, James and Howells (2001) examine the use that Asian companies are making of the research and development facilities they are establishing or acquiring within the United Kingdom. Evidence suggests that these firms are seeking both knowledge for adjustments to markets and broader intellectual capital for their home operations. The British government and the European Commission encourage companies to seek similar alliances and opportunities in the opposite direction. Such contacts can serve both as a means of accessing the market potential of Asia's growing economies and as a means of improving offshore manufacturing resources in relation to both home and export markets (e.g. EC/UNCTAD, 1996). Within the urban cores of advanced economies, low wage and low capital activities continue in the form of outworked and home based labour in industries such as textile, clothing and footwear (Greig, 1991). For the self-employed trader or the small company, the Toyota van, cell-phone and fax, deployed across the conurbations mimic the use of equivalent technologies by large corporations at a global scale.

Design and Development: The Worlds We Live In

Five chapters form the first part of this book which explores our current situation. They deal with the nature and opportunities of a network form of globalisation which places information and communication technologies at the centre of the process.

The current role of information and communication technologies can be traced to decisive events of the Pacific War. In 1941 the large scale deployment of naval aviation in the attack on Pearl Harbor represented the assimilation of Western technology and strategy – military and industrial – by Japan. The Imperial Japanese Navy had already demonstrated its competence in the Russo-Japanese war of 1904, but military success against the United States and Britain in 1941 and 1942 came as a shock. The subsequent U.S. victory at Midway was engineered through the use of information technology – code-breaking of intercepted communications. These two events foreshadowed two shifts in the centre of gravity of global development. The first was the shift of attention to the Pacific Basin for the remainder of the twentieth century. The second shift was that of information and communication technologies to their current central role. Derived from the requirements of the Second World War these became and remain the key technologies of economic globalisation.

The military determination of the development paths of advanced technologies in the crucial Second World War period and beyond is returned to later in the book.

Chapter 2 examines the continuities and discontinuities inherent in the current dynamics of global development.

Shifts in the prevailing view of the global chain of production and consumption are discussed. The development of international trade as a series of flows between centre and periphery, followed by the development of multi-domestic production close to markets is discussed. The subsequent emergence of more global strategies involving trans-national production networks is described.

The shift in characterisations of the multinational company by both proponents and critics is plotted from the seventies to the nineties. The characteristics of the "new" multinational corporations and the emergence of production webs and networks are described. These have blurred the distinction between centre and periphery. Current relationships are contrasted with the more orderly flows of technology from centre to periphery associated with earlier models of multinational development and technology transfer.

The dominant role of the "triad" formed by the developed regions of North America, North West Europe and North East Asia within the world economy is introduced. The locational consequences for investment and economic activity are examined, along with the new forms of "periphery", no longer necessarily physically separated from the core. New forms of exclusion are examined, in particular, the problematic promotion of what Kenichi Ohmae terms zebra strategies. These are directed at only the strongest parts of a regional economy, in order to create sufficient levels of formal economic activity for inclusion in the wider system. The consequences of such strategies for both inclusion and exclusion and for economic and social equity are raised.

Chapter 3 links the emergence of computer-based information systems with the theoretical underpinnings of modernism and bureaucracy and offered a non-place definition of community and association. Modernism and related theories from architecture and planning are examined and the chapter describes an alignment between the information infrastructure of the current form of globalisation and both the physical infrastructure of urban development and industrialisation and the institutional infrastructure of the nation state.

The integral role of information and communication technologies in current changes is emphasised through reference to earlier work. The continuity of technocratic positivism, from the first half of the twentieth century to the first decade of the twenty-first is traced. The "wicked" nature of socio-technical problems as defined by Horst Rittel and Webber is used to enter the debates around the social shaping of technology. A path which avoids the post-modernist cul de sac is sought through critical information systems design methods.

Chapter 4 The diffusion of state power through agreement to and participation in multilateral regulation in areas such as trade, security and environment has been matched by the emergence of trans-national corporations operating in internationalised financial and labour markets. These changes impact not only at national and sub-national levels, but increasingly flow through to the individual household. This chapter considers the impact on the household and local community of the increasing porosity of national boundaries.

The coalescence of communication and computing technologies has transformed government attitudes to communication infrastructure. The national missions of the traditional common carriers of goods and information, focussed on equity of access, have been replaced by the pursuit of commercial opportunities. The informal replacement of national broadcasters by extraterritorial organisations using direct satellite broadcasting has taken place in parallel with telecommunications deregulation. Acceptance of a neo-liberal frame eclipses the ability of national governments to form and control key areas of policy for technologies which impact on both urban and rural infrastructure. This has created a new tension between space and place.

Non-place definitions of community and of citizenship are introduced as a means of understanding the challenge presented by these changes.

Chapter 5 introduces the concept of "windows of opportunity" and the possibility of the appropriation of technologies by the mariginalised. It has been demonstrated that a process of organisational learning is needed to move beyond the technical effects of direct substitution of information technology for manual processes (Zuboff, 1988; Sproull and Kiesler, 1991). The social learning curves associated with the introduction of new electrically-based technologies at the turn of the last century have been described by Marvin (1988). Consensus over the value and application of these technologies emerge only after considerable debate. An agreed paradigm for the rapidly succeeding generations of information and communication technologies being deployed in the current wave of globalisation cannot be expected to emerge without equivalent debate and contestation. Developing regions need some window of opportunity through which to gain access to and influence in such debates.

The metaphor originated in a study of the impact of relatively simple bulletin board technology on a group of users with disabilities whose special requirements highlight the need of peripheral users to appropriate features of mainstream technical developments as far as possible (Earls, 1991). Nineteen-eighties bulletin board technology allowed these users to participate in an electronic community which was unaware of their considerable physical disabilities. The volunteer student cohort who participated developed fruitful and co-operative relationships with a number of individuals, without the preconceptions that would have influenced face to face interaction.

Despite the falling costs and growing flexibility of computer technology there remains a need to identify and exploit equivalent windows of opportunity presented by mainstream technology. Current examples of the use of web-based technologies show that the paradigm remains relevant. It will be argued that access to state of the art technology is necessary for full participation in the global economy, but access alone is no guarantee of its appropriate or effective use. The use of technology, rather than the technology itself is the key to appropriateness, and to sustainable voices from the margins in virtual social and political spaces. However, the huge and diverse range of potential users is inevitably segmented organisationally and culturally. It requires an adequate fit to a wide variety of specific needs and the capacity for adjustment to continuing developments. These need to be informed by social and organisational learning, over considerable time.

Determination and Design: Frames and Paradigms

The second part of this book provides a detailed analysis of the technical design and development process. It takes as its starting point the increased significance of intellectual capital leveraged by information and communication technology in a globalising world economy. Access to both knowledge and material resources determines the policy and design choices available to decision makers beyond the core triad of the global economy described in Chapter 2.

To understand how global flows of information are undermining the distinction between manufacturing and service activities and the distinction between products and services new forms of locational and functional differentiation across a globalised network of invention, innovation and implementation must be examined.

In Part II design is defined as an activity which unifies product, process and organisation across geographical and cultural boundaries, as an aid to understanding the process of technological shaping within the globalising economy. The value of a design perspective is explained in relation to the literature on the social shaping of technology (Mackenzie and Wajcman, 1995).

Part II is concerned with the dynamics of "big design" – the complex and tightly coupled high technology innovations that have allowed the emergence of a global society. The military determination of the development paths of advanced technologies in the crucial Second World War and Cold War periods is evident in the examples used here.

The "small design" of the disintermediated local initiatives aimed at entering the global production system can be mapped on to a generic model of the design process presented here. This model identifies the distinctive intellectual and physical resource requirements of the invention and initial innovation stages of the project and product life cycle and the very different requirements of the mature manufacturing phases of the cycle.

Design as an activity links the service and manufacturing components of the production chain. Rather than the replacement of manufacturing by service activity, we are witnessing the enhancement of the value of manufactured goods by their incorporation into services. As the distinction between products and services blurs we must examine new forms of locational and functional differentiation across a globalised network of invention, innovation and implementation. Design, defined as an activity which unifies product, process and organisation across geographical and cultural boundaries, can play a critical role in placing the strategies presently pursued in both manufacturing and services in a global context.

However, a nexus of conflicting and competing interests determines the outcome of complex design and development processes.

Chapter 6 introduces a design paradigm as an aid to understanding this process of technological shaping within the globalising economy. This builds on the shift in manufacturing from established core to emerging periphery which was presented in Chapter 2. This shift reflects the success of the newly industrialising countries at the convergent stage of the design model presented here. It involves efficient production utilising mature technologies. However, the very different cognitive requirements of each design stage are a measure of the challenges facing countries like Malaysia and Taiwan, both of which have developed policies intended to take them from the essentially convergent tasks of global production to transformative and divergent activities.

The difficulties encountered by the East Asian economies in the 1990s highlighted the stresses inherent in the emerging global system. The tight coupling of the system propagates the diverse problems of these individual nation states across the globe. This chapter examines the emergence of strategies and alliances across regional and organisational boundaries with a model derived from design management.

Arguments around incremental versus systemic innovation in design, the literature on innovation, and implementation, and on the necessity of innovative milieux are introduced.

Chapter 7 develops one aspect of incremental development: time-frames. Conflict between time-frames at different levels within a decision space may conflict with or frustrate the intentions of designers. The chapter looks at three cases of technology driven development strategies spanning several decades and at the impact of conflicting time-frames on the critical decisions in design and management processes.

Chapter 8 describes an overall "metatechnical" framework to encompass the perplexing range of influences on individual design projects. It presents a framework of analysis which allows socio-technical concerns to link national and wider cultural and institutional contexts with the decision-making levels of the individual firm, or network of firms, and with the technical dynamics of the techno-economic paradigm.

Often designers appear to make or acquiesce to decisions which frustrate their own professional objectives. From a systems perspective, such results may be seen as suboptimization resulting from a conflict between the evaluative criteria appropriate to institutional and task environments. To be successful the design activity must address both. The alternative is to allow the conflict between technocratic consciousness originating at a technical level and overconformity attributable to the institutional level to give rise to pathological outcomes. The development of the space shuttle – the NASA Space Transportation System (STS) – is one illustration of this argument, and a "metatechnical" framework is advocated as necessary to the successful linking of task and institutional orientations.

The implications are that the technical environment of design decision-makers must be appropriately linked to the institutional environment in which their organisations as a whole must operate

Chapter 9 explores a means of linking from the technical level to the wider cultural environment. The notion of "design cultures" provides an explanation of distinctive outcomes from processes addressing essentially the same technology in different social and cultural settings.

Established practices and expectations within organisations contain a cultural component. This imparts its own dynamic to the diffusion and adoption of socio-technical systems across cultural settings. The key technologies underpinning the present mode of global development have been modified by cultural orientations and preferences which are in turn incorporated into popular accounts of difference in organisational practices. Such accounts themselves may carry a significant emotional charge reflecting anxieties played out at a national level, especially in North

American accounts of North East Asian developments prior to the downturn of the 1990s in that region.

The design process itself can be seen to reflect its cultural setting. However, reference to culture should not become a means of avoiding further explanation of difference. National associations of style and capability are both a form of stereotyping and a source of value, for example in the marketing of German or Italian automobiles with their respective associations of engineering reliability and design flair. They also reflect distinctive outcomes based on differing priorities among designers in different settings. Culture must therefore be disaggregated into a constellation of tradition, ethnicity, organisational and institutional frameworks. Ironically, the military technology which dominated much innovation transferred to the "third world" during the Cold War period offers clear examples of differences between artefacts which reflect institutionally varied frameworks of invention and innovation. The performance driven extremes of military technologies reveal characteristics that are less clearly exposed in more mundane and robust technologies and this chapter plots changes in the distinctive design cultures of the Cold War protagonists.

From Geography to History: Designing a Place in the World

The final part of this book examines the practical consequences of the dynamics of the emerging global system and the technology that underpins it for decision making in development.

Design itself is a process of compromise to find acceptable solutions within large potential solution spaces. The notion of bounded rationality was propounded by Herbert Simon to explain the limits of human capability in such situations (Simon, 1957). He coined the word *satisficing* to explain the compromise strategy of arriving at an acceptable solution rather than pursuing of an unattainable optimised solution.

One consequence of the inevitable compromise in achieving a design solution in the face of complexity is that any non-trivial solution also contains unanticipated characteristics and consequences. An increasingly well known example is the consequences of robust characteristics designed into ARPANet, the precursor to the Internet. In order to enhance survivability during a possible nuclear war, the core of the system was able to relocate itself between host computers depending upon availability and capacity. As a result the current global network is in no way amenable to centralised control.

Lawson (1982) has demonstrated that design students develop additional rules and constraints as one means of further reducing solution spaces. In some respects the more constrained problem offers easier routes to solution than the less bounded one. At a meta-level the end of the Cold War has removed one clear set of constraints on decision making. As a result it seems that the attention span of developed nations is incapable of dealing with the unconstrained complexity of Ohmae's "multi-polar" world. As a consequence, for better or worse, vast areas lying beyond the core economies of the triad introduced in Chapter 2, merit only intermittent attention from the centre.

The pursuit of greater added value has led to the recognition of the emerging global system as an "information economy" and this relegates developing countries to the peripheral areas beyond the triad core. Information and communication technologies have enabled the disaggregation of the production chain into a network by locating each activity specifically at its point of greatest comparative advantage. The ability to disaggregate the intellectual capital produced by the divergent stage of the design process from the convergent, focused discipline of the production process has been enhanced by the ability to control production lines from across national boundaries. In some instances complementary manufacturing takes place at both ends of such relationships, however, Lipietz (1992) argues that the ability to separate production from consumption signals the end of the "Fordist compromise", his term for the Keynesian social-democratic paradigm which was accepted during most of the Cold War period. In the neo-liberal view, employers need not pay the production workers remote from intended markets sufficiently well to consume the products of their own labour.[3]

Part III looks at past attempts to design development pathways into the industrialised world of the nineteenth and twentieth centuries in order to emphasise the path dependence of such strategies and the complexity of outcomes.

Chapter 10 compares two nations which made a conscious effort to achieve "modernisation" in the terms created by Western industrialisation and colonisation. Turkey and Japan aimed for the same outcome from different starting places and achieved different outcomes. However, comparison of their different trajectories of development reveals the importance of the opportunities and constraints to development set out in the previous sections of this book.

Chapter 11 examines the re-establishment of geo-economic alliances suppressed by recent history, and the emergence of new forms of association facilitated by current communication technologies.

The early 1990s saw the unequivocal end of the Cold War and the removal of barriers arbitrarily created at the cessation of hostilities in World War II. Subsequent political and economic re-alignments have been problematic. In the Balkans they have allowed the resurrection of earlier conflicts, placed in stasis by external threats. Elsewhere in Europe, Darrell Delamaide has identified these linkages in terms of what he describes as "super-regions" across Europe. From this perspective we are witnessing the re-emergence of older international alignments. For example, an emergent Scandinavian bloc within the EU is linking with the Baltic republics, recalling both the Hanseatic League, and the days when Shakespeare's plays opened in Gdansk within months of their London debuts. The resilience of such links reflects a degree of cultural consonance. However, such realignments bring tensions and contradictions and this chapter examines models with which to examine their dynamics.

Chapter 12 examines the technical and social synergies of the current and prospective generations of information and communication technologies. It engages with the consequences of the paradigm shift from hierarchical information and communication technologies to the disintermediated world of solar powered satellite-based technologies with which the planet becomes a single communication space.

The chapter looks at responses to the opportunity for countries and regions disadvantaged by the current distribution of communication infrastructure to enter the communication space of the wealthy. The "window of opportunity" metaphor is applied to the consequent shifts in definitions of centre and periphery in the global economy and shifts in the nature of exclusion from that economy. From critical information systems research, a paradigm through which windows can be kept open is described, and illustrated with some current initiatives from a variety of locations.

Notes

1 Ohmae's conception is of a "borderless world" in which direct foreign development seeks areas of highest GNP regardless of political boundaries – his "zebra strategies". The tensions implicit in Ohmae's concept are discussed at some length in Chapter 2.
2 See http://www.digitaldividenetwork.org/
3 See Bello (1999) and Klein (2000) for detailed discussions of the social and economic consequences of such policies.

Chapter 2

Chains, Networks, Webs: The Topology and Geography of a Global System of Development

This chapter identifies continuities and discontinuities in the situation which faces both developed and developing regions. These differences determine the space for manoeuvre left for the developing regions excluded from the process of formation of key technical systems. Later chapters look more closely at the dynamics of the design of complex systems themselves. This chapter examines the characteristics of the emerging global system within which these are formed.

There have been significant shifts in characterisations of multinational corporations by both their proponents and their critics. The characteristics of the "new" multinationals and the emergence of production webs and networks have blurred the distinction between centre and periphery in the global economy. In response strategies to cope with trans-national production networks have emerged. The shifts in the nature of the global chain of production and consumption have undermined the view of international trade as a series of complementary flows of raw materials and products between centre and periphery, which are eventually followed by the development of production close to markets.

The technologies facilitating this change have created the potential for the co-existence and co-location of activities associated with different stages of production and consumption. These new adjacencies disrupt the orderly flows of technology from centre to periphery associated with earlier models of multinational development and technology transfer (see Hirsch, 1967, 1972).

This chapter introduces the notion of a dominant triad of developed regions within the world economy. This understanding has locational consequences for investment and economic activity. New forms of "periphery", no longer necessarily physically separated from the core, and new forms of exclusion are examined. In this context the promotion of what Kenichi Ohmae terms zebra strategies is problematic. Inward investment is directed at only the strongest parts of a regional economy, in order to create sufficient levels of formal economic activity for full inclusion in the world equation of production and consumption.[1] The contrast between such favoured regions and their neighbours may not be entirely black and white, but the consequences for economic and social equity within a nation can be stark, as illustrated in this chapter with data from China.

The emergent dimensions of micro (city scale) meso, (country/state scale) and macro (international) regional scales of exclusion from the "triad" of North America, North West Europe and North East Asia mentioned in Chapter 1 are discussed. The consequent stresses on the national state are touched on here and in the following chapters.

Global Production/Global Participation?

The complexity of our world has become better appreciated following the removal of what Ohmae (1995) terms the "bi-polar discipline" of the Cold War. This obscured differences within and between members of the Eastern and Western blocs and consigned the remainder of humanity to the disparagingly termed "Third World". The rapid and comprehensive collapse of the Eastern Bloc at the end of the 1980s led some in the West to attribute a key role in the erosion of monolithic state control to information and communication technologies. This led to accompanying assertions that a technically driven globalised economy would solve the remaining problems of global development. In the 1990s such simplifications were increasingly challenged with evidence of the exclusion of economically marginal performers from decision making, by the onset of simultaneous crises across the varieties of capitalism deployed by the developmental states of East Asia and by the subsequent dot.com bubble.

The post-Cold War era has seen rapid growth in global economic integration. Disparate national and regional cultures are increasingly interacting within networked and globalised organisations. Information technologies are facilitating these changes through the reduction of transaction costs and the alteration of the relative advantages and economies of size. However, this is leading to a complex process of layering of labour markets, both internal and external to the developed economies driving this process. The unevenness of development within and between economies threatens the achievement of sustainability as defined by writers such as Welford (1995) who cites the Bruntland report from the World Commission on Environment and Development

(Bruntland, 1987). This establishes a requirement to meet present needs without compromising future generations and emphasises the shift of focus in development from growth to sustainability.

The reorganisation of production around the integrated sectors of an emerging global economy seems to have left the world divided into three major regions, North East Asia, North America and Western Europe. This is the "triad" described by Ohmae (1990) with localities within those regions restructuring rapidly in an attempt to obtain or ensure a continued prosperous place within the new system.

The foundations of an Asian node in the global economy were laid during the nineteenth century by the successful acquisition, adoption and subsequent re-export of externally developed technology by Japan (Morris-Suzuki, 1994). The focus of growth in Asia had shifted westwards to the East Asian mainland by the close of the twentieth century, but the very success of Japan and other Asian economies in transferring, transforming and re-exporting socio-technical systems has already provoked a response from older developed economies. The result has been the rapid cross-diffusion of innovations within an emerging globalised economy dependent on the widespread use of information and communication technologies. These key technologies underpin a global system of production, distribution and consumption.

Orru, Biggart and Hamilton (1991) examined organisational isomorphism in N.E. Asia reflecting a revived interest in "institutional" issues in Western organisation theory (e.g. Powell and DiMaggio, 1998). A better understanding of the dynamics of the strategies employed in East Asia has come through Kim's examination of the significant differences between the historically connected business forms of *chaebol*, *zaibatsu* and *keiretsu* (Kim, 1996). Similarly Redding (1996) and Wong (1996) have provided a better understanding of the nuances of Chinese business practice to the West.

As noted above, the success of Japan and other Asian economies in transferring, transforming and re-exporting socio-technical systems inevitably provoked a response which resulted in the rapid diffusion of innovations in all directions. In many respects, the current unsettled state of several East Asian economies is a reflection of the closer interaction of systems based on conflicting assumptions and expectations. A de facto global system linking Keynesian developmental states to the neo-liberal hegemony of the Anglo-Saxon developed states is likely to exhibit instabilities.

Tensions and contradictions in development are not confined to the newer participants in the global system. The rapid pace of growth in favoured areas also creates regional imbalances within any regions and nation states where available infrastructure and skills cannot support full integration into the global economy. Europe, North America and East Asia all contain the most advanced levels of economic development alongside developing economies. Each region faces the challenge of supporting balanced growth in peripheral areas which are not attracting private inward investment. While these inequities may be most marked within the most rapidly developing economies such as China, they exist to some extent in all economies.

At the same time there seems some degree of consensus that, in the post-Cold War era, difference and diversity are potential resources. For example, Delamaide (1994) explores the synergies flowing from the re-assertion of historical cultural and economic linkages, offering an alternative understanding to Ohmae's "zebra strategies" (Ohmae, 1995) which play to the relative strength of the most developed components of national economies in order to create regional synergies. Both are discussed below.

Although linkages between the advanced areas of developing economies are creating new regions irrespective of national boundaries, few national governments are prepared to relinquish responsibility for the development of the state as a whole. The "strong globalisation" argument that national or even international regional governments no longer have a significant role in development is now increasingly challenged. However, differentials in development are entrenched through dependence upon a global infrastructure constructed around the priorities of the dominant developed economies and the resulting inequities undermine the legitimacy of some national states.

The development of co-operative economic mechanisms such as the North American Free Trade Association (NAFTA) and the Association of South East Asian Nations (ASEAN) suggest that there are means of developing sufficiently large-scale development policies while retaining a role for national governments. However, the emergence of economic groupings as large as the Asia Pacific Economic Co-operation (APEC), with the addition of Russia, Vietnam and Peru to its original membership, or the further enlargement of the European Union to twenty-five members in 2004, threaten the original coherence and logic of some of these associations.

Dicken (2003) and Dunning (1993) show that the majority of direct foreign investment is within and between members of the "triad" but the European Union is particularly keen to encourage European investment into Asia's developing economies. Initiatives such as "Asia Invest" are aimed at smaller and medium sized companies which may benefit from resource sharing between European design and development and low-cost

Asian manufacture, as mentioned in Chapter 1. While this initiative is focussed on the actual and potential resources of the less developed Asian economies, the European Union is keen to direct investment to both developing and developed regions of Asia (EC/UNCTAD, 1996).

Chains, Networks and Webs

The geographical separation of a periphery providing raw resources and a basic market from a core containing transformation processes and sophisticated markets can be identified in European and earlier forms of colonialism. However, the emergence of a global market has led to the progressive relocation of basic manufacturing processes to the periphery and a consequent shift in focus in developed economies towards the end of the production chain where product differentiation and customer support can maintain demand for goods and services.

The integration of this emergent system can be overstated since specific markets and specific technologies are at different points in the cycle of growth, maturity and decline at any time. Consequently, the organisations and alliances which comprise the global production system are presented with the challenge of delivering continuous innovation at the cutting edge while ensuring effective diffusion and exploitation of more mature technologies. Innovation at the cutting edge increasingly requires cross-national collaboration to achieve the necessary levels of resources.

Dicken (2003) enumerates the repertoire of trans-national corporation strategies which include direct foreign investment, joint ventures with local companies and alliances. Alliances can be both permanent, as with the merger of Daimler-Benz and Chrysler in 1998, or temporally and geographically limited partnerships such as that between Siemens, IBM and Toshiba in relation to the European market (Castells, 1996, p.194). Such arrangements involve significant cross-cultural accommodation, as with the acceptance of German workforce representation at board level by the U.S. side of the merged DaimlerChrysler corporation.

Cores, Peripheries and Rims

The divisions within the emerging "global economic system" and the prospects for overcoming them are the focus of this book. These divisions create two particular problems which undermine the broader sustainability of development. The newly industrialising countries that are aiming to catch up with the most advanced regions are engaged in a process in which development and growth are synonymous. They are understandably sceptical of advice which suggests that they should adhere to higher standards than those applying at the equivalent stage in the development of the dominant established economies. However, repeating the short-term strategies of their predecessors may adversely affect their long term choices. Secondly, significant parts of the globe are excluded from this "global" system. Rather than aspiring to catch up, these regions find difficulty in maintaining even modest economic objectives.

Exclusion from policy-making processes or from influence over the emerging global production system reduces the ability of less developed regions to negotiate over the sustainable exploitation of the primary resources they have traditionally contributed to international trade. Just as colonial infrastructure was often aimed more at the exploitation of resources than development, the priorities of trans-national corporations are creating an emergent information apartheid within the global economy. Because of the asymmetry in bargaining power, the spatial strategies of virtual adjacency delivered by information and communication technologies threaten any prospect of integrated development. They allow the outsiders a "cherry-picking" approach to both the human and physical resources of developing regions. Infrastructure investment is driven by external criteria similar to those described by Headrick (1981) in his description of railway development in Africa.

The key twenty-first century communication technologies are in danger of mirroring the uneven development of the key nineteenth century transport technology, with the extreme case of the internationalised enclave of the Free Trade Zone mimicking the trading fort of the nineteenth century.

The Pacific focus of the global economy at the end of the twentieth century reflects the steady migration of the creative source of models of development and innovation from Western Europe. During the first and second industrial revolutions the focus of innovation and technical development moved to the east coast of the U.S.A. and during the third and putative fourth industrial revolutions to its West Coast. As noted above, the basis for the subsequent shift in focus to the Western Pacific rim was the nineteenth century appropriation of Western technology by Japan (Morris-Suzuki, 1994). David and Wheelwright (1989) argue that such regional shifts can only be understood in the context of waves of capitalist development operating on a worldwide scale.

As noted in Chapter 1, Hirst and Thompson (1996) argue that the world economy was highly internationalised by the outbreak of the First World War. The technologies of electric telegraph and steam navigation had delivered a new predictability and reliability to intercontinental communication essential to the growth of global trade. Nevertheless there are further qualitative shifts associated with the near-instantaneous transfer of almost unlimited amounts of information between almost any two points on the surface of the planet. The application of information and communication technologies (ICTs) to globalised financial markets has contributed to the internationalisation of economic decision-making and transformed the volume and flow of resources from David and Wheelwright's waves into tsunami. At the same time, a deeper understanding of the mobility of knowledge and intellectual capital in the production and value chain has developed.

The resulting complex interplay of interests and resources requires some form of representation akin to the logos used by Mintzberg (1979) to illustrate the influence of context on his organisational typology. A basic production chain model is used by Dicken to map a geographical hierarchy involving resources, manufacturers and consumers (Dicken, 1998, Figure 1.1). This metaphor is being superseded by the idea of global production networks. Research and development, routine manufacturing, final assembly and after-market support may all be present in the same location, yet each activity may be contributing to radically different product chains and sectors. As noted above, the orderly transfer of these functions from core to periphery across the product lifecycle described by Hirsch (1967) is replaced by an interpenetration of core and periphery in which market, processing and raw materials source, and production and consumption are increasingly co-located without being integrated into a self-sufficient economy. The re-distribution of these activities during each product life cycle further undermines the traditional concepts of centre and periphery.

Dicken (1998, 2003) demonstrates that information and communication technologies underpin the global system, offering opportunities for participation in the "information economy" to peripheral areas. Information and communication technologies have enabled the disaggregation of the production chain into a network by locating each activity specifically at its point of greatest comparative advantage. The ability to disaggregate the intellectual capital produced by the divergent stage of the design process from the convergent, focused discipline of the production process has been enhanced by the ability to control production lines from across national boundaries.[2] In some instances complementary manufacturing takes place at both ends of such relationships; however, as noted, Lipietz (1992) argues that this ability to separate production from consumption signals the end of the "Fordist compromise" which underpinned the Keynsian social-democratic paradigm.

Harvey (1990) points out that Ford significantly increased wages when he introduced his five-dollar, eight-hour day in 1914 in conjunction with his moving production line. Ford saw the workers as an integral part of a production and consumption process. However, the technical developments underpinning the current globalisation process have created interrelated labour markets, both internal and external to the developed economies. Harvey regards this post-Fordist situation as a regime of flexible accumulation which is tightly organised through its geographical dispersal and flexible responses to labour markets, and which is even more reliant on the creation of scientific and access to technical knowledge.

If Henry Ford implemented his $25 dollar weekly wage in part to create a market for the output of his production line, production workers remote from the destination market no longer need to be paid sufficiently well to consume the products of their own labour. The Fordist compromise was institutionalised in the international bodies created by the Bretton Woods Agreement of 1944. The transformation of these institutions, in particular the mutation of the General Agreement on Trade and Tariffs (GATT) into the World Trade Organisation[3] (WTO) is at the centre of debates over the meaning and nature of globalisation.

The current neo-liberal development agenda is driven by the requirements of capital flows, and backed by the twin resource providers of the International Bank for Reconstruction and Development[4] (World Bank) and the International Monetary Fund (IMF). Both lenders have a strong preference for very particular interpretations of both development and globalisation. The International Labour Organisation[5] (ILO) charged with ensuring that workers rights would converge with the standards achieved in the more advanced economies manages a much lower profile in the public debates and coverage in general news media. The results of the prevailing agenda are catalogued by Bello (1999) and Klein (2000) in their accounts of conditions in the free trade zones of less developed economies.

Despite the tight coupling and complex interaction of the globalising economy, a simplistic isomorphism reappears in models of the development process which still reflects Rogers' (1983) model of diffusion of innovation from centre to periphery. The general dissemination of "lean production", and of models of science cities and science parks derived from specifically U.S. synergies between university and commercial research are evidence of the persistence of a "one-way" view of transfer processes. Both Route 128 and Silicon Valley have been adopted as models for technology transfer and economic development, with varying success: Route 128 around Boston emerged as a centre of high technology industries in the 1960s. Saxenian has compared the developments of industries along Route 128 and in Silicon Valley (Saxenian, 1994). The East Coast paradigm relied upon established companies and a new relationship with universities and central government, the core of U.S. President Eisenhower's "military-industrial complex" (Eisenhower, 1961). The closed nature of these large, individual organisations contrasts with the densely networked environment of the more dynamic West Coast firms. Silicon Valley is dominated by the loosely networked companies which created and in turn were sustained by a new generation of information and communication technologies.

Military projects played a crucial role in the early development of Silicon Valley, but the availability of venture capital from within the region is a key to its continued prominence. Castells and Hall (1994) show that attempts to engineer such creative situations have produced very mixed results, both within their original cultures and beyond and this path dependent aspect of technical, economic and social development will be examined in Part II and Part III.

Castell's (1989) view of the creative milieu captures the complex web of relationships which is necessary to support the genuine innovation required for economic autonomy within an economy of flows. Castells (1996) describes a form of network enterprise which is composed of components of larger corporations, collaborating in specific spatial and temporal circumstances, while the main companies are still pursuing global strategies of direct competition. The framework of the network organisation appears to offer an opportunity for smaller players to access resources from and to compete within global networks. Inoue (1998) describes a "virtual village" in which small enterprises are able to form and reform alliances in order to provide high technology services to larger companies. However, the additional accessibility and flexibility offered to smaller players also allows larger firms to restructure in such a way that they can enter niche markets yet still draw on their wider resource base to maintain economies of scale not available to the smaller incumbent firms. The potential advantages to smaller players are thus offset by the ability of some larger firms to de-couple key business units better to target customers and markets traditionally served by much smaller firms.

Borders versus Hierarchies: The Tensions in Ohmae

Dicken's (1998) use of the production chain to analyse the dynamics of the global economy was introduced in Chapter 1. The view of international trade as a series of developments from flows between centre and periphery, via multi-domestic production close to markets to reciprocal production webs has accompanied Ohmae's formulation of the end of the "bi-polar discipline" of the Cold War.

Organisations, whether commercial, regulatory or voluntary, are increasingly confronted with the need to operate across a multiplicity of boundaries, whether geographical, political or cultural, in order to function within the emerging global system. Some subsequent regional re-alignments, most obviously in the Balkans, have allowed the resurrection of earlier conflicts placed in stasis by external threats. However, recently colonised regions of Africa in particular are faced with regional shifts of even greater complexity. More positively, elsewhere in Europe, Delamaide (1994) has identified what he describes as "super-regions" with, for example a re-emergence of the characteristics of the Hanseatic league in current developments around the Baltic.

Delamaide offers a perspective on pre-existing historical and cultural linkages which predate both the recent Cold War divisions, and the emergence of current nation states. In many areas such as the Danube basin and the Baltic, these older linkages can be seen re-emerging in the pan-European context. Elsewhere, he draws attention to the pivotal role of Turkey as a link between Europe and the Turkic republics of the former Soviet Union. Such cultural synergies offer a means of retaining regional coherence in the face of continuing expansion of entities such as the European Union. Kirlidog (1997) demonstrates the implications for technical support through an examination of the impact of Turkish business practices on the implicit assumptions of imported executive information systems. Cultural inter-operability is likely to become as significant as technical inter-operability in the global economy (Kaye and Little, 1996). These issues are returned to in Part III where Chapter 10 examines the institutional and cultural dimensions of development through a comparison of Turkish and Japanese modernisation strategies and their outcomes.

The logic of the current wave of technology-driven globalisation has impacted on significant sectors of the developed economies themselves. It has been suggested that even countries such as Japan and Britain are finding that only specific geographical areas or economic sectors are benefiting fully from integration into the global economy. As with other forms of technology transfer premised on foreign direct investment, smaller local organisations and enterprises may gain little, finding instead that key resources are diverted to the support of incoming capital, hampering their own development (see Dicken, 1998).

Inward investors may "cherry-pick" demographically, establishing greenfield developments remote from existing competing companies and with a younger workforce entailing less expense in terms of health and retirement provision. Such tactics allow investors both the inducements offered by local governments and a workforce whose age structure represents a significant cost advantage over established indigenous companies. The resulting regional "beauty contests" may result in supporting technologies, in particular the information and telecommunications infrastructure, optimised for these externally-driven actors, just as with the older technologies of more direct forms of colonial relationship described by Headrick (1981).

The differences and tensions between centre and periphery and between large and small scale economic activity become central to an understanding of the impact of globalisation and its supporting technologies. While Ohmae's "zebra strategies" combine the most developed components of adjacent national economies in order to create regional synergies, the resulting patterns of development are dependent upon a global infrastructure driven by the priorities of the dominant developed economies. This can only entrench inequitable development within national economies.

Implicit and explicit in Ohmae's zebra strategy is the view that national or even international regional government no longer has a significant role in development. While this view is increasingly challenged, there are differences of opinion over which level of government: regional, national or trans-national, is best equipped to deal with particular negotiations over a location's relationship to the wider economy.

During the 1990s the roller-coaster of events in the East Asian economies undermined confidence in their status as "miracle economies". Paul Krugman warned against the uncritical acceptance of the significance and sustainability of high growth rates over relatively short periods from very low base levels (Krugman, 1996). Unfortunately the immediate impact in the West was the out of hand rejection of the development strategies which had delivered substantive growth. This was coupled with a lack of awareness of the very different forms of crisis across the affected economies. As the range of responses from the governments and firms involved began to yield differential results, the diversity of former and current approaches within the region became more apparent to outsiders.

The crisis was in part a consequence of the success of the strategies which brought the growing economies to the point at which a paradigm shift from catch-up to sustained production of new technologies was required. At least part of the crisis in East Asia reflected the difference between the problems of technological leadership and those of catching-up with leading economies. Participation in the development of the intellectual resources necessary for this next stage requires more direct integration into the emerging world system and a greater institutional alignment within and between regions. The implications of this point for the technical design process itself will be looked at in detail in Part II. The policy implications of this shift will be dealt with here.

The shift from catch-up strategies to leadership requires different socio-technical paradigms capable of sustaining development in the conditions of lower absolute growth encountered in relatively mature markets. Mature economies seeking to remain at the cutting edge of technology in a maturing global market are themselves shifting focus towards the end of the production chain where product differentiation and customer support can maintain demand for goods and services seems essential. This end of the chain requires closer adjustment to cultural variation among the users and customers and as a consequence of the search for added value the distinction between products and services becomes less obvious. James and Howells' (2001) examination of the research and development facilities of Asian companies within the United Kingdom suggests that knowledge for every stage of the production process is being sought.

The Cold War concept of "Third World" identified the bulk of humanity through its exclusion from either superpower camp. The end of the Cold War has meant reduced attention from the former blocs. In some respects this has been beneficial, as major power confrontations are less frequently played out at the expense of third party proxies. However, there has also been a reduction in the flow of resources and technology, albeit often related to militarisation and its requirements. In the absence of this attention, the legacy of colonial infrastructures whose orientation may owe little to regional needs or potential synergies has become a central issue for development policies.

Realignments in an Emerging Global System

Throughout the emerging global system specific markets and specific technologies are at different points in the cycle of growth, maturity and decline. Rapid growth at favoured locations has created regional imbalances within regions and nation states. The notion of the dominant triad of developed regions within the world economy – North America, Europe and North East Asia – has become widely accepted in debates on the nature of globalisation (e.g. Mol, 2000; Ohmae, 1990; Rugman, 2001). Localities within each region of the "triad" are restructuring rapidly in an attempt to obtain or ensure a continued prosperous place within the global system. The great majority of world trade is within and between these regions. Beyond it new forms of exclusion are arising along with new forms of "periphery", no longer necessarily physically or geographically separated from the core regions.

Europe, North America and East Asia all contain the most advanced levels of economic development alongside developing economies. Each region faces the challenge of supporting balanced growth in peripheral areas where available infrastructure and skills cannot support full integration into the global economy. However, it is in the rapidly industrialising nations that the greatest disparities exist. In China the differences are even more striking. Using 1991 statistics, Ohmae (1995) shows that China's national average per capita GDP of US$317 masks regional variations in GDP ranging from US$164 and 197 in Guizhou and Guangxi to US$1,218 and 1,527 in Beijing and Shanghai. While continuing rapid economic development has raised all of these measures since 1991, the differentials remain, and are now openly acknowledged by the Chinese government (State Council of the P.R.C., 2001).

China, as East Asia's largest economy has the advantage of size and continuing scope for the established high growth paradigm. The attractiveness of its domestic market to foreign companies places both national and regional governments in a strong bargaining position. For example, in the automotive sector there are a number of substantial joint ventures. Rivals such as Ford and Nissan are happy to co-operate in order to access this market. However, by the late nineteen-nineties only the Shanghai Volkswagen Automotive Company's operation was judged profitable (Ishibashi, 1998) and this on the basis of substantial government and public sector and taxi fleet sales of their Santana model. This suggests that longer term market potential was the main motivation behind investment.

China's size also increases the problems of regional differentials in development. Ohmae celebrates such variation as evidence of the need to pursue his "zebra strategies" which play to the relative strength of the most developed components of national economies in order to create regional synergies. However, while linkages between the advanced areas of developing economies are creating new regions irrespective of national boundaries, few national governments are prepared to relinquish responsibility for the development of the state as a whole. The emergence of co-operative economic mechanisms in the Asian region, such as APEC and ASEAN suggest that there are means of achieving development which are acceptable to national governments. While the assertion that national or even international regional government no longer has a significant role in development is now increasingly challenged, differential development seems likely to be entrenched through dependence upon a global infrastructure driven by the priorities of the dominant developed economies.

There is a danger of the development of two-tier technologies, addressing the less developed local markets and more demanding overseas markets separately, and adding little to indigenous capacity to enter the global market. The GM-Shanghai mid-size luxury Buicks designed and produced for the local market indicate that at least in the automotive sector, this is less of a concern in China. However, the sustainability of local demand will depend on continuing infrastructure development, both in support of manufacture, and of the use of the resulting automobiles, bringing in its train all of the issues confronting resource sustainability in the more developed economies.

Chains versus Networks

Picking up an earlier point, the organisations and alliances which comprise the global production system have to deliver continuous innovation at the cutting edge while ensuring effective diffusion of more mature technologies. For prospective participants, the infrastructure and skills necessary for full integration into the global economy may be lacking. The shift from catch-up development strategies to technological leadership of a globalising system of production requires a shift in socio-technical paradigm. Sustaining development in the conditions of lower absolute growth encountered in relatively mature markets is a very different proposition. The organisational forms of the late twentieth century world economy and corresponding emergent require adjustment if they are to deliver a developmental infrastructure. Historical and cultural particularities ensure both diversity and friction throughout the emerging global system Nevertheless, this heterogeneous system is too often presented as a seamless technological artefact.

This chapter argues that the idea of global production chains consisting of a geographical hierarchy linking resources, manufacturers and consumers is being replaced by the idea of global production networks in which research and development, routine manufacturing, final assembly and after-market support may all be present in the same location. The re-distribution of these activities during the product life cycle further undermines the traditional concepts of centre and periphery. Krugman (1996) points out that internal trade still dominates many major industrial countries, but linkages among members of the Triad account for the majority of global trade and have established a pattern which disadvantages substantial areas and populations by excluding them from the global cycle of technical innovation and improvement.

The emerging global system is not a uniform network, it presents different challenges for the new century for each member of the dominant economic "triad" of Europe, North America and East Asia identified by Ohmae. Both proponents of globalisation such as Ohmae and more critical reviewers such as Dicken (1998) recognise that differences within individual national states may be at least as significant that those between them. As noted above, these may be most marked within the developing economies but the logic of the current wave of technology driven globalisation has impacted on significant sectors of the developed economies themselves. Japan and Britain are finding that only specific geographical areas or economic sectors may benefit fully from integration into the global economy. As with other forms of technology transfer premised on foreign direct investment, smaller local organisations and enterprises may gain little, finding instead that key resources are diverted to the support of incoming capital, hampering their own development. Key supporting technologies, in particular the information and telecommunications infrastructure, may be optimised for these externally-driven activities.

In addition, the challenges of technological leadership differ from those of catch-up growth. Economies such as South Korea which have been highly successful during the catch-up phase of development show that different socio-technical paradigms are needed to sustain growth in the conditions of lower absolute growth encountered in relatively mature markets. The greater emphasis on basic science and emerging technologies now evident in both Japan and South Korea shows the response that is being made.[6]

European and North American companies have sought to emulate aspects of Asian strategies for some time and comparative advantage has been eroded as Asian methods, building on the Western industrial model have been re-exported to the original industrial core of Europe and North America. Japan's earlier lead means that the debate over new economic strategies has intensified further since the collapse of the bubble economy which was sustained by inflated share and property prices. However, consensus has not been achieved over exactly what changes should be made to the institutional structures which supported post war development.

Networks, Globalisation and Sovereignty

The idea of a global marketplace reflects economic developments which came to fruition in the second half of the twentieth century and are set to continue into the twenty-first. The new forms of internationalised business organisation which are now emerging represent the culmination of processes of downsizing, separation of core and peripheral activities through concentration on critical success factors, and the medium to long term effect of technical changes which have been visible for some time. The recent maturation of a number of capabilities within information and communication technology has allowed these processes to reach fruition. Computer-based information systems are now capable of facilitating or even substituting for organisational structures and standards. This phenomenon has been evaluated from a variety of social and organisation theory perspectives. For example, computer-aided design systems may substitute for organisationally enforced standards and alter the economies of scale in favour of smaller, flatter organisations. Standards for software and electronic data interchange (EDI) are increasingly presenting organisations with externally derived standards and procedures. The standards are increasingly the result of market-based de-facto processes and not of governmentally supported formally constituted committees.

The emergent concept of the "networked organisation" has focused attention on the development and maintenance of organisational relationships through computer-mediated communication. The prospect of organisations primarily dependent upon information systems for both structure and social cohesion also implies a new range of locational choices for business. More recently EDI and networking between formally separate organisations has produced a counter-trend to down-sizing and outsourcing by permitting coalescence into federated forms of organisation. Diverse human and material resources can be managed through the electronic adjacency delivered though ICTs. The outcome of these processes has been a marked shift in employment patterns with new opportunities and access reflecting new locational opportunities.

Telecommuting by some members of an organisation has become the corollary to the outsourcing of other activities to separate undertakings. More flexible forms of work contract are leading to the incorporation of households into formal business organisations in a way which recalls the pre-industrial household, as much as any post-industrial scenario. Home-based work offers an alternative to the enforced leisure of unemployment, however, in developed countries, the association between casualisation and home-based work raises concern for the quality of that employment. Gains such as improved employment access for women with dependent children, or workers with disabilities, must be set against corresponding costs of isolation and fragmentation within this "virtual" workforce, and the potential loss of the social dimension of working life. Technologically optimistic accounts subsume these dimensions into generalised "resistance to change". The reality of current achievements is far from the seamless visions of integrated technologies critiqued by Zimmerman (1986), but is likely to be experienced as incremental, fragmented adjustment and change.

The remaining chapters of this section examine the origins of the technocratic view of the new spatial and organisational relationships, and the implications for the meaningful participation by regions, communities and households in the formation of global networks.

Notes

1 For Ohmae full engagement with the developed economies requires a per capita GDP of US$10,000.
2 See Chapter 6 for a discussion of the model presented by Jones (1980) of a basic design cycle from divergent to convergent phases.
3 http://www.wto.org
4 http://www.worldbank.org
5 http://www.ilo.org
6 See for example the Korean Ministry of Science and Technology's plan for science and technology development to 2025, MOST (n.d.), http://www.most.go.kr

Chapter 3

Wicked Problems and Evil Empires: Positivism, Complexity and the Cold War Origins of the Information Society

The preceding chapters have outlined the information infrastructure of the current form of globalisation on one hand and the institutional infrastructure of the nation state on the other. Both of these determine the space in which developing countries can develop their responses to their global context, alignment between them is necessary for coherent and inclusive development. These issues will be further developed in the remainder of Part I and this chapter looks at the historical origins of the communication technologies central to the current mode of globalisation, and the underlying positivist assumptions about technology and development.

The influence of modernism and related theory from architecture and planning on current implementations of physical infrastructure, urban development and industrialisation is described. A view of complex systems that engages the social complexities which undermine determinist projects is introduced.

As argued in Chapter 2, the information and communication technologies underpinning the current mode of globalisation are not the first spatially significant technologies. Headrick (1981) demonstrates the key role of technologies ranging from transportation to medical prophylaxis in the extension of the influence and sovereignty of the European powers and the globalisation of their model of the nation state. Chapter 1 and 2 examined how continued developments in technology and economic scale have led to the internationalisation of economic activity and to the emergence of consequences beyond the capacity of individual states to manage. The emergence of trans-national corporations (TNCs) and the internationalisation of both financial and labour markets have created a rapidly evolving world system. Currently this is characterised by progressive integration at a world scale. Camilleri and Falk (1992) argue that power and authority have become diffused with national states participating in a variety of multilateral arrangements covering not just trade, production and finance but also increasingly inter-related environmental and security issues. Paradoxically, the model of nation state central to international relationships is both undermined and constrained by the commitments, explicit and implicit, created by such international ties.

The previous chapters examined how the imperatives of an emerging global market have led developed economies to shift their focus towards the end of the production chain where product differentiation and customer support can maintain demand for goods and services. This has provided an opportunity for the inclusion of new contributors whose capabilities lie at other points in the production and consumption chain. However, segregation and exclusion are producing an unevenness of development both within and between economies and this unevenness impacts on regions, communities and individuals. Whether such exclusion is socially or geographically based, it threatens the prospects of achieving economic development which is environmentally or socially sustainable. Natural resources exploited by external actors may be developed in order to deliver high extraction rates at low cost rather than longer term sustainable exploitation. With human resources, skill-bases may be developed to serve the external priorities of imported capital, instead of around a more balanced strategy for the development of a host economy.[1]

Two issues raised so far merit further consideration. The first is the scepticism of newly industrialising countries engaged in catching up with the dominant established economies. Governments are unwilling to adhere to higher standards than those applied to their competitors when they were at the same stage of development, but by ignoring improvements in practice they run the risk of undermining their own longer-term interests. The second issue is the partial nature of an allegedly "global" system. A significant proportion of humanity is excluded from both the catch-up process itself and the policy making processes which determine the nature of the emerging global production system. In Chapter 5 it will be argued that imminent shifts in the information and communication infrastructure offer a window of opportunity for players marginalised by the status quo to make a meaningful contribution to the social shaping of an emerging techno-economic paradigm. This chapter traces the origins of the framework which currently underpins that paradigm.

Engines of Development: Modernism in Architecture and Planning

The roots of the determinism implicit in modernism in architecture and planning, its relationship to "scientific management", and its influence on the design of the physical infrastructure and the information infrastructure of the global system are central to the thesis of this book. The application of a pre-war modernist project to post-World War II reconstruction coincided with developments in information technology which ultimately transformed the range of spatial configurations available to organisations. Urban studies and organisation research have both been influenced by general systems theory. This influence is critical to both definitions of modernism, and to developments underpinning postmodernism.

In the last quarter of the twentieth century postmodernism appeared as both a reactionary and progressive influence. Esher (1981) talks of British post-war reconstruction as a "broken wave". In architecture and planning postmodernism first gained ground, paradoxically because of its critical continuity with modernist sentiment in terms of the democratisation of design and the claims to a shared understanding of aesthetic and technical expression between designers and users. However, the critique of the inadequacies of modernism in architecture and planning voiced by Venturi (1966) foreshadows the narrowly stylistic interpretation of post-modernism that followed.

During the same period, however, new definitions of community in urban theory emerged which challenged the determinist assumptions of the modern movement in architecture and planning and which voiced the concerns of those whose space for action was being determined by design professionals. Participative design (Cross, 1972) was advanced as the means to overcome the deficiencies of the implementation of the modernist project.

International Style – Global Intent

The International Style, in the form of the Bauhaus aesthetic, stood for the determination of form by machine production, yet the archetypes promoted through international publications were in fact hand crafted prototypes, at some remove from the reality of mass-produced products in the marketplace (Banham, 1960). The Soviet constructivist movement demonstrated the greatest gulf between aspiration and available infrastructure in its attempt to create built forms to support the socialist transformation of society (Kopp, 1970).

In constructing a retrospective narrative of modernism the architectural historian Nicholas Pevsner (1949) included designers such as Eric Mendelsohn, firmly rooted in German expressionism, and Charles Annesley Voysey from the British Arts and Crafts movement in the Modernist pantheon. This indicates a post-priori justification of modernism in Darwinian terms as the climax of design evolution. Venturi (1966), echoing Sir John Summerson, argues that the programmatic approach of modernists tends to stake a claim for architecture rather than produce architecture. Subsequently a new narrative has relocated individuals such as James Stirling or Isozaki Arata and sub-movements such as Brutalism, and Metabolism, to take European and Japanese examples respectively, from late modernism to early post-modernism. This indicates that a similar process of justification operated in the 1970s and 1980s as postmodernism began to be identified retrospectively in architecture and design (e.g. Jencks, 1989).

As Banham (1969) and Russell (1981) demonstrate, there were tangible technical, social, and economic pressures influencing the development of planning and construction during these periods, but not in the physically deterministic fashion assumed by the promoters of modernism.

Banham (1960) argues that technical and aesthetic innovations were not strongly coupled in the period that saw the emergence of the modern or international style. The most innovative buildings technically were often aesthetically conservative while aesthetic innovations, pursued through technically obsolescent means, were presented as demonstrations of a technical determinism in which form followed function.

Globalisation was implicit in the modernist agenda. In 1927 the French architect and polemicist Le Corbusier advocated a worldwide internal temperature standard of 18 degrees Celsius (Corbusier, 1946). In the United States, the engineer, Richard Buckminster Fuller proposed the global distribution of factory-built prefabricated houses by airship.

In a comprehensive study of the development and implementation of the concept of industrialised building, Russell (1981) demonstrates that large-scale convergence of social and technical forces were needed to bring about substantial changes in design and construction practice. The availability of pre-war and wartime innovation, coupled with relative labour shortages and a government sponsored policy of increased capitalisation in the building industry produced a coincidence of interest during the 1950s and 1960s which led to large scale industrialised building programmes in the U.K. and elsewhere. The drive towards standardised volume production also led to the direct application of information and communication technologies in the form of computer aided design (Little, 1988).

Russell (1981) provides a detailed analysis of the dynamics of the discourse within the technical design community and their institutional clients. These led to what generally became regarded as massive social and technical failures. By the late 1960s large scale-social housing projects were being cited as examples of spectacular systems failure (e.g. Webber, 1968). These perceptions prompted the crisis of confidence from which post-modernism emerged as a dominant architectural aesthetic.

The modern movement architects were happy to pursue the detail of design down to the micro level. A striking example is the design of St Catherine's College, Oxford by the Danish architect Arne Jacobsen. His interpretation of an Oxford college was designed down to the furniture in the students' study-bedrooms, and the cutlery used at High Table. At the more mundane level the design standards for U.K. public housing from the 1960s to 1980s were articulated in design manuals portraying, hour by hour, the "typical" day in a household (Roberts, 1991). Specific items of furniture had to be indicated in each room of a house plan to qualify it for housing subsidy. The standard itself, originating in a 1961 report (Parker Morris Committee, 1961), did not reflect subsequent social and technical developments which affecting space usage. For example, the diffusion of domestic freezers during the 1970s was ignored. Instead the presence of a radiogram, a key aspiration of the 1950s, was preserved in every living room until the abandonment of the design standard in the early 1980s.

The detailed implications of this level of attention are examined in Part II. It is worth noting both the totalising approach and the heavily gendered understanding of domestic labour institutionalised in the design of domestic architecture. This totalising view of human activity was derived from the technocratic sensibility which is examined below.

The critique of the modernist narrative was a partial and selective one, from within the determinist framework. Biased towards physical implementations rather than underlying social drivers, it focussed on the interests of the design professions. By the 1980s, in the U.K., for example, high rise housing became unacceptable all circumstances, low rise housing was an unalloyed public good, regardless of socio-economic context. Two decades earlier the established wisdom was that sufficient accommodation to replace unfit low rise housing could only be provided by high rise construction. Neither set of assumptions had any basis in reality. To go beyond such simplifications it is necessary to look at the origins of the positivist view of technology and design implicit in a form of modernism, both mandated by government policy and funding regulations and supported by public discourse.

Beyond Physical Spaces: Technology, Technocracy and Modernism

The output of the modern movement in architecture and planning was physically obvious. The equivalent discourse in the design and development of organisations and institutions produced less tangible but equally significant outcomes. It is therefore worth tracing the origin of the corresponding philosophy in management and administration.

Weber's definition of bureaucracy is regarded as a major underpinning of modernism in organisation theory and sociology.[2] The claim to superiority over traditional forms of authority and control made by bureaucracy was based on the notion of a rational means of evaluation of individuals and their capabilities. The scientific management movement which arose in the first half of the twentieth century built upon this understanding of rationality. This generated a positivist narrative which underpinned both the rapid advances in management and production of the Second World War and the Cold War period. Climaxing with Robert MacNamara's incumbency as U.S. Secretary of State this period was one of rational analysis of quantified data, placing scientific management at the centre of national survival.

The foundations for the "military-industrial complex" identified by US President Dwight Eisenhower in his farewell address (Eisenhower, 1961) were laid in the period leading up to World War II. Rearmament, mobilisation and the associated managerial methods formed the basis of those used in the Cold War. The strategic distribution of production during the war laid the basis for post-war policies of "complementarity" in which production resources were both distributed and replicated (Little and Grieco, 2003). The same logic of distribution of production applied to the subsequent period of nuclear confrontation.

The modern movement in architecture had been articulated during the inter-war depression, but implemented on a large scale in the renewed activity of post-world war reconstruction. The U.S. military-industrial complex is a product of the impact of World War II and the Cold War on science and technology policy, but it too reflects a pre-war technocratic sensibility. This had been given a formal expression in the political flux immediately before the implementation of the Roosevelt administration's "New Deal" programme. A Technocrat Movement rose to short-lived national prominence in the United States on a political programme of technical rationality. The Movement aimed to place engineers in charge of all facets of society, claiming that the economy would prosper in the hands of engineers. Developing Veblen's (1904) conception of the role of technical workers, the Technocrat Movement adopted energy consumption as a single unifying metric through which the rational management of economy and society could be achieved.

Ultimately, according to Akin (1977), the movement withered precisely because its narrow technicism precluded the formulation of a programme of political action. The Technocrat agenda lost momentum in the face of the success of the New Deal, but the Second World War gave an added impetus to the underlying view that any problem, however complex was amenable to quantitative analysis, provided that analysis was sufficiently sophisticated.

The continuity of technocracy pre and post World War II needs to be emphasised. Belief in the power of technical rationality to deal with almost any economic or social problem has proved enduring. It received reinforcement through the comparative success of the New Deal policies in the U.S. and the successful application of new management techniques during the Second World War. The rapid advances in military and other technologies ensured a continuing acceptance of such views in the post-war period. One former Technocrat Society member, the engineer Richard Buckminster Fuller, mentioned earlier in connection with the aerial delivery of standardised housing, promoted the original Technocrat principles up to the end of the 1960s. As noted, the career of Robert MacNamara, narrated by Halberstam (1971), offers a paradigm of this post-war flowering of technocratic consciousness. MacNamara's career in the automotive industry, government and the World Bank reflects the movement of these sensibilities from industry to governance and to development.

It could be argued that Cold War strategy elevated technocracy above democracy. Chalmers Johnson's study of post-war Japan illustrates the continuity of personnel between the post-war Ministry of International Trade and Industry (MITI) and the pre-war technocrats of the administration of Manchukuo, Japanese occupied Manchuria (Johnson, 1983). U.S. influenced constitutions were imposed on Japan and Germany, but the former Japanese colonies of Taiwan and South Korea benefited primarily from the attention of U.S. advice in technical development and productive capacity with democratic development coming only late in the Cold War period.

Cold War Traces: Information Systems and Surveillance

The information and communication technologies facilitating the global distribution of Western models of production were created in the same wartime and post-war milieu. However, the continuity of Cold War concerns for secrecy with wartime security meant that the narrative of this crucial period of development was determined without reference to some key components. In particular, the wartime creation by British code-breakers of the Colossus electronic computer used to calculate settings on the German Enigma encryption machines was left out of the narrative of the introduction of computer-based information systems to governance and commerce.

The work was only revealed fully by the publication of F.W. Winterbotham's *The Ultra Secret* in 1974. In the following decades a number of documentary and fictional accounts of the work undertaken by the Government Codes and Cypher School (GCCS) appeared, providing the basis for a revisionist narrative of World War II. These accounts contradicted many assumptions implicit in the established view of a British victory based around Churchillian "Blood, toil, sweat and tears" plus the judicious use of operations research techniques. Instead it was revealed that at key points in the war allied commanders had access to German high command orders before their intended recipients, via the use of captured or purloined Enigma coding machines and the computational analysis of intercepted signals traffic.

Alan Turing, a key figure in assembling the core team, was cast as the central heroic and eccentric genius. In the best British tradition, fictionalised accounts of the work of Turing and his colleagues emphasised a small group of boffins in a remote country house and the documentary accounts of survivors of the key groups at Bletchley Park tell of inspirational breakthroughs by individuals and small teams. However, the Taylorist organisation for the volume production of information from a vast range of intercepted messages contradicts the carefully cultivated image of lonely genius and individual inspiration. Much of the site, fifty miles north of London, is still covered by temporary and permanent buildings occupied by the 8,000 workers, many female, who made use of state-of-the-art business data processing technologies in the form of Hollerith tabulators and card indexes. The creation of massive databases of signals traffic and the development of increasingly sophisticated traffic analysis techniques, not the discovery of the content of individual messages, led to many of the significant results produced.

By the time the work of Bletchley Park became public, Turing's fame had already been established by his early specification for a generalised computational machine (Turing, 1936/7) and as the "father" of artificial intelligence through his formulation of a test to determine whether a machine was exhibiting intelligence.[3]

The post-war deployment of computer-based information systems in commercial organisations diffused a particular model of strategic and operational management. Individuals who passed through Bletchley Park played a leading role in the post-war development of electronic computing, both at Manchester University in Britain and in the MIT Whirlwind project in the U.S. The sharing of intelligence and knowledge between the U.K. and the U.S. meant that with the destruction of the British records, the reconstruction of the Colossus computer, the star exhibit of the Bletchley Park museum, was expedited by archival information only available from U.S. sources (Sale, 1998).

By the time the gaps finally were filled in the U.K.'s wartime narrative, however, a history of electronic computing had been constructed from U.S.-based activities, including a range of successor projects to the secret British efforts. Ironically, despite the close relationship of these activities to defence in general and the U.S. nuclear weapons programme in particular, these had long been in the public realm.[4]

In the U.K. Churchill had ordered the physical destruction of key equipment and files at Bletchley Park on the cessation of hostilities in 1945, effectively concealing the wartime contribution of code breaking. However, the Government Communications Headquarters (GCHQ) was established in 1946 as the post-war successor of the Government Code and Cipher School. In the U.S. the Signals Intelligence Service, based in Arlington Hall, Virginia, and comparable in its origins to GCCS, re-emerged in 1952 as the National Security Agency (NSA).

Bamford (1983) provides a history of the NSA which characterises its Cold War resource levels as computer capacity measured by the acre. According to its website,[5] the NSA is currently the second largest user of electrical power in Maryland with an annual bill in excess of $21 million.

A range of significant innovations in computational capability followed from the capacity required by both code breakers and the developers of nuclear weapons. York's narrative of the post-Manhattan project technologies and politics (York, 1976) was noted above. During and after the Cold War the NSA led significant initiatives in the development of computing. It promoted joint development with IBM of second generation general computers with features such as the high speed tape drives, prominent in every 1960s movie featuring computers. They also sponsored the first Cray supercomputers and in 1990 established a Special Processing laboratory for in-house fabrication of highly specialised micro-electronic devices.

Innovations such as finite element analysis in engineering calculation and the related practice of constructing production aircraft without physical prototypes (Sabbagh, 1995) as well as the mathematical modelling which allows "in-silico" pharmaceutical development, all make use of massive computational power first developed either for code breaking or for the mathematical simulation of nuclear explosions.

Technocracy, Systems and Solutions

The confluence of scientific and military resources and the effect on the wider arena of technical design is a major theme of Part II. The continuing role of the signals intelligence community at the cutting-edge of computing developments in the post-war period has ensured that the information economy emerged in step with the surveillance state.

In the U.K. the post-war reactivation of GCHQ was closely followed by civilian scientific and commercial applications of electronic computers. The Lyons Electronic Office (LEO) implemented the key concepts of management information systems at a stroke. However the low profile of Bletchley Park allowed an alternative narrative to be constructed. As recently as December 2000, John King of the University of Michigan provided a keynote address to the International Conference for Information Systems in Brisbane which traced the post-war history of commercial computing with no mention of the critical LEO innovations (King, 2000).

The established narrative is a Cold War one, leading from the SAGE[6] real-time system developed for aircraft interception, to the critical innovation of the SABER real-time airline reservation system. This was as much the key to affordable mass air travel as the wide bodied jet and, disintermediated through the Internet, real-time booking systems remain the core technology of budget airlines.

The Cold War ARPANet origins of the Internet are well known,[7] as are the survivability and web characteristics which were in part a response to the physical vulnerability of the SAGE system. The computer centres of this system were located at Strategic Air Command (SAC) bomber-bases, prime targets for any enemy nuclear strike. Allegedly this was for staffing reasons since, under General Curtis Lemay, SAC had secured the best quality officers' facilities, in the U.S. military and SAGE relied on the attentions of highly skilled and highly sought after technical personnel.

At the end of the Cold War the NSA's mission statement[8] distinguished between external foreign signals intelligence and "classified and unclassified national security systems". In the post-9/11 environment, the civil dimension is represented by a separate Information Systems Security Organization (ISSO).[9] The NSA promoted their own "Clipper" encryption chip as the answer to commercial security problems on the information superhighway.[10]

Joint development and commercial programmes provide a direct link between military and diplomatic concerns and the world of commerce. Despite measuring its computing resources in acreage, the NSA outsources data processing to commercial organisations such as TRW, also a major credit data agency, as illustrated in the 1980s film *The Falcon and the Snowman* (see also Bamford, 1983). Yet another link between military and commercial projects is through technique. The continued refinement of signals traffic analysis has led to the emergence of what Roger Clarke (1989) terms "dataveillance" in which sets of data collected for a variety of disparate purposes can be processed to reveal unanticipated information and associations. Both governments and private organisations like TRW are able to assemble revealing pictures of organisations and individuals through the correlation of individually trivial data. In the nineteen-eighties Clarke campaigned against the introduction of a national identity card – the "Australia Card" – on these grounds. Again, in the post-9/11 environment fresh demands for the introduction of electronic identity cards for citizens are being made in the U.K. and elsewhere.

At the workplace level, equivalent electronic surveillance has been described in a Japanese electronics factory, where data derived from production equipment was used to discipline work teams (Sewell and Wilkinson, 1992, see Chapter 4). Such coercive practices are now an accepted part of the call-centre economy. The electronic version of the panopticon (Foucault, 1979) involves constant monitoring of workers, consumers and customers.

Technocracy offers a deceptively simple solution to the cultural problems which a globalising economy presents. Rather than responding to local needs, variety of response is replaced by a range of top-down standard solution which can be promoted as technologically ordained.

Systems analysis became synonymous with technicist initiatives in the 1950s and 1960s. The general systems theory perspective on which it is based provides a relatively rigorous framework in which to advance the claims of modernity. However, the same perspective can also expose the partiality and post-constructed nature of the modern movement in architectural design and the closed-system logic of its axioms.

General systems theory emerged in the 1940s, as a means of comprehensive explanation in the natural sciences. The formulation of a general systems theory by von Bertalanffy (1950) provided a hierarchy of levels, each providing the environment for the subsystems on the level below, and the notion that internal differentiation reflects the complexity of transactions across the boundaries between systems.

A determinist and literal reading of general systems theory is reflected in the first generation design methods and theories that emerged in engineering and design during the 1950s. These attempted normative explanation of optimum design practices and procedures. They enjoyed acceptance among practitioners because they utilised familiar and straightforward techniques, such as the check-list.

Scott (1987, 1992) classifies the evolution of all the major strands of organisation theory as a progression of increasing sophistication from a closed rational systems view associated with classical management theory to an emergent open natural systems view, closer to von Bertalanffy's position.

The natural systems view incorporates the perspective of the human relation school of management theory which accounted for the complexity of the behaviour of human actors within their system view, in contrast to the rational systems view that regarded job titles and descriptions as the determinants and predictors of behaviour. However, the classic Hawthorne studies encapsulating this approach (Roethlisburger and Dickson, 1939) and which first theorised informal relationships within the workplace remain controversial. The findings suggested that worker behaviour reflected the manipulation of the physical environment of the plant, without reference to the external, hostile economic environment. There were lay-offs and redundancies taking place during the studies.[11]

Contingency theory (Lawrence and Lorsch, 1967) most clearly reflects the open systems view by relating the internal state of an organisation to the environment with which it has to interact and the means of that interaction.

"Wicked Problems"

Postmodernism can be characterised by a move away from hierarchical determinist structures and the unified rationality of a single metric as exemplified by first generation design methods.

The type of strictly hierarchical decomposition derived from classical general systems theory was incorporated in first generation design methods, typified by Alexander (1964). Alexander himself quickly modified this approach through the use of semi-lattice networks to account for the rich and subtle social and physical interactions he associates with "natural" as opposed to "artificial" cities (Alexander, 1965). There exists a critical lag in the diffusion of his ideas, however, such that even Alexander's revision of his original position has yet to reach many of those influenced by him and who utilise his work. Venturi (1966) also argues for "complexity and contradiction" in his early formulation of what was soon to became post modernist architecture. However, Goodman (1972) argues that complexity is acknowledged only through physical appearance in what remains a traditional architectural approach; the design process itself is not modified.

In contrast, Rittel and Webber typify the second generation of design methods in that they forsake a simplistic view of systems theory. Rittel and Webber (1973) tackle the context of complex design decision making head on. They argue that they are responding to growing dissatisfaction with the performance of professionals among their clients, particularly the "general public" despite an apparent growth in professionalism, training and qualification, and the development of an increasing range of supporting technologies.

By the early 1970s the American and European public were becoming more vocal and discerning, but the classic professional approach to decision-making was seen as increasingly ill-suited to "conceptions of interacting open systems" and "contemporary concerns with equity". Ten distinguishing properties of "wicked problems" were identified by Rittel and Webber:

1: There is no definitive formulation of a wicked problem.
2: Wicked problems have no stopping rule.
3: Solutions to wicked problems are not true-or-false but good-or-bad.
4: There is no immediate and no ultimate test of a solution to a wicked problem.
5: Every solution to a wicked problem is a "one-shot operation"; because there is no opportunity to learn by trial-and-error, every attempt counts significantly.
6: Wicked problems do not have an enumerable (or exhaustively describable) set of potential solutions, nor is there a well-described set of permissible operations that may be incorporated into the plan.
7: Every wicked problem is essentially unique.
8: Every wicked problem can be considered to be a symptom of another problem.
9: The existence of a discrepancy representing a wicked problem can be explained in numerous ways. The choice of explanation determines the nature of the problem's resolution.
10: The planner has no right to be wrong.

(Rittel and Webber pp.161-166)

These properties take the problem space beyond Simon's formulation of bounded rationality (Simon, 1969). Jones (1980) points out, in support of Simon's notion of satisficing, that a ten component system with ten alternatives for each component has a solution space of 10^{10} configurations, but in Rittel and Webber's formulation, the system boundaries will always be subject to re-formulation and the introduction of more or different variables.

The first and second properties acknowledge the complexity of solutions to wicked problem and the difficulty of consensus among those affected by them.

The third and fourth argue that the evaluation of wicked problems is ultimately a question of judgement.

The fifth, sixth and seventh properties indicate why formal decision support systems have met with limited success at strategic planning levels.

The eighth property: each problem existing as a symptom of another problem, reflects the interconnectedness implied by a systems framework for the task of modern technical design (e.g. Jones, 1980). Treatment of a wicked problem in isolation implies the risk of suboptimization within the larger system context.

The ninth property is suggestive of a post-modern frame: the selection of a particular framework of analysis or explanation is seen as a significant determinant of acceptable outcomes. Rittel subsequently produced the concept of an "issue-based information system" as the vehicle for providing a second generation systems approach to planning decisions, by allowing the implications of differing viewpoints to be incorporated into the analysis of a problem (Rittel, 1982).

The tenth property indicated that, unlike a Popperian scientist who can be satisfied with the disconfirmation of a hypothesis, the prescriptive planner could not regard the falsification of premises as a useful outcome. Action research may be viewed as one response to a commitment to deliver some resolution for the designer's client (e.g. Clark, 1972), and the first generation of design research in the 1950s and 1960s led many designers to view practice as a form of research with the experience of each project being utilised in its successors. Even here, however, the fifth and seventh properties question the value of past experience. The modernist project of universal rational design and development systems is severely compromised when analysed with this framework.

Conflicting Formulations of Planning, Design and Development

In 1970 Chris Jones both summarised the first generation of design methodologies from the 1950s and 1960s, and opened the debate on the nature of second generation methods which was to occupy much of the 1970s (Jones, 1980). He applied a general systems theory hierarchy to open up design decision making to community and political levels of discussion above the traditional arena of the technical core. This represented a generally non-determinist reading of systems theory, but, as explained above, the determinist strand from the Technocrat Movement had survived the Second World War and flourished in post-war conditions. Indeed, the conflict had enhanced the reputation of quantitative analysis and numerical decision-making methods. Thus, the mundane but significant applications of operations research at a technical level were elevated to the glamour of the strategic arena and a post-war generation of managers typified by Robert MacNamara attempted to solve "wicked" problems with rational, numerical methods (Halberstam, 1971).

A paradox emerges: general system theory in the hands of Jones (1980) is used to reveal the limited, deterministic frame of traditional technical decisions in the face of more complex socio-technical design problems, while in other hands applications of general systems theory ultimately supported a resurgence of technocratic, de-politicising assaults on modernist assumptions of social equity. For example, Forrester (1969) argues for the elimination of poor peoples' housing as a component of urban economic revival, the poorer inhabitants simply decamp across the system boundary to another town with less "enlightened" policies, and the real estate they vacated becomes available for inward investment and industrial development.[12]

In systems thinking the devil is on the boundaries and where they are drawn defines what is inside and outside the system under consideration. Unfortunately Forrester's argument that complex systems require counter-intuitive responses has led to, among other things, decisions leading to the destruction of British mining communities in the 1980s, Chilean democracy in the 1970s and Vietnamese villages in the 1960s. Weather patterns, nuclear explosions or complex engineering structures may be amenable to such a deterministic approach to mathematical modelling, but political and economic systems are not.

A pluralist view is inherent in Rittel and Webber's check-list of criteria for wicked problems, and pluralism was a focus of 1970s concerns in planning and development. Goodman (1972) mounts a sustained critique of the values concealed by the implementation of both modernist and emergent post-modernist planning and design practices. A range of participative design and advocacy planning concepts emerged as an alternative. Design participation generally left ultimate control with the professionals, and shared the strengths and weaknesses of the socio-technical systems approach to job design. Advocacy planning corresponded in many ways to the substitution of markets for hierarchies emerging in organisation theory during this period (Williamson, 1975). Marketplace rhetoric neglects the issue of ability to participate and to voice concerns meaningfully. Participation and advocacy in such limited forms have in effect de-politicised issues such as housing provision and employment opportunity which have been among traditional working class political demands by moving decision making into a technocratic framework.

Paradoxically planning in the 1970s and 1980s also saw the promotion of the key features of a deterministic modernism under the guise of critiques of modernism. Oscar Newman (1973) and Alice Coleman (1985) combine elements of behaviourism with environmental psychology and perceptual modelling in the service of the political status quo. They focus on a behaviourist interpretation of the physical characteristics of the built environment, suppressing discussion of underlying social relations through the use of a non-political "scientific" discourse. Newman however, takes time to berate post-war planners for attempting to create social diversity, arguing that strict separation of classes and land-use was the only means of arresting urban decline through the creation of defensible socially homogeneous enclaves. Jencks (1989) compares such "New Right" positions with Marxian critiques to demonstrate the collapse of the previous modernist consensus.

The reallocation of key modernist components to the post-modernist canon, noted above, suggest that the change from modernism to post-modernism is a Kuhnian paradigm shift (Kuhn, 1962), wherein existing marginal evidence becomes central to the new thesis. Just as categories of artefacts such as Brutalist architecture were shifted from late modern to post modern canon, so individual architects substituted neo-classical post modern forms via for the modernist aesthetic they had previously embraced.

In the U.K. an intermediate "neo-vernacular" style was briefly associated with the aesthetic conservatism of clients of the welfare state empowered through process-oriented participative design methods. It also accommodated the process-oriented Long Life, Low Energy, Loose Fit design strategies prompted by the energy crisis of the mid-1970s. However, these genuine innovations and the style itself were swamped by the high-tech aesthetic which appeared in response to the subsequent economic upturn, where, just as in the 1920s, the image of high-technology construction was pursued in preference to any serious concern for resource consumption over the lifetime of buildings.

It is significant that both modernism and post-modernism in architecture and planning were formulated at the bottom of an economic cycle. Implementation took place in the subsequent upturn, to a programme established in the absence of direct practical experience and constraints. Even more marked transformations can be seen in a journal such as Architectural Design. Following a change in ownership in 1976 serious examination of process-oriented technical innovation was replaced by purely stylistic exercises. When changing economic circumstances led to a direct economic as well as "moral" threat to the standing of the professions involved, ranks were closed and a traditional, physically-oriented view of design reclaimed the centre of architectural discourse.

Modernism, Postmodernism and Information Systems Design

By the end of the twentieth century the domains of information systems design and physical design had coalesced. Systems analysis provides the instantiation of general system theory in a form suitable for city planning, warfare or information systems development. Cost-Benefit Analysis was promoted as the means to compare complex variables on the basis of an equivalent to Technocracy's energy metric: in this case a financial bottom line. As computer-based information systems have become ever more pervasive, there has been a differentiation of technical skills into information systems development, software engineering, and computer science, in rough analogy to planning, architecture, and building science in urban construction. .

In information systems the role of the systems analyst is analogous to that of the architect. The social support requirements of users must be interpreted into technical requirements for system implementation by the software engineers who apply principles derived from computer science. Information systems are the most socially embedded technical artefacts. Galbraith (1977) first indicated how the task of information systems design inevitably involved organisation design, since the consequent organisational changes could only be regarded as effects, not side-effects.

The socio-technical systems approach which originated in work carried out in the U.K. in the late 1940s and early 1950s supports this view of the social formation of technology and the influence of technology on organisations. Research into new work methods in industry looked at the social consequences of changes in work methods (Trist and Bamforth, 1951). This work represented a significant change from the view that the introduction of technology was a neutral process leading to predictable outcomes. These views saw technology as determining these outcomes. However, the subsequent notion of social shaping of technology (Mackenzie and Wacjman, 1995) led to a position in which technical outcomes were determined by social actions. This collection of studies into the development of technologies ranging from military equipment to consumer durables demonstrate the predominance of human intention, over technical constraints.

Mumford and Wier (1979) bring socio-technical systems to information systems design and Checkland (1981) defines the concept of soft systems, each an attempt to incorporate a broader social component in design considerations. The "Multiview" approach (Wood-Harper et al, 1985) is a conscious attempt at an eclectic use of available methods in the early stages of design, but reverts to the established "life-cycle" sequence for the technical phase of design and implementation. Multiview 2 (Avison et al, 1998) adheres more closely to the "garbage can" approach to decision-making (Cohen et al, 1972) by retaining a choice of perspectives throughout the design process.

While Goodman (1972) condemns the asocial nature of post-modernist historicism, there is an analogy with emerging software engineering techniques supporting information systems development. Alexander, having started out with a direct application of systems decomposition to architectural design, eventually turned to a radical conservatism in which buildings were designed on site, drawing on a range of pre-existing and socially significant design elements (Alexander, 1977, 1979).

Object-oriented development techniques are intended to allow pre-existing modules of computer code to be readily re-used. The aim is to improve reliability and economy by developing a library of tried and tested components over a range of projects. In this respect they mirror the intention of Alexander's "pattern language".

Rapid prototyping and other so-called fourth generation information systems design technologies have raised the prospect of "end-user computing" becoming a genuinely postmodern design methodology, driven by users in their own terms. However, by incorporating both social and technical elements, actor-network theory provides a seamless representation of socio-technical systems.

Actor-network theory can be traced to work in the area of social studies of science (Latour and Woolgar, 1979) and of the study of technical innovation. The actor network itself is a heterogenous network of actors and interests that may include people, organisations, standards and artifacts. Callon and Latour (1992) coin the term "actant" to cover both human and non-human "actors". Their treatment of people and machines as equivalent may seem simply a deliberate provocation and an attempt to court notoriety.

"Quasi-objects" are introduced by Latour to express the influence of social processes and collective understanding on certain classes of constructed object. The "black box" is a key term in general systems theory. It is applied to a sub-system which is modelled in terms of its inputs from and its outputs to the larger system while its internal processes are not the immediate subject of investigation. Latour uses the term to imply that an element of the network may incorporate a set of conditions and decisions that have in effect been concealed within the box. These decisions determine the behaviour of the "black box" within the larger system. In this sense the behaviour of the box can exhibit the intentionally of those who contributed to its design yet at the same time conceal it.

Technocracy and Development

This chapter traces the origins of a philosophy which drove technological development during much of the twentieth century. It links the emergence of computer-based information systems with the theoretical underpinnings of modernism and bureaucracy and provides a definition of "wicked problems" not amenable to solution through the positivist assumptions of hierarchical models of design and development.

The technocratic focus of the first generations of design methods has been softened by the inclusion of social considerations of both design and use of artefacts and systems. However, a hard technocratic view still influences the design of both technologies and the organisations which are increasingly dependent upon them.

Approaches such as actor-network theory offer an equal role for the social and technical components of systems, and the opportunities provided by such views of design are examined in Part III. Chapter 4 raises issues of space, place and identity for communities and individuals seeking alternative understandings of a globalising system.

Notes

1 Both Headrick (1981) and Dicken (1998) provide a historical perspective for such patterns of development.
2 See for example Beetham (1985), Clegg (1990), Elwell, (1999).
3 Turing's famous test for machine intelligence (Turing, 1950) initially speculated on the ability to distinguish between male and female respondents via teletype communication, and only then discussed a human versus machine distinction. The gender blindness of most accounts of Bletchley Park is intriguing. For example, it was a low ranking Wren who alerted the Admiralty to an imminent sortie by the battle-cruiser Scharnhorst on the basis of signals traffic analysis on Christmas Eve 1942, allowing its destruction.
4 See York (1976) for a detailed account of the U.S. nuclear weapons programme in the relevant period.
5 http://www.nsa.gov
6 The Semi-Autonomous Ground Environment pioneered real-time control of interceptor aircraft supported by fault-tolerant dual computer systems.

7 ARPANet was eventually split into the secure Milnet and the public Internet.

8 Available at http://www.nsa.gov/about_nsa/mission.html

9 See http://www.nsa.gov/isso/bao/index.htm

10 The Enigma machine, the focus of the attentions of Bletchley Park, was itself originally a commercial product touted at pre-war trade shows and used by German state railways for commercial communications, as well as by the German Wehrmacht. In effect the NSA is returning technologies distantly descended from a German commercial patent to the world of business. In this context it is not surprising that there are claims that the U.S. signals intelligence community has from time to time acted in support of U.S. commercial interests through the interception of foreign business communications (European Parliament, 2001).

11 See Parsons (1974) and Gillespie (1991) for two analyses of these studies conducted decades after the original observations.

12 Edwards (2000) provides a sympathetic account of Forrester's work and its context.

Chapter 4

Virtual Working: Public and Private Presence in Cyberspace

Chapter 2 described the consequences of shifts in sovereignty flowing from the advent of the World Trade Organisation and other supra national constraints. The diffusion of state power through agreement to and participation in multilateral regulation in areas such as trade, security and environment has been matched by the emergence of trans-national corporations operating in internationalised financial and labour markets. These changes impact not only at national and sub-national levels, but increasingly flow through to the individual household. Chapter 3 linked the emergence of computer-based information systems with the theoretical underpinnings of modernism and bureaucracy and provided a definition of wicked problems not amenable to solution through positivist assumptions of hierarchical models of design and development.

The increasing porosity of national boundaries means that the household becomes the end-point of trans-border data flows. This disintermediation and the consequent collapse of hierarchies required the coalescence of communication and computing technologies. These changes transformed government attitudes to communication infrastructure. National monopolies with a remit to provide equal access for all citizens have been replaced by privatised and de-regulated alternatives. Governments perceive this as the only way to meet the rapidly expanding demand for capitalisation to deliver new forms of service.

Similarly national broadcasters now compete with a range of domestically and externally based competitors. This demonstrates the eclipse of the ability of national governments to form and control key areas of policy for technologies which impact on both urban and rural infrastructure (Camilleri and Falk, 1992). In such conditions new understandings of place and association are required.

Beyond Physical Place: Non-place Realms in Planning and Development

As indicated in the previous chapter, the systems approach had entered planning and development discourse by the 1960s (eg. Doxiadis, 1968; McLoughlin, 1969). It had shifted the focus from built form to the processes that underpin the development of that form.

In the U.S.A. Melvin Webber (1964) went a step further by seeking to move away from the agenda of city planning with its focus on "small scale physical aspects of urbanisation" (Webber, 1964, p.80). He suggests his view is

> oriented to metropolitan *processes* (a verb view) from which it seeks to identify the matching spatial *form* (a noun view), and hence it seeks to pose a dynamic portrait of metropolitan *form in action* (a gerund view).
> (Webber, 1964, p.80, emphasis in original)

Urban communities are presented as spatially structured processes, with the physical fusing of U.S. Atlantic seaboard settlement providing a striking example of the outcome of such processes.

In order to move from the physical bias of established planning conceptions, Webber proposes the "city as communications system" (Webber, 1964, p.84). Planners "share a conviction that the physical and locational variables are key determinants of social and economic behaviour and of social welfare" (Webber, 1964, p.85). According to Webber, the unique commodity offered by the city is accessibility and he cites Meir's (1959) development of a system of social accounts as the basis of an index of cultural wealth reflecting the volume and variety of information flowing through public communication channels (Webber, 1964, p.87, note 9). Such an approach switches the emphasis of urbanity from physical built form to the quality of interaction in cultural life through the exchange of information. Castells (1989) produces a corresponding analysis of economic activity in terms of the "space of flows" into which a location must enter in order to fully participate in the emerging global economy. Webber argues that this new definition implies that suburban and exurban dwellers enjoy a measure of urbanity not previously acknowledged.

Webber argues that planning must engage with three components of metropolitan social structure:

1: spatial flows of money, people and goods
2: location of the physical channels and adapted spaces that physically house activities
3: locations of activity places

(Webber, p.96)

The third component is approached through the traditional land-use view of development.

He suggests that the first component can be derived from the effectiveness with which communications systems may substitute messages for physical movement of persons or goods (p.97).

He cites the significance of railroad location in North American development as an indication of the importance of the second component in determining urban form. The subsequent significance of street car and suburban lines, and freeways suggests that developments in telecommunication capability and capacity had been equally instrumental in freeing access and range of locational choice.

Face-to-face communication becomes a special need, and traditional central locations are therefore still of value for particular forms of business.

Webber provides a descriptive schema for spatial structure using the three components, and points out that "(p)atterns of functional interdependence will become increasingly complex at the same time that major developments in transportation and communications systems will be opening up unprecedented possibilities for whole new spatial patterns" (p.107). He constructs a matrix to facilitate the exploration of the character of accompanying change in spatial structures.

Webber formulates a "non-place community" in terms of Interest-Communities. Accessibility, rather than the propinquity aspect of "place" is the necessary condition for this form of community (p.109). Extensive webs of specialised professionals can be regarded as communities without propinquity. Specialised professionals are acknowledged to be at one end of the spectrum of residents in a metropolitan area, with many other similar association patterns present in non-professional communities. Webber argues that such a traditional "place community" is in fact a special case of a larger genus. With developments in technology and education allowing wider participation in non-place groups a hierarchical continuum from highly specialised communities spanning the entire world via less specialised intra-national networks, to metropolitan and neighbourhood networks may be envisaged. Individuals can expect to play roles at a number of these levels at any one time. At each level, the appropriate spatial field is shared by a number of interest communities, and Webber calls such levels of interdependence and interaction "urban realms" (p.114). Webber is providing new definitions of adjacency which fit with those now created by ICTs.

Place in Urban Theory, Design and Development

Webber argues that if an analysis of the distribution of each individual's time between realms were possible, it would reveal that rich and diverse human communication was present in conditions of low density and low concentration. He suggests that, in his terms, the urbanity of Los Angeles may not be that different from that of New York. Webber argues that certain approaches to the classification of urban centres were more amenable to the consideration of the range of interactions which he identifies, but that any reconsideration of definitions of centrality in the terms outlined by him would call into question the traditional notions of centre and hinterland, citing locational decisions of emerging high technology companies in California at that time.

A range of other approaches combined to shift attention from the physical to the social and psychological dimensions of environment. Mental mapping is the application of a technique from geography, evaluating perceptions of actors in an environment, coupled with observations of their actions in space. This allows a cognitive approach to the definition of place and neighbourhood. Environmental psychology emerged as a discipline providing support for spatial decisions at a "proxemic" level of personal space (Hall, 1966; Canter, 1977), at a regional level mapping geographical preference revealed striking distortions in perceptions of geographically and culturally remote regions (Gould and White, 1974).

Spatial formation can be approached from the phenomenological perspective of the postmodernist Robert Venturi in which, with luck, the "relationships and power will take care of themselves" (Venturi, 1966, p.12). A Marxist approach from Feenberg (1980), argues that the alienating effects of urban existence, in contrast to the contentment of rural community, may be seen as potentially politically liberating. In this context, non-spatial relationships, and the wider networks provided through greater private mobility can be seen as destructive of the cohesion of traditional urban centres.

Advances in information technology have problematised definitions of centre and periphery in development. The contrast between the telecommuting scenarios of technologically optimistic futurists such as Toffler (1970) and Bell (1979) and subsequent developments in trans-national work organisation is considerable, however. Telecommunications have allowed real-time off-shore location of white collar work, for example from the U.S. mainland to the Caribbean or from the United Kingdom to India. While information technology appears to offer a means of redressing relative locational disadvantage, and widening access to the "non-place realm" described by Webber, practical experience suggests that the impact on locational mobility has been overestimated for the majority of the working population. Webber himself discusses the relative disadvantage of the "by-passed pre-industrial locals" (Webber, 1968, p.1101). Whether the elite component of the workforce required by trans-national corporations are the only actors meeting Webber's definition of non-space interest communities will be explored later in this book.

Place, Non-place, Community and Network

The "global village" concept, a cousin of Webber's non-place realm, is perhaps the culturally acceptable face of globalisation, but it represents a top down diffusion of cultural hegemony. Only now can the diffusion of information technology at various levels of sophistication support a two-way traffic. Gender was little theorised in relation to the application of technology in the 1960s, and Aungles (1994) demonstrates how it can still be largely ignored in technological debates through her examination of electronically monitored domestic detention. The state places the burden of incarceration upon the family and responsibility for monitoring that process on female members in particular. When coupled with Sewell and Wilkinson's analysis of electronic surveillance in the workplace (Sewell and Wilkinson, 1992), there is a complete penetration of both the domestic and employment sphere by the technologies of global commerce. Sewell and Wilkinson describe an electronics factory transferred from British to Japanese ownership. Both unobtrusive electronic monitoring of work and error rates plus highly visible physical labelling of under-performing workstations are used to engender an atmosphere of close self-monitoring by the workforce.

At the same time as the separation of domestic and public space is being eroded, the concept of nation state is becoming problematic. The close of the twentieth century saw the revival of sub-national and regional sovereignties. Such shifts have been readily supported by developments in global communication technology. The most striking example was the briefly canvassed suggestion during the 1992 Iraqi occupation of Kuwait that the dispossessed national government might continue to function on the world financial markets without access to its country, but with electronic access to its funds.

Jane Jacobs was one of the first to report the negative effects of applications of modern urban planning theory in terms that affected the popular consciousness of the sixties (Jacobs, 1961). She illustrated how the strict hierarchical decomposition of mainstream land-use planning failed to acknowledge either long established economic mechanisms, or more recent changes in the nature of industry and employment which made rigid separation of housing, industry and commerce less important than accessibility and diversity. This positivist view of planning and development and the strict hierarchical view of systems were discussed in the previous chapter. Twenty years later Jacobs (1982) placed the development of Quebec separatism in a global context. Sub-nationalism can be seen as an inevitable outcome of changes wrought since the post-World War II high point of modernism.

Webber (1968) argues that the replacement of the city state by the nation state weakened the power of the traditional urban community. Supranational government may in turn revive city and regional status, as it erodes the status of national governments. The nature and quantity of European Community funding directed to research into definitions of citizenship reflect concerns over the implications of continuing enlargement of the European Union. However, equally significant funds are directed towards the development of physical communications infrastructure in the candidate states and beyond.

Experience with the development of transport informatics in support of road pricing policies suggests that direct negotiations between European Community institutions, metropolitan governments and trans-national corporations may diminish the influence of national governments over crucial standards for information and communications technologies. Indeed, as will be discussed later, many of the key standards are essentially de facto, as the rate of change in the relevant technologies outstrips the pace of formal processes of ratification.

Ohmae (1990) argues that regional and city level interests have replaced direct international competition. However the question remains how powerful "city states" might be in the face of direct competition with their neighbours for the attention and resources of trans-national corporations (TNCs). The TNCs strive for a position of "currency neutrality" so that relative shifts of exchange rates between the major world currencies have a negligible impact on their activities across the "Triad". Similarly location policy is also informed by the potential formation of trading blocks, and facilities and resources are planned so that operations are self-sufficient within each potential block. Ford Europe first implemented a policy of "complementarity" across Europe by replicating key facilities in two or more European states (Dicken, 1992). During pay negotiations, British workers could be compared unfavourably with their German counterparts in terms of productivity, while the German workers were compared unfavourably in terms of pay levels. The relative capitalisation of the two locations was conveniently ignored. This strategy has been overtaken by the development of the single European market, but is now played out in a different form on a global scale by Ford and other large corporations.[1]

Webber (1964) considered the growing importance of non-governmental and specialised governmental groups and bodies in urban life. Industry and de-facto standards as well as formally agreed international standards are key elements of the emerging supranational infrastructure, just as railways, roads, and national telecommunication carriers were cited by Webber as historically significant influences on locational decisions by individuals and organisations. In this context, the widespread deregulation of national telecom carriers may mark the final decline of purely national sovereignties. As these are privatised their key social role of equalisation of access to communication resources under their control is replaced by various targeted funding initiatives aimed at communities and groups identified as being the wrong side of the national digital divide.

The situation is even more problematic in countries such as Russia where neo-liberal policies unleashed unfettered privatisation in a situation of much greater existing inequity between centre and periphery (Giglavyi, 1993). By the end of the twentieth century, local governments were competing for the availability of new communication resources, just as they competed for access to railway routes during the nineteenth.

In developing states the national telecom carrier may be seen as a source of income and political leverage by government and be priced and controlled in a way that discourages growth and diversity of telecom-based services. Nevertheless, the privatisation and/or corporatisation of national telecommunications carriers and broadcasters and the introduction of market competition means a loss or reduction of the redistributive, social role implied by such public monopolies.

This produces a paradox: private providers are delivering the access once regarded as a social responsibility of the state. In Britain, cable television companies initially attracted a significant proportion of first-time local telephone subscribers for whom the economic barriers to entry to the former state system had been set too high. Pre-paid cellular phones now fill this gap in the social marketplace and their contribution to developing economies will be dealt with later.

Non-place Resources and Developmental Inequities

Obstacles to infrastructure development are not a simple reflection of relative lack of resources and experience, but of the very specific skills and techniques necessary for full integration into the global economy. Unlike the "appropriate technology" approach promoted during the 1970s, the current situation requires an "appropriated technology" approach which implies access to the key technologies at the core of the global economy.[2]

The new forms of virtual adjacency delivered by recent developments in information technology challenge the value of physical centrality. Recognition of the existence of "cyberspace", a non-place realm of computer-supported relationships, has taken Webber's original conception of non-place realms considerably further, as we will see below. The key issues around access and equity which are highlighted by the emergence of "non-place" reflect the tensions between big technologies and small implementations. Big technologies drive the processes of globalisation but small scale implementations of the same technologies can facilitate local and regional development initiatives. The big technologies include the complex wide area networks which support global business exchanges and global broadcasting: synchronous satellites, fibre optic networks and massively distributed computing facilities, such as the Internet. Here an institutional perspective is needed to understand the driving concerns which are shaping the emerging "new world order". The small scale implementations are those points at which entry cost, in terms of both finance and skill acquisition, is low enough for individuals and small groups. Often this is because of transferable social learning from older infrastructures which provides the "windows of opportunity" to be discussed in Chapter 5. The fax and mobile phone, for example were sufficiently close to existing technical experience for users such as self-employed trades-people to appropriate them rapidly and successfully.

Trans-national companies themselves are undergoing a series of transformations. Real-time off-shore location of white collar work from the U.S. mainland to the Caribbean was the logical extension of the less dramatic division between "front office" tasks which remain in the prestigious Central Business District and "back office" tasks (Nelson,

1988). The latter often involve part-time and female workforces relegated to the periphery of suburbia.

While information technology appears to offer a means of redressing relative locational disadvantage, experience so far suggests that the impact on employment opportunity has been overestimated for the majority of the working population, raising the prospect of Webber's "by-passed pre-industrial locals" being joined by many post-industrial workers.

Belussi's (1989) study of the Benetton company fuelled discussion of an alternative to the established form of international enterprise which links small and medium companies with global markets. Clegg (1990) and Perez (1985) describe the utilisation of a number of technical strands by the company which result in a computer-based network which is both trans-national and trans-organisational in extent. In this example, ownership and control of the core of the information network substitutes for ownership of production and distribution and for a formal hierarchy. The core of this enterprise links a network of world-wide franchised retail outlets and a network of subcontractors who provide the wholesale products.

One view of the advent of the network organisation sees it as an opportunity for smaller players to access resources from and to compete within global networks. The decreasing cost of Internet access has already allowed more spontaneous associations such as "virtual villages" described in Chapter 2 in which small enterprises form and reform alliances in order to service large companies (Inoue, 1998). These have been observed in both Asia and Europe.

However, as noted in Chapter 2, the additional accessibility and flexibility of advantage offered to smaller players is accompanied by the equivalent capability of larger firms to restructure in such a way that they can enter niche markets yet still draw on their much wider resource base. Castells (1996) describes the temporary "network enterprise" which allows global competitors to collaborate in a specific context, for specific purposes. While Castells provides examples from the electronics sector, the pharmaceutical industry presents the most radical structure with key research and pre-clinical development activities de-coupled from the core companies. These crucial specialised activities are increasingly handled by separate contracted partners, and specialist companies are offering to orchestrate the re-integration of these efforts into a research-discovery-development chain. This leaves the core pharmaceutical companies free to concentrate on brand management, and marketing.

Potential advantages to smaller players are thus offset by the ability of some larger firms to de-couple key business units better to target customers and markets traditionally served by much smaller competitors. For developing regions this exacerbates the dilemma of encouraging the entry of foreign firms and capital which may displace less well resourced and less experienced local capacity. By locking in scarce local skilled labour with superior conditions and rewards, the incoming companies may actually restrict indigenous development (see Dicken, 1998).

Non-place and Cyberspace

As noted, nation states are relinquishing one of their last remaining means of redressing regional imbalances in accessibility through the privatisation of telecommunications. One result of such withdrawal of state influence can be seen in the highly selective targeting of cable services in U.K. cities. This has produced results comparable to those of the earlier "red-lining" of areas deemed a poor risk by mortgage providers. The denial of access to housing finance hastened the development of urban blight in those areas. Despite the potential of emerging technologies and concepts such as Virtual Reality and computer supported collaborative work (CSCW), uneven infrastructure means the comparable exclusion of a significant minority of any region's citizens. Redressing the imbalances of global development will involve not just technical prescriptions, but an awareness of location within global production networks. Potential participation strategies achievable with the assistance of a design paradigm, and sensitivity to windows of opportunity are discussed in the next chapter. However, in questioning the value of physical centrality, the contrast between the telecommuting scenarios of technologically optimistic futurists such as Toffler (1970) and Bell (1979) and the reality of emerging practice highlighted in Chapter 2 must be considered.

The potential of computer-based information systems to facilitate or even substitute for organisational structure and standards has been evaluated from a variety of social and organisation theory perspectives. Little (1988) shows how very different strategies may be pursued with the same equipment, but that technical developments may lag behind organisational ambitions. Sproull and Kiesler (1991) emphasise the difference between immediate technical gains from such technologies and the longer term process of social gains for organisations. Specific technologies like computer-aided design may substitute for organisationally enforced standards, while software standards and electronic date interchange are increasingly presenting organisations with externally derived standards and procedures.

The ethnocentric focus of much of the thinking in this area is reflected by the equation of modernism with Western (U.S.) urban forms and structures which are seen as the end product of a process of social evolution. Clegg (1990) indicates how North American organisational forms are established as a norm, and argues that cross cultural examination of alternative organisational form, building on Lammers and Hickson (1979), is necessary to evaluate the full range of available possibilities.

As noted, Clegg (1990) and Perez (1985) use the practices of the Benetton company to show how a clever weave of technical strands can result in a computer-based network which is both trans-national and trans-organisational in extent. The physical non-space aspects of ARPANet, mentioned in Chapter 3, are a striking indication of how far such tendencies may take organisations. The operating software could relocate itself across its own network to the least busy host machines. Such non-space aspects of "netland" have been exploited by "cyberpunk" enthusiasts but have also attracted more respectable attention from researchers such as Canter and Perin, who apply respectively their cognitive mapping and environmental psychology methods to the mental images and organisational relationships developed by users of complex interactive computer systems (see Canter, 1977; Perin, 1970, 1991).

The critics of the urban planning of the seventies attacked redevelopments that privatised previously public spaces, yet the virtual space of computer networks is primarily private, with the deregulation and privatisation of common carriers widening this trend. The process of globalisation and deregulation has accelerated the privatisation of this previously public infrastructure.

Contesting the Core Technology: The Household as Public and Private Place

The relatively benign scenarios of increased personal choice which have been built around the prospect of "telecommuting" and "electronic cottages" are already compromised by the realities of tele-marketing and other forms of white-collar outwork. The background of casualisation across all sectors of the workforce in developed and developing countries should be grounds enough for caution. With a renewed emphasis on the productive role of households, competition between cities and sub-city regions might be reflected at the micro-level in competition between neighbourhoods or even households.

Silverstone, Hirsch and Morley (1992), in describing the moral economy of the household, identify "boundary maintenance" as one of the problems set for the household by information and communication technologies. Concerns in this area have generally been aimed at the content of mass media and other leisure activities such as video games and, most recently, the Internet. The boundary problems of the "globalised" household are as likely to revolve around the technologies of production as around those of consumption, as evidenced by the work of Aungles (1994) on home detention and Sewell and Wilkinson (1992) on workplace surveillance described above.

A considerable body of work covers the development of Western domestic technology up to the Second World War (e.g. Cowan, 1983; Hayden, 1981), and the significance of the reorganisation and re-definition of the household in utopian enterprises, particularly in the United States (Hayden, 1976). The pre-industrial household was a locus of production, and the redefinition of the household as locus of consumption and reproduction, distinct from the public sphere of "work" emerged with the onset of the industrial revolution.

Ravetz (1987) points out differences between the pre-industrial situation prevailing in North America as described by Cowan (1983) and that in Britain, where paid domestic employment was a significant feature of economic life, so that "housework" retained both domestic and public association. Change in the domestic division of labour continued into the twentieth century, with many pre-industrial features surviving in the agrarian sector of developed economies to within living memory (Kleinegger, 1987). The separation of domestic and productive spheres was never complete, and in some senses current technological and economic developments are simply reversing a slow moving trend.

It remains clear that electronic networking alters the size/performance equation and removes many of the traditional buffers between smaller and larger social and economic players and between public and private places. The key issues which are revisited in Part III revolve around access to the big technologies driving the processes of globalisation and to those related technologies underpinning the small scale implementations which facilitate meaningful participation at local and regional levels.

The staggering development of information and communication technology in the forty years following Webber's formulation of "community without propinquity" (Webber, 1964) has confirmed many of his assertions. Globalisation and deregulation of economies has produced a number of nomadic communities. Attali (1991) predicts the emergence of a nomadic international elite, in line with the examples provided by Webber but movement is not restricted to the elite employees of trans-national corporations. A range of skilled, semi-skilled and unskilled workers, legal and illegal are moving into and between the more developed economies in growing numbers (Castles and Miller, 1993).

Migration patterns and improved physical and electronic communications have produced transcontinental extended families in all types of society, and the anxiety and confusion between categories such as asylum and economic migration point to the tensions produced by the growing scale of physical movement within the globalising system. Remittances from these workers to their relatives and dependants in the home country have become a significant component of global financial flows and they represent a very different form of global workforce than that posited by Webber in 1964. The establishment of a Los Angeles office by the British Labour Party prior to the 1997 general election was one indication that the legal and semi-legal flows of migration are not just from developing to developed regions.

Information networks are emerging as the social milieu of non-place communities and the next chapter looks at a number of examples. However, the emerging problem of "information asymmetries" (Lamberton, 1995) raises a wider problem than the "digital divide", since it encompasses the significant proportion of humanity living in communities more than forty minutes travelling time from even basic telephonic communication. The concept of "information justice" is required (Lamberton, 1995). The next chapter looks at the technologies which now offer to bridge this gap. Meanwhile the ubiquity of the base technology of the Internet means that access to non-place community does not depend on large investment, nor on esoteric technical skills, a point sometimes missed in otherwise justifiable criticism of technological optimism. The growing maturity of the contributing technologies means that relatively stable standards are emerging, allowing both commodification (and consequent cost reduction) of components and the diffusion of appropriate technical literacy and skills among the general population. The major hurdle at present is the selection of an appropriate strategy from the confusing range of opportunities currently being promoted with a great deal of hype.

As noted earlier, the fax and mobile phone were sufficiently close to existing technical experience and practices for users such as self-employed trades-people to appropriate them easily. These relatively simple technologies can alter the size versus performance equation for businesses. Equally significantly, even the smallest companies may employ state-of-the-art technologies. Diffusion of technology to smaller players may be sponsored by the larger players as with the deeply layered subcontracting systems in Japanese manufacturing. These link top-level suppliers, themselves TNCs, with small family companies which may be assisted with the acquisition of key technology (Miyashita and Russell, 1994).

However, big technologies still underpin the complex wide area networks which support global business exchanges and global broadcasting, for example geo-synchronous satellites, fibre optic networks, and the massively distributed computing facilities supporting the Internet. Here an institutional perspective is needed to understand the driving concerns which are shaping the emerging "new world order" and Part II of this book considers how design processes, technology and institutional structures interact.

Cyberspace and Citizenship

Webber's original conception has been extended by the emergence of "cyberspace" as a non-place realm of computer-supported relationships.

Benedikt (1991) traces the term "cyberspace" to William Gibson's dystopian novels of the 1980s and 1990s (e.g. Gibson, 1984). The cyberpunk culture which has grown around the themes first articulated by Gibson has both utopian and dystopian strands. Their value lies with their focus on the gap between technologically optimistic futurists such as Toffler (1970) and Bell (1979) and the reality of technical determination driven by the assumptions of neo-classical economics.

Cyberpunk literature emphasises the intellectual and cultural possibilities of the emerging global "non-space realm". The non-space aspects of "netland" have been explored by the enthusiasts but have also attracted more respectable attention from a number of researchers. Harasim (1993) assembles a broad overview of the "official" dimensions of its use and development. In line with Webber's observations in the nineteen-sixties, specialised scientific communities provide the most impressive evidence of global social networks.

The adverse publicity given to the use of the World Wide Web to distribute pornography and its association with other unsavoury forms of criminal activity has obscured the positive aspects of its accessibility. It has also led to a variety of attempts at control of either access or content, doomed in essence by the Cold War lineage of the underlying technology and its ability to continuously reconfigure itself, an asset during nuclear bombardment.

It has been argued that the pornography industry has also promoted web-based commerce, by providing a paradigm for on-line business and web-based forms of revenue collection (Robinson, 2002). The globalisation of organised crime (Castells, 1998) which has accompanied the globalisation of more legitimate economic activity has also made use of the web.

The phenomenon of "hacking" is indicative in part of resistance to emerging patterns of ownership and control. It can be seen to parallel earlier resistance to privatisation and regulation of public space within the physical environment, from mass trespass in Britain in the 1930s to "green bans" against urban re-development in Australia in the 1960s and 1970s.

Early attempts at commercialisation of the Internet brought retaliatory responses from the established "hacker" community who promoted their libertarian notion of freedom of access as incompatible with commercialisation. The "cyberpunk" sub-culture represents the first example of an increasingly global non-space community inhabiting the "virtual space" of communication networks. It became global as the technological base diffused from the nations that developed it.

The view of hackers as romantic outlaws was enhanced by the association of virus attacks with political resistance at the close of the twentieth century. A great deal of traffic across the networks in the summer of 1991 originated in Russia and described the events of an abortive coup to the outside world. In Britain at the height of the anti-Poll Tax campaign an elaborate hoax was staged to persuade local authorities that a computer virus had been introduced in order to corrupt the databases essential to the collection of this unpopular charge. In China, following the suppression of the democracy movement in 1989 there was a massive increase in the incidence of computer viruses. Subsequently the Ministry of Public Security became a market leader in computer virus protection in China. The employment of faxes and laptop computers by the Mexican Zapatista rebels (*Newsweek*, 1995) is the latest manifestation of an effective incremental and interstitial use of relatively low tech aspects of the emerging global infrastructure first seen in the Russian Interfax news agency.[3]

In this context there may be a positive role for the cyberpunk sub-culture, if the collective community action of the 1970s can be facilitated by the technologies of the nineties. However, the "hacker" in the spare bedroom has been demonised. Criticism of the sub-culture focuses on the genuinely criminal and destructive activities of a minority and Sterling (1992) recounts the lengths to which national authorities may go to control such activities.

In a post-Cold War environment it is clear that a number of institutions are reassessing their roles, just as enforcement institutions shifted their attention from alcohol to other drugs after the repeal of prohibition laws in the United States (Grinspoon, 1994). "Cold Warriors" are viewing this non-space arena as their new fiefdom and Chapter 3 described how the U.S. National Security Agency has become involved in the development of data verification and encryption, to the extent of proposing standards for commercial transactions which would enable them to monitor traffic. The proposals have been vigorously opposed by groups such as Computer Professionals for Social Responsibility (CPSR[4]). At the same time NASA has become involved in a reconfiguration of SDI or "Star Wars" projects which are directed not at the defence of the United States, but at denial of near-earth space to competing nations: policing the infosphere for the benefit of one nation.

If the respectability of CPSR brings to mind the ACLU or the NAACP of the 1960s, then the demonised hackers of the networked world may yet emerge as the twenty-first century equivalent of the Black Panthers and urban guerrillas of the 1960s. "Hacking" itself can be traced back to "phone phreaking", an activity at the fringes of the anti-war movement in the U.S.A. in the late 1960s and early 1970s, which targeted the traditional telephone system to "liberate" communication resources (see Bowcott and Hamilton, 1990).

Each new stage of development in information and communication technology has led to exploitation and counter-exploitation by criminals and regulators. In the post-9/11 environment, the urgency of Cold War data analysis has returned. Surveillance and intelligence are once again seen as the thin line separating us from oblivion. Ever closer attention is paid to these flows of information and resources by national and international security agencies.

In the next chapter Webber's paradigm of non-place realms, is set alongside that of appropriate technology and windows of opportunity in the formation of that technology. This will provide some guidance for the development of effective local responses to the globalising pressures resulting from the continuing development and coalescence of advanced information technologies.

Notes

1   This strategy had its origins in the strategic dispersal of wartime production in Britain and the United States (Little and Grieco, 2003).

2   This shift can be seen in the focus of the Intermediate Technology Development Group from the re-discovery of superseded but sustainable technologies applicable to developing countries, to the appropriation of aspects of state-of-the-art technologies. See http://www.itdg.org

3   This approach to access to and use of technology will be returned to later in the book.

4   http://www.cpsr.org

Chapter 5

Windows of Opportunity: Supporting Development with Appropriate Technologies or Appropriated Technologies

This chapter provides a link to the second part of this book which describes facets of a design paradigm with which to develop paths of access from the margins to the central processes of globalisation and development.

It steps backwards, beyond the debates touched on in Chapter 3 concerning the nature of rational modern design, to look at predictive literature from the end of the nineteenth century onwards. This review of the value and pitfalls of prediction is followed by an overview of some emerging forms and paths to inclusion which will be revisited in the concluding chapters. It has been demonstrated that a process of organisational learning is needed to move beyond the technical effects of direct substitution of information technology for manual processes. The nature of this social learning process is examined in the final section of the chapter.

The modern information and communication technologies derived from Second World War innovations are essential to the level of control required over back offices and subsidiary plants located across national boundaries. They are therefore key determinants of the replacement of a spatial hierarchy involving resources, manufacturers and consumers with complex interlocking layers of labour and resource markets.

Private investment can be allocated on the basis of favourable polices on infrastructure provision, taxation and other incentives from competing local governments (Lipietz, 1987).

Inspired by the new organisational relationships made possible by the merging of computer and communication technologies (ICTs), observers such as Negroponte (1995) and Mitchell (1995) argue for the transformative potential of new forms of networked organisation and "virtual" workplaces. The locational strategies which allowed white collar work from the U.S. mainland to be relocated off-shore to the Caribbean as far back as the 1980s have been described already.

Less developed regions find themselves increasingly in competition for such lower value work, and their infrastructure is likely to be developed primarily to support it. At the same time, potential consumers with limited economic resources are less able to influence the direction of development of technologies, artefacts and services. These are targeted at the most lucrative component of global markets but they also determine the nature of access from the less favoured regions.

The opening chapters argues that across the new networked economy as a whole research and development, raw materials sources and routine manufacturing, final assembly, markets and after-market support, are increasingly co-located. The emergent global system is one of complex inter-penetration of peripheries and cores and these terms now refer to competence in the underpinning information and communication infrastructure, rather than physical location.

These innovative forms appear to alter the relationship between organisational size and performance. The contemporary notion of the "network organisation" and decreasing Internet costs appear to present an opportunity for smaller players to access resources from and to compete within global networks. However, using the reduction on transaction costs delivered by ICTs, larger firms can restructure to enter niche markets yet still draw on their wider resource base. Castells (1996) describes a form of "network enterprise" which presents a formidable challenge to smaller and medium scale players: monolithic large scale planning is being replaced by opportunistic niche infiltration.

Previous chapters pointed out that the growing separation between intellectual capital and physical production has consequences for both core and peripheral economies. Lipietz (1992) argues that the ability to separate production from consumption in these systems signals the end of the "Fordist compromise" which underpinned the Keynsian social-democratic paradigm. Meaningful engagement from the margins requires a means of challenging such approaches to the development and distribution of resources.

Looking Backwards, Looking Ahead: Moving into a New Century

Rosenberg (1982) illustrates the problem of being even partially right in technological forecasting by quoting a late nineteenth century prediction that ultimately every American city would be provided with a telephone. Webber (1968) cites significant high speed surface and air transport developments, although supersonic transportation and not the sub-sonic wide-bodied jet is mentioned and mass air travel is not discussed. However, improved communications, including public real-time access to computerised databases are identified as potentially critical developments. Toffler's (1970) pro-technology assertions were subsequently given fictional form by science fiction writer John Brunner. However the predicted world of *Shockwave Rider* (Brunner, 1975) in which it was possible to exist in the interstices of massive computerised domestic credit and surveillance systems had been exceeded by Clifford Stoll's factual account from the end of the 1980s (Stoll, 1989). Billed as a new kind of detective story, the latter describes the global pursuit of miscreants across several international computer networks, while Brunner's fictional twenty-first century network was confined to the U.S.A.

In many respects the technical component of predictions from the 1960s were reasonably accurate, what was lacking was any intimation of parallel changes in the institutional settings of those technologies. Large institutions managing large main-frame based resources are the paradigm implicit in the technological forecasting of this era, the desk-top computing revolution and the distributed nature of current resources, and consequently organisations, was not foreseen. The central issue – access to and exclusion from key resources – was not part of the discussion.

In addition, an ethnocentric bias is reflected in formulations of progress and development in which Western (U.S.) urban forms and structures are seen as the end product of a process of social evolution, as noted in the previous chapter.

The question of what leverage is available to small players in terms of influence over the emerging new "techno-economic paradigm" (Dosi, 1986) becomes central to participation in or effective exclusion from a global system of development. Harnessing the key technologies for development beyond Ohmae's dominant triad raises the question of what leverage can be achieved over outcomes. The perspective that is appropriate here is that of the 1970s "intermediate technology" movement. Forbes and Wield (2001) use examples from Africa and India to show that a variety of strategies can be used to achieve innovation in the face of competition from global leaders.

The prospect of non-place community does not depend on the big technologies, rather on appropriate use of a range of technical opportunities. If local and regional initiatives are to be possible, then the notion of an intermediate or appropriate entry point to the technology becomes central.

As noted in the preceding chapter, the current situation requires an "appropriated technology" approach rather than the "appropriate technology" approach promoted during the 1970s. This implies access to the technological core of the global economy. Despite the continually falling costs and growing flexibility of computer technology there is considerable debate over the realisation of its potential benefits by organisations (e.g. Hartamis and Lin, 1992; Kling, 1993; Landauer, 1995). Much of the argument is around the way in which the core concerns of computer science should be broadened to encompass the usability and usefulness of its products. The skills required to assess and monitor the practices and requirements of end-users are now recognised as very different from the technical skills required for the development of a technical infrastructure.

Sometimes strategies favourable to national players in the global community may offer an unanticipated advantage to minority users within a local community. Such "windows of opportunity" inadvertently offered by shifts in the dominant technical realm must be recognised and exploited. They can be used to reduce the growing inequities that threaten the prospect of effective participation in a globalising economy.

At each location, relevant aspects of the world economy and corresponding emergent organisational forms must be related both to the developing technical infrastructure. As noted in Chapter 3, this system is often presented as a seamless technological artefact despite the historical and cultural particularities that ensure diversity and friction throughout it.

The emergence of English as a global language emphasises the existence of both cultural and linguistic barriers within the world economy (Crystal, 1997). Key innovations in information technology have succeeded where they were mapped on to existing cultural frameworks. The spreadsheet package became the "killer application" that ensured the commercial success of the micro-computer because it could readily mimic the twenty column analysis paper already in use in Western economies (Kaye and Little, 1998). In East Asia a number of economies have been relatively late adopters of many facets of office automation because of a range of cultural differences, not least their use of non-Roman characters. Shepard (1993), writing from direct experience, sets out the technical complexities of networking in an environment that must move beyond the ASCII standard.[1] Technologies that do not incorporate the requirement of a specific alphabet have been adopted, and Castells and Hall (1994) attribute the refinement and promotion of fax technologies by Japanese companies as evidence of their need to support logographic text. Rather than attempting to overcome cultural barriers, such users have applied available technologies to more directly relevant areas of advantage. However, for China in an era of bit-mapped graphics and machine translation, the simplified script provides a clear advantage through its independence from regional variations in spoken language (Kaye and Little, 1998).

The rapidity of technical development, particularly in ICTs, is constantly reducing entry costs, and rendering obsolete extant technical infrastructures. Such a situation favours later entrants, and permits them some chance of catching up. In many developing countries the colonially oriented communication infrastructures are already obsolete. Current technical developments such as direct satellite mobile communications via large numbers of low earth orbit satellites or wireless fidelity (WiFi) protocols offer unintended advantages to groups marginalised by the current technologies. Unless the late entrants can find a point of entry, these technologies will be shaped entirely by the interests of users who are already well resourced. Nevertheless, forms of distributed development and pathways to resources are becoming evident.

Emerging Forms, Emerging Strategies

Continuing development in technology and economic scale has led both to the internationalisation of economic activity and to the emergence of environmental consequences beyond the capacity of individual states to manage. Camilleri and Falk (1992) argue that power and authority have become diffused over a considerable period, with national states participating in a variety of multilateral arrangements covering not just trade, production and finance but also increasingly inter-related environmental and security issues.

The potential of computer-based information systems to facilitate or even substitute for organisational structure and standards has been evaluated from a variety of social and organisation theory perspectives. Little (1988) shows how very different strategies may be pursued with the same technology, but that technical development may lag behind organisational ambition. Sproull and Kiesler (1991) emphasise the difference between immediate technical gains from ICTs and the longer term process of social gains for organisations. Specific technologies like computer-aided design may substitute for organisationally enforced standards, while software standards and electronic data interchange are increasingly presenting organisations with externally derived standards and procedures.

Suchman (1986) has looked at the collective and collaborative use of computer systems by groups of users, breaking with a human-computer interaction research tradition which has emphasised usability of systems in terms of the performance of individuals. The concept of Computer-Supported Collaborative Work (CSCW) subsequently emerged with the move from an individual to a collective view of users in a socially constructed workspace which includes computer-based information systems. Such technically created non-spaces for both work and social activity can be achieved with relatively unsophisticated equipment. Increasingly such non-place workplaces are appearing within the home, as discussed in the previous chapter.

The demonstrations against the World Trade Organisation in Seattle in 1999, and subsequent events in Prague and Stockholm represent one set of reactions to the shifts in employment practices described in the preceding chapters and their impact on communities which derive their identity from economic activities now under threat. They also represent a powerful alternative paradigm for organisation at a global level that will be discussed further.

Kanbur (2001) argues that they also reflect a perception that the activities of the Bretton Woods institutions, including the World Bank and International Monetary Fund, are increasing rather than reducing global poverty and inequality. For Kanbur a Group A mentality on the part of the governments and international institutions clashes with a Group B view of the non-governmental organisations (NGOs). Conflicting views of the appropriate level of aggregation at which to gauge progress, of the appropriate time horizon that should be addressed, and of the nature of markets structures and power relationships ensure that agreement is impossible. NGOs stress the short-term effects on actual communities of medium-term focussed policies, while environmentalists stress the much longer term sustainability of policies. Both sides disagree upon the nature and function of market mechanisms, with the NGOs perceiving substantial market power accruing to large scale established players from developed countries.

The real-time management of a sequence of large, international demonstrations shows that the key technologies of the Internet and World Wide Web do offer opportunities for voices and visions from geographically disparate locations to enter the world of global communication. These can build a dynamic between traditional cultural practices and modern communication forms to provide an enrichment of global symbolic life. Little, Holmes and Grieco (2000) describe a symbiosis between the use of the Internet for e-commerce purposes and the maintenance of living and differentiated cultures, a pattern which is already evident in Canada, Africa and Indonesia. The richness of this medium also allows a challenge to the hierarchical nature of the established global political discourse.

Castells has described "informational politics in action" (Castells, 1997, p.333). He is concerned that one aspect of globalisation, the reliance on simplified mass communication, inevitably reduces the complexity of political discourse. However, in the same volume he describes very different and complex forms of electronically mediated communication by dissident minorities: the Zapatista rebels in Mexico and militia groups in the U.S.A. In both cases movements premised on the championing of the local and specific and a rejection of the global economy are achieving a presence and a voice in a global arena through the appropriation of the technologies of globalisation.

Castells (1997) cites the Zapatista movement in Mexico as an example of an oppositionist response to the exclusion from the benefits of the global economy of those bearing its greatest social and economic costs. Significantly it utilises the very information and communication technologies that facilitates the system under criticism. The image of the laptop and satellite phone in the rain forest is a potent one, however, in regions of less stark contrast between those included and those excluded, similar forms of resistance and opposition can be found. Castells also points out that fundamentalist appeals are not confined to the Muslim world, as evidenced by the rise of the U.S. militia movements which draw on specific historical precedence, and make an equally significant commitment to the Internet. While the Zapatista example is a well worn one, it is significant that the Mexican Federal Government itself now provides links to independent and critical coverage of events via its own web-site, shifting political discourse into cyberspace and in front of a limitless audience (Little, Holmes and Grieco, 2000).

In Japan, the Internet has been widely used for political debate, for example over airport location and development in the Kansai region. The Japan Local Government Centre has set up a site through which it links with local governments globally to explore solutions to new urban problems.[2]

On-line electronic petitions systems have been established in Scotland (see Griffin, 2003) and, for the U.K. as a whole, SMS (short message service) text from mobile phones as well as traditional postal voting has been trialled at local government elections in an attempt to increase voter turnout.

Providing grassroots access to the ICT domain has been identified as a means of reducing the cost of health and educational servicing, as with the current planned expenditure in the U.K. National Health Service (Cross, 2002). However, the channels established for electronic commerce and for top down monitoring of public sector performance create new forms of bargaining. The transaction costs for the least powerful to gain visibility are also greatly reduced.

In California the notion of "community informatics" has been used to justify the provision of access to information previously freely available, but increasingly commercialised (Pitkin, 2001). Across Europe city governments are co-operating across national borders through fibre optic technologies and other forms of electronic networking in the identification of municipal problems shared and solutions sought. Similarly within the European Union locations along particular lines of transport communication have begun to co-operate electronically in the management of traffic (Little, Grieco and Holmes, 2001).

Along with U.S. ownership of the strategic components of global communication technology, most particularly the dominance of Microsoft, the emergence of English as a global language is seen as an important element in a flattening of cultural terrain. Such a view cannot be entirely discounted but it ignores many of the new cultural capacities of new forms of global communication. Just as Crystal (1997) argues that the global English language is no longer under the control of its original native speakers, so are the technologies of globalisation appropriated by users at the margins.

New technology can assist the civic empowerment of the individual in relation to the state and also the capability of remote locations to influence the world of global government and global commerce: there are now powerful electronic counterbalances to historical policy remoteness. Networking small states and islands through a combination of new technology and face to face meetings can generate new economic and social structures within global functioning. Miller and Slater (2000) explore the question of local improvisations in the case of Trinidadian diaspora:

> Indeed the significance of studying the Internet is the degree to which it transcends dualisms such as local against global. It forces us to acknowledge a more complex dialectic through which specificity is a product of generality and vice versa. (Miller and Slater p. 7)

Trinidadians undertake a distinctive set of social activities on the global Internet. What they experience are specific and local practices at a remote location. Malta, with a population of 420,000, the smallest of the candidate states joining the European Union in 2004, has a much bigger virtual presence as the centre of another diaspora.

The rise of the portal metaphor as an organiser of web access has allowed countries such as Estonia, to provide public access in its own Finno-Ugric language (Abbate, 2000). The use of "front-end" translation software can now overcome the language barrier. Estonians can surf the Internet in their own language from public access kiosks provided by their government.

The portal is a home page which provides structured links into resources appropriate to its users. As an organising device it can reduce search time for newer users. The World Bank recognised the role of knowledge in the 1998-99 "World Development Report" (World Bank, 1998) and subsequently re-branded itself as the Knowledge Bank. Stephen Denning, former Director of Knowledge Management for the Bank, has presented this approach as a necessary dialogue between all parties concerned with the development process (Denning and Grieco, 2000). A component of this realignment is the development of a web portal for Global Development Knowledge.[3] The Bank has opened a web-based debate with non-governmental organisations which has inevitably raised the issue of power relationships. These can be seen in the framing of access pathways by the resource rich on behalf of the resource poor. Part III will look at some of the issues raised in this venue.

The emerging global system described in these chapters is far from complete and far from determined, but it has already had a profound impact on social and working life in the regions included within and excluded from it. Information and communication technologies are driving the distributed processes of globalisation. By providing new forms of adjacency they are also providing avenues of engagement for excluded constituencies. They offer a means for entry or challenge and a means of refining and developing and managing the knowledge which has been foregrounded by the new relationships.

The speed of change in markets, competition and technology means that there is a socio-institutional lag as the new paradigm emerges (Dosi, 1986; Perez, 1986). For example, e-commerce is already mutating into m-commerce: mobile delivery of services. Despite the relative inadequacy of current WAP (Wireless Application Protocol) mobile telephony, the combination of low earth orbit (LEO) satellites with Global Positioning Systems (GPS) in proposed systems such as the European Galileo GPS will allow location-sensitive services to be delivered to individuals and groups on the move (Taplin, 2000). Wireless broadband (WiFi) has been co-opted where fibre-optic infrastructure or even copper wire telephony is not available.

New forms of community of practice may arise, together with a reassessment of the spatial dynamics of knowledge creation and application. With LEO direct satellite systems, the network coverage will of necessity be equally dense and universal across the majority of the planet's surface beneath the hundreds of orbiting satellites. The lag caused by severe problems with the initial business models of the pioneer systems presents an opportunity for a diversity of models and approaches to be discussed and developed by potential users outside those models.

The next section of this book contains four chapters which introduce design as a set of processes which reflect resources, capabilities and context. A design perspective offers a means of identifying opportunities within the complex constraints on development at the centre and participation from the periphery which have been described in this opening section.

Social Learning, Social Networking

Marvin (1988) quotes from the debates and disagreements over the significance of the electrically-based technologies of the second industrial revolution. She notes the time taken for a general understanding of the appropriate social use of the telephone to emerge. It is not surprising that a global consensus on the more recent generation of information and communication technologies underpinning the current wave of globalisation is still to emerge. What is clear is that the necessary paradigm will not emerge on its own. Would-be participants in the development process need some window of opportunity through which to gain influence and access.

Kalpinsky and Posthuma (1992) demonstrate the transferability of organisational technology in the form of Japanese manufacturing practice without high levels of capitalisation. Marginal players, in this case East African manufacturing companies, can make significant improvements in their performance without substantial capital investment. The adoption of the organisational approaches utilised in Japan can transform efficiency and effectiveness in companies in developing economies without the supporting technology usually associated with it. Gains from relatively low-cost reorganisation were achieved through the use of intellectual resources which had some consonance with the cultural assumptions embedded within the imported techniques. However, to compete directly with developed economies access to similar levels of capital resources is required. Ultimately access to state of the art technology is necessary for full participation in the global economy. However, access to such technology is no guarantee of its appropriate use. The use of technology, rather than the technology itself is the key to appropriateness, and to sustainability but the organisational and cultural segmentation of potential users requires an adequate fit to varying needs and the capacity for adjustment over time. This implies a cultural wrapping for the technical standards. The technology also must be available in a mature and robust form capable of adaptation to specific situations (Kaye and Little, 1996).

Sproull and Kiesler (1991) show how a process of organisational learning is needed to move beyond the technical effects of direct substitution of information technology for manual processes. Unfortunately the direct technical costs and benefits dominate information systems planning and investment. The gains reported by Kaplinsky and Posthuma were achieved through the use of intellectual resources which needed some cultural consonance with the cultural assumptions embedded within the imported techniques. The transformative gains in effectiveness represented by Zuboff's (1988) "informated organisation" will come about in the globalised arena only through an understanding of the need for cultural interoperability at both pre-competitive and competitive stages of development (Kaye and Little, 1996).

Standards are the vehicle used to achieve interoperability and the notion can be applied to each level of interaction within and between organisations. Standards themselves cannot solve the problems confronting actors in the global economy. The cultural dimension of organisational practice impacts on the diffusion and adoption of socio-technical systems across cultural settings. Simply ascribing differences in outcomes to "cultural difference" between adopters offers little guidance for either potential adopters or for policy-makers.

O'Hara-Devereaux and Johansen (1994) argue for a distinction between work cultures, both professional and corporate and the primary culture in which an organisation is embedded. For them the synergy between levels is a potential resource, but the tendency towards a convergence determined by the primary culture is seen as an obstacle to cross-cultural working. Culture needs to be de-composed into issues related to the historical, geographical and institutional setting in which organisation and individual must operate. The business recipes and frameworks grounded in these differences offer a view of "culture" of more direct value to actors (see for example Marceau, 1992).

Chapter 2 introduced Castells (1996) notion of network enterprise which is composed of components of larger corporations, collaborating in specific spatial and temporal circumstances, while the main companies are still pursuing global strategies of direct competition. Japanese companies have demonstrated the value of pre-competitive collaboration and joint development of key technologies. Collaboration between Sony and Phillips over audio media has created global standards for consumer products. The framework of the network organisation appears to offer an opportunity for smaller players to access resources from and to participate in global networks. This was illustrated in Chapter 2 with the "virtual village" (Inoue, 1998) in which small enterprises are able to form and reform alliances in order to provide high technology services to larger companies. However, it was noted that a dual challenge is provided to smaller firms, since the advantages offered are matched by the ability of some larger firms to de-couple key business units better to target customers and markets traditionally served by much smaller firms.

During the 1980s the Centre Mondial Informatique et Ressources Humaines in Paris promoted the use of state-of-the-art computing technology in Saharan and sub-Saharan Africa (Roper, 1983). While the national basis of the institution might say something about its post-colonial orientation towards Francophone Africa, it deployed the work of Seymour Papert (1980) as evidence of the ability of the new information and communication technologies to short-circuit the learning curve of earlier industrialisation processes. However, it was only at the end of the twentieth century that technical progress offers to solve the chronic infrastructure deficit of less developed regions. The shift from geostationary Earth orbits (GEOs) to medium Earth orbit (MEO) and low Earth orbit (LEO) satellites (Price-Waterhouse, 1998), described earlier, has the potential to render the current communications infrastructure largely obsolete. A range of proposed systems will use various combinations of direct inter-satellite communication and a low number of ground-stations. The planned systems target current affluent users of mobile communications, rather than the 3.9 billion people judged to have no telephone service available.

The Teledesic system originally proposed a total of 840 broadband LEOs communicating directly with individual personal computers. By 1997 a revised system of 288 satellites was planned. In 2002 this was replaced by a scheme for 30 satellites in Middle Earth Orbit (MEO) reflecting the take over of a failed competitor. In July 2003 Teledesic surrendered its broadcast frequencies to the U.S. Federal Communication Commission. The Iridium system, re-launched under a new company in 2001 consists of 66 low-earth orbiting (LEO) satellites plus 14 orbiting spare satellites. Following the failure of optimistic business plans which assumes the technology would compete with the existing terrestrial cell phone, the services are now marketed to businesses and workers remote from established communications infrastructure.

The technology to achieve low and middle earth orbit is simpler and more accessible than that for geostationary orbits which is dominated by Ariane and NASA-based launches with a small contribution from Russia, Ukraine and China. In addition, the laws of geophysics ensure equally intensive coverage of all areas below the satellites, regardless of OECD status.

Clearly such shifts in technology offers a window of opportunity for countries and regions disadvantaged by the current distribution of communication infrastructure to make up considerable ground, if not to leapfrog to the forefront. However, the removal of the barrier of physical and technical infrastructure leaves the problem of social and institutional infrastructures.

Windows of Opportunity

The need for peripheral users to utilise features of mainstream technical developments as far as possible is exemplified by a study of the impact of relatively simple bulletin board technology on a group of users with special needs[4] (Earls, 1990). Bulletin board technology of the 1980s allowed these users to participate in an electronic community which was unaware of their considerable physical disabilities. The features which were of particular advantage to this group, such as the "narrowness" of the communication bandwidth which produced a levelling and bland alphanumeric interface, or the asynchronous nature of communication are those which characterise access to the global communication technologies by those at the margins, reliant on obsolete equipment and relatively poor connections. These features were eliminated in the mainstream push for ever greater sophistication.

Initial results revealed a slight lowering of self image by the board users at the end of the experimental period. After two years, however, case-studies revealed individuals who had become politically active, gained employment (over 50 per cent of the experimental group), taken up further study and begun to live independently. These clear benefits also evoked positive changes in their peer group, structural changes in the organisation and a policy response from government.

These outcomes emphasise the importance of longitudinal studies. Vitalari (1985) argues the need for such an approach in the broader investigation of computing environments and in effect supports Sproull and Kiesler's (1991) call for consideration of both the short- and long-term implications of the introduction of computer-based communications.

Much of the available data on the impacts of computer-based information systems and communication is cross sectional in nature. Such studies have often presented conflicting findings on, for example, the employment implications of the introduction of word processing (Buchanan and Boddy, 1983) because they have examined organisational relationships which have still been in flux following the deployment of the technology.

In this instance the initial negative results may be interpreted as a reflection of the increasing standards of performance and the wider technical community against which the participants measured themselves and their new skills.

The impact of relatively simple bulletin board technology highlights the need to utilise features of mainstream technical developments as far as possible. The features which were of particular advantage to this group, such as the "narrowness" of the communication bandwidth which produced a levelling and bland alphanumeric interface, or the asynchronous nature of communication might be eliminated in the mainstream push for greater sophistication. Such shifts might not be useful for the particular disabilities examined by Earls (1990) although other emerging techniques and technologies might offer similar advantages to different groups and disabilities. The long-term, qualitative nature of the benefits suggests that such research methods would be appropriate for the evaluation of more sophisticated computer-based technologies for any group of users. The evaluation of the use and impact of the experimental computer bulletin board on people with disabilities illustrates one paradigm for a diverse range of minority users and their relationship with information technology and the opportunities it affords.

Despite the falling costs and growing flexibility of computer technology there remains a need to identify and exploit equivalent windows of opportunity presented by mainstream technology. Considerable sophistication in the evaluation and use of elements of mainstream technology is needed by any group wishing to access the potential benefits of a mainstream solution, in order to minimise the use of low volume, expensive specialised hardware and software. The evidence of the ability of current protest movements to achieve real-time direct access to a global audience through a combination of mobile computing and World Wide Web technologies is encouraging.

Part II presents a detailed discussion of the nature of design paradigm taken from high technology innovation and design management. An understanding of design and technical development as embedded socio-technical processes is a necessary precondition for engagement with the technical dynamic of the emerging global system.

Notes

1   ASCII refers to the American Standard Code for Information Interchange. This numerical representation of alphabetic was developed to allow the Roman alphabet to be used with teletypes.
2   See http://www.jlgc.org/
3   See http://www.edc.org/GLG/gkd/ for an on-line archive of these contributions and debates.
4   A full account of the study in which clients and therapists in an Australian Spastics Centre were linked with computing students for a period of three months is available in Earls (1990). The most striking feature of the findings of the study was the contrast between the short-term results which reveal no change in attitude over a three-month period and the significant changes revealed by a repeated application of the Measurement of Attitude Towards Disabled Persons Test (Yuker, Block and Campbell, 1960) after two years.

PART II

DETERMINATION
AND DESIGN:
FRAMES AND PARADIGMS

Chapter 6

Finding a Lever to Move the World: The Design Paradigm and Its Value*

The foundation of the current form of globalisation is a technical system designed in a social context. This chapter introduces a framework for its analysis derived from design research and design management. This is developed in the following chapters and can be used to analyse strategies and alliances intended to diffuse innovation in design and development practice across regional and organisational boundaries.

The stresses inherent in the emerging global system described in Part I were highlighted by the difficulties of the East Asian economies following a period of unprecedented growth through the 1980s and into the early 1990s. The tight coupling of the emerging system propagated the diverse problems of these individual nation states across much of the globe while the failure of a number of states in Africa and elsewhere emphasised the problems of exclusion from the system.

A design perspective is critical to the consideration of opportunities and obstacles for effective participation in a globalising system and the achievement of meaningful development. Local initiatives aimed at entering the global production system can be mapped on to a generic model of the design process. This model accounts for the distinctive intellectual and physical resource requirements of the invention and initial innovation stages and the very different requirements of the mature manufacturing phases of the product life-cycle. This gives a means of gauging the effectiveness of participation in the global nexus of production and consumption by both newer entrants and established players. A design framework offers a means of evaluating potential technology transfer and the developmental value of the participation on offer from inward investors.

The design and development of a range of advanced technologies are discussed in this chapter and the following chapters of this section. These technologies have been determined by the priorities of advanced economies. They in turn determine the prospects for less developed economies of either joining or abstaining from a growing global system.

Crisis and Continuity

At the close of the twentieth century events in the East Asian economies undermined the idea of a rapid and unproblematic process of globalisation, driven by "miracle economies". As noted in Part I, Krugman (1996) criticised the acceptance of high growth rates over relatively short periods from very low base levels as evidence of such miracles. Unfortunately the immediate impact in the West has been the rejection of the development strategies which had delivered genuine growth. It was argued earlier that at least part of the current crisis in East Asia reflected the difference between the problems of technological leadership and those of catching-up with leading economies. The very different forms of crisis across the affected economies and the different responses at national level reflected the diversity of approaches within the region. Chapter 2 noted the work of Orru, Biggart and Hamilton (1991) which revealed strikingly different forms of intra-societal isomorphism among the relatively new industries of Japan, Taiwan and South Korea, despite their close historical associations.

Part III will return to the cultural and institutional dimensions of development, this chapter considers the consequences of the success of the strategies of the growing economies described by Orru et al (1991). Eventually a paradigm shift is required from catch-up strategies which involve identification and adoption of best practices to the sustained innovation of new technologies and associated practices.

Economies such as South Korea which have been highly successful during the catch-up phase of development show that different socio-economic paradigms are needed to sustain growth in the conditions of lower absolute growth encountered in relatively mature markets. Korean companies have invested in the developing markets of the candidate states due to join the European Union in 2004, while accessing the intellectual capital of developed economies through the acquisition of research and development resources, as noted in Part I.

Participation in the development of the intellectual resources necessary for the next stage of development requires even more direct integration into the emerging world system and a greater institutional alignment within and between regions. Japan's failure to build a new policy consensus following the collapse of the bubble economy has led to the term "lost decade" being used to describe the apparent hiatus of the last decade of twentieth-century

Japan (e.g. Hayashi and Prescott, 2002). Key institutional arrangements, such as the readily available long-term finance sourced from within the Japanese *keiretsu*, are increasingly recognised as a liability not an asset both within and beyond Japan itself. The resulting accumulated bad debt is a major component of the current economic and political impasse.

China, as East Asia's largest economy, has continued with high growth policies. However, this size also increases the problems of regional differentials in development. For example, the successful business networks of Hong Kong can only be developed so far into the wider hinterland of the Special Administrative Region before cultural and linguistic differences impede their further extension (Yu and Robertson, 2000). As noted in Chapter 2, the Chinese government now acknowledges the problem of differential growth and the difficulties of matching the rapid advances in favoured coastal regions in the interior provinces (Information Office of the State Council of the P.R.C., 2001).

European and North American companies have sought to emulate aspects of Asian strategies for some time and comparative advantage has been eroded as Asian methods, building on the Western industrial model, have been re-exported to the original industrial core of Europe and North America. Nuki (1998) shows that this in turn has engendered a response based on accelerating the product life cycle through the application of ICTs at all stages of development and production. This aspect of direct engagement with the timeframes of technical development is taken up in the next chapter.

Repositioning Across a Global Production Web

Mature, developed economies are committed to remaining at the cutting edge of technology in a maturing global market. The opening chapter argued that many companies are directing their attention to the end of the production chain where product differentiation and customer support can maintain demand for goods and services. As a consequence, the distinction between products and services becomes less obvious. The high value end of the chain requires closer adjustment to cultural variation among users and customers and gives high cost regions some prospect of retaining these activities. James and Howell (2001) suggest that access to both broader intellectual capital for technical development and local knowledge for precise market adjustments are the objectives of East Asian inward investment in European research and development. The encouragement of both the British government and the European Commission to companies seeking alliances and opportunities in the opposite direction was noted in Part I. This reflects both aggressive movement into potential markets and defensive development of low cost offshore manufacturing resources to support home and export markets.

The repositioning of ICL (International Computers Limited), from computer hardware manufacturing to information services provider was mentioned in Chapter 1. Further evidence of a "value chain" approach (Porter 1990) can be seen in a very different industry. Two EU-based trans national corporations, Imperial Chemical Industries (ICI) and Unilever have been engaged in shifting their assets along the production chain, to the area of higher added value. Unilever passed its specialist chemical division to ICI in 1997 in order to concentrate on the delivery of differentiated brands based on these generic materials (Bennett, 1997). Meanwhile ICI has off-loaded it own bulk chemical business to firms content to compete primarily on price at the commodity end of this chain (Chemical Week, 1998).

Dicken's (2003) use of the production chain to analyse the dynamics of the global economy is revealing. In common with Porter's representation of the value chain,[1] a range of critical support activities is modelled at each stage of this generic model. Dicken demonstrates the traditional view of the service sector as evidence of a "post-industrial" or advanced economy. The emergence of a dominant quaternary sector is seen as the logical development of a preponderance of intellectual capital over physical capital. The dynamic growth of deregulated financial services and the broadly perceived shift from manufacturing to service industries supports such a view.

The diversification of as prestigious an engineering company as General Electric into financial services that now yield greater turnover than its engineering efforts might seem to confirm services as the successor to primary, secondary and tertiary activities. However, primary production is linked with quaternary, post-delivery support of goods and services, a variety of service activities is wrapped around the core thread of the production chain. A clear distinction between primary, secondary and quaternary activity is difficult to justify since primary production is the essential precursor to all the other forms of activity. Consequently the most advanced technologies have been applied at every stage of the production process. Sophisticated artificial intelligence programs have been developed to optimise primary extractive mining activities in Australia. Currently global positioning (GPS) equipment is available in agriculture to monitor productivity via harvesting equipment (Forristal and Keppel, 2001) while satellite imagery is available to monitor the extent of reserve resources or environmental hazards (e.g. Bastiaanssen, 1998; Sudhakar et al, 1996).

Design Paradigms and Paradigm Shifts

For developing economies a successful paradigm shift from catch-up strategies based on rapid growth rates on a low cost base to technological leadership requires a broad level of analysis. Global links to regional economic activities must be considered. In addition, the repositioning of effort across the production network can be better understood from the perspective of the design philosophies and methods that have been applied to both product and processes during the second half of the twentieth century. A critical view of a region's resources and capabilities and their relevance to development requires a shift in the view of innovation and product life-cycle to that of process life-cycles. This is akin to a shift from single to double loop learning (Argyris and Schön, 1974).

Galbraith (1977) staked the claim that information system design was in effect organisation design. Information systems designers have in turn drawn heavily and effectively on the wide body of more general design research and theory outlined in Chapter 3.

In parallel to the development of organisation theory through and beyond the framework of systems theory discussed in Chapter 3, design methodologies have reflected a changing understanding of the processes and the role of the participants and wider stakeholders in them. Scott (1992) argued that organisation theory could be seen as developing from the closed rational systems view of classic management theory to an open natural systems view able to accommodate influences from the institutional and technical environments. Chapter 7 introduces the notion of institutional and technical time-frames while Chapter 8 looks at the wider relationship between institutional innovation and the absorptive capacity (Cohen and Levinthal, 1990) of national economies. This chapter examines the internal characteristics of the technical design process and in particular the nature of incremental and systemic change.

Jones (1980, pp.63-69) presents design methods extant in the 1960s and 1970s, and relates them to generic models of the design process. This model, introduced in Chapter 1, consists of three stages:

- Divergent Search
- Transformation
- Convergence

In the *divergent* searching of the possible solution space for a design problem, the objectives are unstable and tentative, the problem boundary is unstable and undefined and the evaluation of alternatives is deferred. The design sponsors' brief is a starting point, subject to revision and the aim is to increase uncertainty and widen the range of possibilities.

The *transformation* process involves the imposition on to the results of a *divergent search* of a pattern which will allow convergence to a single solution. At this stage of the design process objectives, briefs and boundaries are fixed, critical variables and constraints are recognised and the problem is divided into sub-problems for parallel or serial treatment. The freedom to change sub-goals, and to evaluate alternative choices rapidly are needed and the personal capabilities and orientation of the design team are critical at this stage.

The *convergent* activities have as their objective the reduction of uncertainty. This stage requires a very different orientation and according to Jones, persistence and rigidity of mind become a virtue. Unforeseen sub-problems may present problems at this stage, and cause recycling to earlier stages. The models used to represent remaining alternatives become more detailed and concrete.

The transfer of mature technologies, and the cost-driven relocation of relatively labour intensive manufacture and assembly processes can be seen to reflect the convergent stage of design. In the context of the production chain presented by Dicken (2003), the relative success of the newly industrialising countries can be seen as a highly effective entry at the convergent stage of the design and production process. This requires mastery of efficient production utilising mature technologies.

The creation of new products from available technologies, is associated with the success of Japan, particularly in consumer electronics and automotive products from the 1960s to the 1980s. These capabilities map on to the transformation stage, and represent a more demanding set of analytical skills. Arguably Japan is accomplished in the transformation stage with highly innovative products derived from newer technologies, but less proficient at the divergent stage which can be likened to the development of basic research strategies and requires the uncertainty-generation of the divergent phase. Part of the recent policy response has been to increase the budget for basic science and to embark upon education reform (Goodman and Philips, 2003).

Economies such as Malaysia, despite efforts to shift to transformative and divergent activities via the Multimedia Super Corridor[2] and related initiatives, still retain a high proportion of the essentially convergent tasks of global production (Wilkinson et al, 2001).

Jones' essentially linear model of design can be seen in a different form as the "waterfall" model of information systems design (e.g. Birrell and Ould, 1985). Here the need for re-cycling indicated by Jones is accommodated between successive stages of development and refinement. The waterfall model can also be reflected in Dicken's chain: the global redistribution of the components of production can be seen to be dependent upon effective communication across the feedback loops linking each stage. In practice these are dependent on globally available ICTs.

The variety of responses of players to the emerging new web-oriented "techno-economic paradigm" (Dosi, 1986) is instructive for both nation states and sub-national regions. For example, Taiwan's relatively effective response reflects a range of cultural and economic linkages, both to Japan as former colonial power, and Greater China.[3]

Taiwan has followed a classic route of state sponsored development, particularly in the area of information technology (Tsai, 1993). Companies such as Tatung reflect the same Japanese colonial influence which produced the sprawling portfolios of the Korean *chaebols*. However, the *chaebols* closely mimic the strict hierarchies and rigidities of the pre-war Japanese *zaibatsu*. In addition, the nature of state patronage through credit rationing in Korea (Zeile, 1996) encouraged companies to second-guess areas of potential state support by moving into business sectors in anticipation of future support. This has created even greater diversity within the company groupings than in the original Japanese model.

In Taiwan the mix of traditional Chinese business networks described by Numazaki (1996) with a state provided or sponsored infrastructure has produced a different outcome from Korea, although both countries were colonised by Japan. The relatively narrowly targeted strategies of Taiwanese firms have delivered world class performance in key areas of information technology. Global dominance has been achieved in motherboard design and fabrication. The manufacturing capability in the "silicon forge" service provided to overseas designers requiring prototype microprocessor chips has allowed participation at key points in the production network. Foreign companies operating in Taiwan, such as Texas Instruments, do so in order achieve the timely production of high-value products, not to pursue outright cost advantage. From this level of performance, companies such as Acer have developed a more integrated presence as full-range manufacturers.[4] This chapter looks at aspects of design decision-making that reflect the capability to make such a transition.

Design Strategies: Incremental and Systemic

Part I argues that the accepted view of organisational relationships has moved towards a network or web paradigm. Models of the design process have shifted to accommodate less linear and more situational views of design. This shift from a hierarchical to a network or web view of organisations was foreshadowed by Williamson (1975) in his description of the substitution of markets for hierarchical relationships, Thompson (1967) in terms of coalition formation across the organisation, and by Mintzberg (1979) in the form of work constellations. Within design the acknowledgement of design participation by users (e.g. Cross, 1972) also shifted models of the design process into less hierarchical and more situated paradigms. Avison et al (1998) describe the evolution of Multiview-2, an information systems design methodology intended both to encompass soft systems methods and to accommodate a view of organisations as networks of related but varying interests and priorities.

Design can be regarded as the unifying activity or process throughout the production chain and across the production network. Design determines the output, whether artifact or service, it also determines the configuration of processes and deployment of resources across the network.

Design: Artefacts and Process

Design and engineering history often focuses attention on the visual aspects of the designed artifact, rather than the design process which gave rise to it. Smith (1983) complains that design historians tend to ignore the non-visual criteria which often determine success or failure. He argues that innovation in subsystems is often studied without reference to overall measures of relative performance. For example in aviation dramatic changes in propulsion from propeller to jet should not be considered in isolation from less obvious but equally significant performance related variables such as take-off weight and payload in aircraft. The invisible organisation underlying the selection and development of new technology is equally crucial to the resulting innovation. The preconditions of successful change inevitably involve the interaction of new and existing technologies.

The difference between successful and unsuccessful innovation can be examined through both physical and non-physical qualities. Innovations need to be robust to survive. Gardiner (1986) defines a *robust* design as one bringing together several divergent lines of development to form a new composite design. This radical or systemic innovation phase can then be followed by consolidation and stretching phases. The latter phases distinguish the robust design, which can be extended beyond its original capabilities by incremental change. A correspondingly innovative design which cannot be developed to this extent is termed *lean* by Gardiner. These arguments also encompass the role of clients in determining design specification and strategy (Gardiner and Rothwell, 1985).

The client-designer relationship is one of a range of contingencies affecting design decisions. However, the strategy which emerges during a complex project largely reflects the underlying range of technical choice available, which in turn reflects a range of contingencies which may be beyond the control of the designers themselves. The analyses which follow are based on developments in two key transportation systems: aviation and railways. They emphasise the importance of resources to the success of innovative design. Access to and competence with relevant resources are equally critical to meaningful participation in the development process.

Entering the Jet Age: Resources and Resourcefulness

Developments in the civil aviation industry provide evidence of the alternative trajectories of systemic, or radical innovation and the incremental, step by step introduction of innovation. Aerospace is a significant global industry, and one in which developing countries have attempted to compete. For example, Indonesia has used licensing arrangements to acquire the skill base for aircraft manufacture while Brazil has enjoyed significant success in competing in the design and manufacture of small capacity regional jet airliners.

Aircraft are a key resource for both development and disaster relief in most developing regions and, for better and worse, mass air transport has transformed the opportunities for the development of the global tourism industry.

In post-World War II Britain, systemic innovation can be seen as an attempt to compensate for lack of breadth in technical development, in contrast to the position of the U.S. industry at this time. The lag in British civil aviation is often credited to the wartime agreement that the United States would meet allied requirements for transport aircraft, so that Britain could concentrate on combat types. However, Smith (1983) argues that considerable disparities in performance levels between British and North American civil aircraft already existed by 1939, as a result of British complacency developed in a captive imperial market.

The post-war application of state-of-the-art military technology to civil aviation, through the Comet airliner programme, was an attempt to overhaul U.S. practice in a single step. The result was an aircraft which Gardiner (1986) has termed a "lean design". It was adequate for the traditional Empire routes with short route stages allowing frequent refuelling, but less well suited to the emerging transatlantic routes, and difficult to re-engine or stretch in specification. The Boeing 707, its U.S. rival, was much more successful commercially, although appearing in prototype form five years after the Comet.

Detailed examination of the development of the Comet design, from the original Brabazon Committee No.4 specification for a "jet-propelled mail plane for the North Atlantic", to the 1949 prototype airliner, reveals the successive revision of a radical design to a more conservative one (Air International, 1977). Early design studies indicated either canard or tailless layouts. By 1945 the DH106 was a 24-passenger four-jet passenger aircraft, but by May the following year a conventional tailplane had been added, although a 40 degree wing sweep was retained. The prototype finally appeared with a modest 20 degree sweep-back to the wing and a conventional unswept tail unit.

This development profile is in marked contrast to that of the B-47 and B-52 bombers, the precursors of Boeing's 707 airliner. Initially the B-47 medium bomber was a straight-wing design. Marschak et al (1967), in tracing the development of the B-47 and B-52, show just how late in design studies the final six and eight engine layouts were determined. A total of fifty engine configurations were explored for the B-47 after it was selected in design competition in 1944. Subsequently further experimental bomber configurations were explored. In 1949 the XB-55 proposal utilised four T-40 turbo-props. In 1950 the XB-56 substituted four J-35 engines for the six J-57s of the B-47. During the development of the B-52, straight wings were replaced by swept as captured German war-time research was analysed and assimilated. Both turbo-props and turbo-jets were considered, as initially the latter were assumed essential for the required fuel economy and range. The final choice of J-57 turbo-jets came only after serious difficulties emerged in the development of the T-35 turbo-prop engine.

The brief account reveals a striking difference between the progressive retreat from a highly innovative design to a buildable compromise for the British project and the progressive radicalisation of relatively conservative designs for the U.S. programme. U.S. technical development involved no ab-initio commitment to a particular technology. This was the crucial difference from the British approach which was, from the outset, focussed on turbo-jet propulsion, a technology in which the country has a clear advantage. The U.S. designs were focussed on the problem of the intercontinental delivery of nuclear weapons, a military problem of little concern to the U.K.; from that perspective the precise technology employed was secondary.

The development of Boeing's commercial jet transports followed a similar path to that of the preceding military aircraft. The forerunner to the 707 was the Boeing Dash-80 private venture prototype. This was a speculative venture to demonstrate the practicality of air-to-air refuelling from jet powered tankers for the growing fleet of high-speed jet bombers. Consequently it benefited from the enormous research effort put into military aviation in the immediate post-war period in the U.S. Gardiner argues that the design exhibits 'robustness', as evidenced by the progressive extension of performance through successive versions. The relevant design features were derived from military requirements. These included placing engines in under-wing pods, not at the wing root, as in the Comet. This dispersed vital components and reduce the risk of catastrophic damage from aerial gunfire. Gardiner points out the advantage this gives in allowing the substitution of more advanced engines with minimum modification to the airframe in contrast to the wing-root location used in the Comet. Currently a new generation of engines for the surviving fleet of B-52 bombers which will extend their operational lives in to the second quarter of the twenty-first century is under consideration (Air International, 2003).

The Dash-80 design represented the effective assimilation of the rapidly growing understanding of the new technologies. The earliest design studies were essentially jet versions of the piston-engined Model 377 Stratocruiser and KC-97 tanker. Pentagon permission for the production of a civil version utilising the military jigs, was given in July 1955 (Gunston, 1980). This represented a considerable cost advantage over rival aircraft, including the projected DC-8 from Douglas, even though not all of the jigs could be utilised.

From the outset Boeing offered a range of fuselage lengths and engine versions, including an adequate competitor to the intercontinental DC-8. Douglas offered only one fuselage length until the DC-8-61 model of 1966 which was stretched by 11.18m. What differentiated Boeing from both Douglas and de Havilland was an appreciation of the marketing advantage of exploiting the flexibility inherent in their design. Subsequently Douglas took this philosophy to heart with the development of its DC-9/MD80 model offering a variety of fuselage and wing combinations (Chant, 1980; Whitford, 2002). Following the 1997 merger of Boeing and McDonnell-

Douglas, the basic DC-9 design continued in production in the recognisable form of the Boeing 717, with radically updated engines, wings and avionics.

In Britain progressive development of the Comet design, from Comet 1 to 1A and 2 was halted after the discovery of extensive metal fatigue problems following several crashes in 1954. Despite the wing root location of the engines, the original de Havilland Ghost centrifugal flow jets had been replaced by axial flow Rolls Royce Avon engines. This option had first been discussed with its main customer, British Overseas Airways (BOAC), at the end of 1946 (Air International, 1977). In the Comet 4 series alternative outer wing sections produced short range and long range versions. While this version enjoyed brief fame in initiating a jet-powered transatlantic service, Gardiner (1986) points out, that it was operating at the extreme margin of its range and payload in comparison with the Boeing 707-120 and the later 707-320 intercontinental model. Gunston (1980) argues that, despite its original design specification as a trans-Atlantic mail carrier, the Comet was best suited to a medium haul role. A 4A version, with 2.14m cropped from its wing-span and 1.02m added to the fuselage, was developed but not built for the U.S. Capitol Airlines. This led to the Comet 4B version for British European Airways (BEA), with 1.98m added to the fuselage length. The 4C assimilated the long fuselage and the Comet 4 transatlantic wing. Such changes may have been more difficult than with the 707 configuration, nevertheless they represent the manipulation of sub-systems expected in the mature stage of a product life cycle, as suggested by Gardiner and Rothwell's diagram of stages in the evolution of robust design (Gardiner and Rothwell, 1985). "Lean" must be regarded as a comparative term in relation to the two designs and arguably the Comet proved robust within the envelope of its initial performance conception.

It should be noted that, while Boeing's subsequent 727 and 737 models enjoyed some 30 per cent commonality with the 707, the 720 medium range version of the 707 was a substantially re-designed and re-tooled aircraft, despite its very similar appearance.

Gardiner and Rothwell (1985) argue more persuasively that such differences in design are a reflection of the quality of relationships between manufacturers and clients. They cite Boeing's collaboration with Pan American Airlines in the development of the 747 project as crucial to the ultimate success of the venture.

Gunston (1980) confirms the importance of client participation in arriving at a marketable design, by recounting the restrictions placed upon the size and performance of the Hawker-Siddeley Trident jetliner by British European Airways. These prevented it competing effectively with

Boeing's 727. The aircraft was one of three similar designs offered by Bristol, Avro and deHavilland in response to a 1957 BEA specification for a short-haul jet. As late as December 1956 BEA had insisted that the turbo-prop Vanguard, developed as a replacement for the highly successful Viscount, would meet its requirements for the 1960s.

At the insistence of BEA the Trident aircraft was reduced in size, then recognised to be too small. Downsizing the original RB141 6350kg thrust engines for the RB163 4445kg Spey engine caused difficulties in the subsequent re-enlargement.

Attempts at development through the Trident 2 and 3 were hampered by the restriction of this crucial subsystem, ultimately producing the compromise of a fourth RB163 booster engine in the 3B to improve maximum take-off weight. By the time the 3B offered payload and performance equal to its American rival, Boeing's 727 had achieved a dominant position in this sector of the market. Only 117 Tridents were built, against more than 1,800 727s.

Gunston (1980) also acknowledges the delays in the development of the Trident design caused by a government insistence that the company selected by BEA should merge with at least one other manufacturer. This reflected the U.K. government's concern with the size and number of companies in the U.K. aviation industry. A consortium of the deHavilland, Fairey and Hunting companies was attempted, but this collapsed in 1959, with deHavilland joining the Hawker-Siddeley group. Given this kind of exogenous pressure it is not surprising that the designers should have concentrated on BEA's requirements, to the exclusion of broader marketing considerations.

The ultimate consequence of the disparity in resources between Britain and the United States in aviation has now been played out. While Britain retains a significant industry, it is networked into a number of partnerships and international collaborations. Airbus and the multinational Eurofighter provide significant activity, while British Aerospace Systems is a partner of Lockheed Martin in the development of a new fighter, the F35, most of which will be produced for the U.S. military. An advanced military trainer, the BAe Hawk, is the only completely British aircraft in production. In this key area of technology, even a major economy can no longer stand alone in the development and creation of new products.

British Railways: Truncated Incremental Change

Almost from their inception, railways have been a tool of colonial development and a determinant of development prospects (Headrick, 1981). In railway technology the change from steam to diesel traction represents a shift equivalent to that from piston engine to gas turbine propulsion in aviation and shows similar outcomes.

In Britain the motive power policy pursued immediately after the nationalisation of four large constituent companies in 1948 illustrates the successful application of an incremental approach to an existing, well understood steam technology. Failure to repeat the process with the then rapidly developing diesel technology reflected financial and commercial pressures rather than any lack of understanding of the difficulties involved. These pressures led in 1956 to the abandonment of a pilot diesel evaluation scheme intended to generate sufficient experience for informed selection of a small number of standard designs. Instead the wholesale construction of almost untried designs was initiated. The result was both an unnecessary variety of equipment for identical tasks, and, in several instances, outright failure to produce a useable locomotive.

Post-war conditions indicated that steam traction was most economical in both capital and running costs in comparison with electric and diesel haulage. The operating conditions favouring the adoption of the diesel in the United States during this period did not apply, except in the case of diesel shunting which had been investigated by the major British companies prior to nationalisation. Prototype diesel-electric and turbine main-line locomotives had been ordered or placed in traffic by three of the four private railway companies and these were used by the new owners to gain operating experience.

However, government restrictions on capital investment ruled out any large-scale experiments with new types of traction. Instead existing designs of steam locomotive were exchanged between the former companies, now operating as regions of British Railways, for comparative trials. The result was a range of standard locomotives built to a variety of power classifications for both freight, passenger and mixed traffic reflecting the best of existing practise. Adaptations for post-war conditions included attention to ease of maintenance and the ability to deal with indifferent quality fuel.

With the exception of certain components, the designs reflected the practice of the London, Midland and Scottish Railway (LMS), the largest of the four companies nationalised in 1948. Under the direction of William Stanier a policy of standardisation had been followed in the pre-war period.

LMS standard designs reflected an incremental adaptation of innovations which Stanier had brought from his training with the Great Western Railway (GWR), following Churchward and his successors. Churchward had produced the definitive design for the twentieth-century British 4-6-0 locomotive in 1902 and 1906 with the Saint and Star classes respectively. He achieved this with a careful blend of current British and European innovations, such as tapered boiler and four-cylinder engine – in Jones' (1980) terms, convergent developments within a mature technology.

The other two companies, The London and North Eastern (LNER) and Southern Railways pursued, through Nigel Gresley and Oliver Bulleid respectively, a more adventurous policy. The latter, having worked under Gresley in the LNER, produced the last wholly innovative steam locomotive design in Britain. The Leader class was intended to achieve the operating efficiencies of diesel with steam traction. The LNER was a relatively under financed company in comparison with the LMS; on the Southern Railway the majority of traffic was carried by electrified lines in and around London. The more innovative approach to steam traction design could be attributed to a lack of the resources needed for a broadly based incremental approach, and to the relative marginality of steam operation on the Southern Railway.

In the modernisation plans drawn up in 1954 it was decided to build no new passenger steam locomotives after the 1956 programme and to terminate the construction of all steam locomotives soon after. The availability of labour was seen as a problem, given the character of steam maintenance work in contrast to working conditions offered by competing industries. Additional concern with the shortage of suitable coal and growing awareness of air pollution had already led to serious examination of alternative sources of motive power. Electrification was the ideal alternative, since the capital cost of such locomotives was between steam and diesel while maintenance was simpler and cheaper than either. The attendant capital costs of power supply equipment and re-signalling meant, however, that these advantages could only be applied to the most heavily used lines.

Diesel traction was chosen to replace steam on an area by area basis so that operating and maintenance practices could be adjusted to the new technology and a clear assessment of the cost and implications of diesel traction made. Nineteen thousand steam locomotives remained in use, although the post-nationalisation standard types had been used to replace the oldest and least efficient classes. It was envisaged that the process of transfer and consolidation of modern steam locomotives would continue with the introduction of diesel types.

According to Rogers (1980) adequate diesel locomotives were available from foreign manufacturers. In particular the Electro-Motive division of General Motors had already established a standard range of locomotive types. In Britain the English Electric company had the capacity to produce all the components of a locomotive within its subsidiaries and had constructed the main-line locomotives introduced on an experimental basis to LMS and Southern designs. Industry lobbying and government policy favoured British construction, if necessary under licensing agreements however, General Motors were not prepared to enter licensing agreements at this time.

The opportunity was taken to utilise public investment to create a capacity among British firms in the new traction technology and to create an export potential. A pilot programme of diesel types was developed. Different designs were ordered from a range of manufacturers for assessment during a three-year period, prior. Haresnape (1982a, 1982b) details the pilot designs and their proposed distribution across the rail system. Each diesel type corresponded to an existing steam power classification so that traffic managers could readily substitute diesel for steam power on their rosters. The individual manufacturers, their designs and the power typology were to be assessed in use.

Private manufacturers, and BR's own workshops at Derby and Swindon contributed locomotive designs with diesel engines of both British, foreign and licensed manufacture. Both diesel-electric and diesel-hydraulic types were included. The latter were based on current German practice and offered weight advantages. On the Western Region, which alone had no electrified lines, hydraulic transmission was thought to offer greater continuity with steam practice than diesel-electric technology in which the diesel engine provided power for electric traction motors.

Before the 174 pilot scheme locomotives were delivered, however, the British Transport Commission ordered the abandonment of the trial period and the accelerated adoption of diesel traction. The rationale for this decision was poor financial performance by the railway and the urgent need to realise projected savings in operating costs from the abandonment of steam in favour of diesel. A reduction in the variety of types was requested, and working parties representing each region convened to produce guidelines. The pilot scheme was a divergent exploration of a new technology, designed to utilise the widest variety of equipment at all levels: control, transmission and power. With little operating experience available, decisions for large scale production were made on the basis of the general performance of the manufacturers involved and reported experience from other railways.

Differential capacity between the companies involved meant that orders had to be tailored to the availability of components rather than traffic requirements. The result was a mixture of medium-speed diesel engines linked to electric transmission and high-speed engines linked to both electric and hydraulic transmission. The issue of electric versus hydraulic transmission was only resolved by comparative tests in 1965 which came down on the side of the former and the abandonment of hydraulic types was not completed until 1977. Several of the diesel engines and the locomotives utilising them were outright failures. One in particular, the Clayton Type 1, was not actually part of the pilot scheme, being ordered in bulk from the drawing board in an attempt to utilise diesel passenger rail-car experience.

Designing the Design Process

Successful innovation and subsequent adaptation to changed circumstances or new applications reflects the availability of technical choice. Success cannot be predicted from the examination of the specific instantiation of a technology in an individual design, since it reflects underlying processes. Continuous or incremental innovation will reflect a well resourced organisation which is able both to construct a range of choice and to identify intermediate stages of innovation, even in conditions of high technical uncertainty. Bold, large-scale single steps in systems innovation are as likely to reflect pressures of time and resources as any greater insight.

Gardiner (1986) regards incremental improvement as evidence of "robust design", and relates this robustness to the adequacy of the brief. Rothwell and Gardiner (1985) contrast the policies observed in two automobile companies, one British, one American, responsible for two models which had been judged equal "best buy" by a consumer magazine.

Ford of Britain held patents equivalent to all the innovations produced by their British rival, the British Motor Corporation (B.M.C.), during the 1960s, but chose not to put them into production. The result was a greater range of customer options and retail pricing which delivered double the profit margin of B.M.C. (Gardiner 1986). The Ford designers were able to choose not to innovate. The less capitalised British company pursued technical innovation as a marketing strategy during the sixties, yet was unable to generate a level of profitability sufficient to improve its relative position or to sustain an adequate level of further technical innovation. Within twenty years, as British Leyland, the company was producing the Montego, a model which relied on a gear-box produced by Volkswagen, a significant competitor, alongside a fully licensed Honda model marketed as the Triumph Acclaim.

While the aircraft examples raise doubts about the characterisation of particular designs as lean or robust, it supports Gardiner and Rothwell's (1985) focus on the client relationship. The British Railways example indicates how a basically sound design policy can be frustrated by the intervention of exogenous variables, and particularly the imposition of inappropriate decision time-frames, which will be discussed further in the next chapter.

The "Robust versus Lean" design dichotomy introduced by Gardiner (1986) is a reflection of the technical base supporting a design. This base may offer a broad or narrow range of technical options on which specific designs may be based. Incremental innovation involves the manipulation of sub-systems through time to facilitate the introduction of a new technology and associated practices This is also a means of tailoring the technology to an extended range of applications. Such a view raises the issue of how clear the separation between incremental and systemic innovation can be, and whether in fact the key is an adequate understanding of the complex interaction of subsystems. The evidence from Marschak et al (1967) suggests that, when entering a new technology, existing understanding of the implications of design decisions must be extended through experience. The quality and effectiveness of the learning process will depend upon the character of the industry into which the technology is introduced and the nature of existing practices. The term systemic, rather than radical, acknowledges the continuum which leads from the incremental manipulation of variables within a well understood context, to a new design environment.

The product life-cycle perspective indicates a role for continuing innovation in both product and process. Process innovation allows the well-understood product to maintain a comparative advantage over a newer rival with great potential, by reinforcing economies of scale of production. At its initial deployment, a new technology may not achieve any of its potential advantages over a mature and well established alternative. The level of understanding of an existing technology will influence the point at which a commitment to a new alternative will be made. Such understanding may differ between organisations for the same technological base.

With its pilot scheme British Railways attempted to create both the knowledge-base and infrastructure necessary to the successful introduction of diesel traction. Exogenous factors forced the premature adoption of an immature technology and a laudable attempt to produce informed choice resulted in the propagation of untried designs. The forced abandonment of the incremental adoption of diesel traction was doubly unfortunate. The disinvestment from steam meant that many of Chief Mechanical Engineer Riddles' standard locomotives went to the scrapyard after only a small fraction of their economic life. The investment in an unnecessary variety of diesel replacements and the need to recover the greater capital outlay delayed the subsequent electrification of suitable lines, a result foreseen by Riddles in 1948 (Rogers, 1980).

The Electro-Motive Division of General Motors Corporation was able to continue its own modular and incremental design policy to provide an increasingly powerful and varied range of locomotives utilising a range of well-tested sub-systems. British Rail Engineering was only able to place a comparable product in service in the 1980s when the Class 58 freight locomotive was designed with consideration of its export potential. In the late 1990s, following privatisation and the creation of a variety of passenger service providers and a single U.S. owned freight operator, General Motors designs finally appeared in significant numbers on British tracks.

Gardiner (1986) relates incremental innovation to the "consolidated" phase of a robust design, at a point where the basic parameters are understood, and can be manipulated to provide a range configurations and performance characteristics. Rothwell and Gardiner (1985) illustrate this point with the Rolls-Royce RB-211 family of fan-jet engines. The current Trent family of triple-shaft gas turbines represents a systemic innovation within a clear incremental framework.

Incremental innovation is a strategy more easily achieved by large and well resourced organisations. It requires a base of thorough and wide-ranging research which can provide a range of alternative solutions to main and sub systems. A less thorough research base and restricted resources will result in a premature focus on specific technologies and solutions. The range of configurations indicated by Marschak et al (1967) in U.S. post-war bomber studies, and the complex interrelationship between engines and airframes generated by the programmed transition to turbo-jet and turbo-prop propulsion indicates that effective consolidation depends on access to a range of significant alternatives.

The difference between the retreat from the original highly radical proposals for the deHavilland Comet, and the successive introduction of innovative sub-systems into the Boeing aircraft proposals of the same period reflects a fundamental difference in design strategy. A high-risk strategy of systemic innovation typified by the Comet programme indicates a relative lack of resources available to designers. The difference in design policies pursued by the major British railway companies prior to nationalisation can be attributed to similar disparities in resources between them. Paradoxically, well resourced conservatism seems the route to sustainable innovation.

The distinction between incremental and systemic innovation may appear to correspond to Kuhn's (1962) concept of normal science and paradigm shift. However, the accumulated change achieved through incremental design can at least equal the performance improvement of a systemic change. The problem for designers is that radical change reached by this route may not be recognised, and insufficient regard may be given to a new system environment.

Lack of practical experience with the emerging technologies led to similar mis-perceptions in the British Railways pilot diesel programme. The complexities of diesel-hydraulic locomotives were not fully recognised by Western Region engineers. They hoped to avoid the intricacies of electrical engineering in a region with no electrified lines, but as Rogers (1980) points out the control systems alone of these locomotives required sophisticated electronic and electrical care and management.

A specific difficulty with the new aircraft technologies of the post-war period was the difference in characteristics between the prototype aircraft, effectively hand-built, and those subsequently built on the production jigs. This loss of the previous level of continuity between development and production aircraft increased the importance of modification in the light of service experience. At the same time more sophisticated aircraft were being produced in smaller quantities and at much higher unit costs than in the previous decade, a trend that continues, and is discussed in Chapter 9.

The solution attempted was the elimination of separate prototype construction, and the modification of production aircraft on the basis of tests on the initial output of the line (Marschak et al, 1967). Such an approach appears attractive, but offers considerable cost penalties if production jigs must be substantially altered, and early aircraft retrospectively modified. Such a strategy was inadvertently imposed on British Railways by the revised diesel modernisation plan.

The earlier caveat for the users of incremental strategies is reinforced. The incremental adjustment of a number of design components can lead, unwittingly, to a systemic change in terms of performance and environment. Such change may not be recognised, especially in new areas of technology, since it results from an accumulation of apparently minor adjustments.

In a complex environment, the alteration of a single design variable can lead to considerable interactions. Perrow (1983) examines the example of a change in U.S. naval propulsion systems to improve performance by increasing steam turbine working pressures. He points out that the contingencies of this single variation were not appreciated and necessary adjustments in the working environment were not made.

Perrow argues that the interactions exhibited in such situations consist of unfamiliar, unplanned or unexpected sequences of events. These may be either not visible or not immediately comprehensible. He labels such systems "complex". They are characterised by proximity of parts not in the principal operating sequence. Common-mode connections may exist between such parts, so that a single error produces effects in apparently remote parts of the system. Unfamiliar or unintended feed-back loops, and many potential interactions between control parameters exist. Only indirect or inferential information sources and limited understanding of some processes may be available to the operators of such a system.

Perrow is principally describing the management of physical transformation processes, as in the chemical industry. However, his terminology can be applied to design problems generally, since a relatively simple design may be deployed in an environment which could involve it in complex interactions.

Perrow (1984) characterises the complexity of a variety of systems on a matrix with two dimensions: interaction – from linear to complex and coupling – from loose to tight. Perrow's argument is that either high complexity or tight coupling can be handled separately, but when they coexist system management can become problematic, if not impossible. Here it is argued that incremental alteration of an established design can move a system into the area of high complexity and tight coupling, but such a change may not be recognised. Systemic innovation may place a design there, but in such circumstances, designers and operators are more likely to recognise a new environment.

Design and Development

Those characteristics of a problem which are amenable to design intervention may be obscured by complexity and uncertainty from a variety of sources. If "robustness" can better be expressed in terms of client relations and resource availability and if the effects of uncertainty can be minimised through an incremental approach, will a new environment be recognised if it is entered by such a route?

The disbenefits of transition to a new technology reflect the relative expense of first generation applications, and the lack of advantages of scale or established support infrastructure. Innovation case-studies indicate that in many areas of manufacturing technology, innovation is associated with new and growing companies which do not face the abandonment of existing capital assets related to the displaced technology. For developing countries there is the prospect of entry into a technology after initial risks have been explored by the early adopters, and with less sunk investment to abandon.

The adoption of specific innovations such as jet propulsion may be prompted by critical comparative advantage in performance that may be sufficient to overcome extreme drawbacks, such as the ten hour operating life between rebuilds of the 1943 Junkers Jumo turbojet. Clearly military technology is an area where small margins can yield decisive advantage and the design cultures engendered in military work are examined in Chapter 9. Kaldor (1981) argues that if an overview of the interactions of increased complexity is not maintained, innovation may become increasingly counter-productive in terms of realised, as opposed to potential, performance. Thus Perrow's (1984) model of complexity might prove a valuable guide to the management of incremental innovation in complex systems.

The 707 aircraft and all its derivatives through to the 737 can be said to have benefited from the military market support enjoyed by the KC-135 air-to air refuelling aircraft and its transport variants. However, Gardiner and Rothwell (1985) argue that the lack of a military base for the 747 project was an advantage. It enabled the exacting commercial requirements of Pan American, their sponsoring customer, to be met while their main potential rivals, Lockheed, were engaged with the military C-5 transport. Increasing differentiation between military and civil requirements may be taken as a sign of a mature, or consolidated design environment compared with that existing at the opening of the "jet age" in the nineteen-fifties.

Military transport aircraft must meet a much wider range of airfield conditions than civil designs of a comparable capacity. However, several civil designs, including the 747 itself have been adapted for a variety of military uses. The military derivative of the Comet, the Nimrod anti-submarine aircraft, is still in front-line Royal Air Force service and a programme to re-manufacture the aircraft into a new version was embarked upon recently (Dawes, 2002), then abandoned on cost grounds.

Clearly for new entrants an adoption policy for technical innovation should aim at the point of greatest immediate comparative advantage. As understanding of the new technology increases, the range of application can be extended beyond the entry point. The Rolls Royce RB-211 engine family is a successful example of such a strategy, with development to both higher and lower power ranges following the troubled development of the initial models. Rothwell and Gardiner (1986) suggest that this initial systemic innovation was facilitated by the existence of a back-up programme. At the insistence of customers, a more traditional alternative to the Hyfil carbon-fibre fan blades originally selected was developed. When the innovative blades failed conventional impact tests, this back-up was the salvation of the development programme. This is therefore a case of technical choice being generated at the insistence of the product users.

The cost of developing new designs has increased steadily in the last fifty years. Gardiner (1986) illustrates changing design trajectories, by plotting design engineering time against development date. The utilisation of computer-aided design, shown by the correspondence of the development cost of the Boeing 757 with the 1960's 727 model, has to some extent broken this inexorable trend. Nevertheless Boeing and other companies are pursuing several strategies to broaden their design base without compromising the commercial prospects of new designs. The design programme for the Boeing 777 model was highly dependent on integrated computer aided design systems which allowed significant savings in development time, and reduced the need for physical models and prototypes to a minimum (Sabbagh, 1995).

One strategy, that of commonality, is not new to Boeing. The pre-war XB-15 bomber prototype, then the world's largest, provided the wing and tail surfaces for the Model 314 transatlantic flying boat. Both the B-17 and B-29 bombers provided wings, engines and control surfaces for corresponding civil aircraft, and some of Boeing's early jet transport studies were based on the B-47 bomber. As noted, the first Boeing 707 derivative, the re-engineered, lightweight 720, shared few components, but the later 727 and 737 shared 60 per cent of components. The current 757 and 767 models, while being narrow and broad fuselage respectively, still enjoy over 40 per cent commonality.

Airbus has followed Boeing's lead in producing a complete range of aircraft models, including the A-380, under development to outclass the Boeing 747. The focus of commonality has shifted, however, to the key systems of the aircraft rather than its basic structure and extends to the computerised flight control systems, minimising the re-training required when shifting crews between different types within the range (Airliner World, 2001). The "fly-by-wire" A320 model introduced a cockpit design which became standard for all subsequent types.

Boeing has adopting a risk-sharing approach to production. For example, in 767 production, aluminium extrusions are sent from Pittsburgh to Japan. Fuselage sections fabricated in Japan are then shipped to Seattle, for assembly. The involvement with the domestic industries of customer nations in production also tackles environmental uncertainty by increasing customer commitment, as with the 747 wing components produced in

Australia. This is of importance in an economy operating at the scale of Australia, where the delivery of a single 747-400 aircraft can produce an adverse monthly foreign trade balance.

Both commonality and complementarity benefit from computer-based support. However, the development of computer-integrated manufacturing systems offers a means of eliminating many of the constraints on design variation. It may be possible to offer more diverse options to customers, or to implement revisions in design at relatively little cost by utilising flexible manufacturing techniques. This key process innovation has begun to impact on design maturity and product life-cycle, as evidenced by the claims made for gains in the development of the Boeing 777 aircraft (Sabbagh, 1995).

The sophisticated integrated computer-aided design and manufacturing systems pioneered in the aerospace industry have the potential to alter the time required for critical stages of development and production. Interactions between the decision-making time-frames of the different levels of a design system add to the overall uncertainties facing designers. In the case of the British Railways modernisation scheme, they disrupted the generation of knowledge essential to sound technical choice. Any adequate design strategy will have to offer some means of dealing with them.

Chapter 7 examines in more detail the interaction between time-frames. inherent in technologies and in the organisations that develop and utilise them.

Notes

*   This chapter includes material derived from an article published as 'Incremental and systemic innovation strategies: reflections of strategic choice' *Design Studies*, 8 (1) January 1987, 41-54.
1   See Dicken (2003) fig 2.3, figs and Porter (1990) figs 2.3 and 2.4.
2   See http://www.mdc.com.my/
3   This term first appeared in mandarin business literature in the early 1990s. As the handover of sovereignty approached it became the accepted term for the People's Republic of China including the Special Administrative Regions of Hong Kong and Macao plus Taiwan.
4   See Poon (2002) for a detailed account of the development of this sector of the Taiwanese economy and of the key companies involved.

Chapter 7

Time-frames and Design Decision-making*

The previous chapter looked at technical innovation from the perspective of the resource implications of systemic and incremental approaches to design and development. Innovation can also be seen as a temporal trajectory representing diffusion from a point of origin to a wider population of adopters. Diffusion also takes place through the life cycle of a particular technology or across an entire industry based on a specific set of technologies. Time becomes a key component of the diffusion of innovation in the notion of early and late adopters of technologies. Plotting an S-curve of diffusion, the vertical axis is the percentage of a given population of users adopting the innovation, the horizontal axis is time.[1]

For late adopters of a technology, or for economies or regions seeking to participate in an established industry, these "time-frames" determine the freedom of action available and the points of entry and catch-up strategies that will best serve the development of capability and capacity.

'Time-frames' consist of a distinctive orientation to past, present and future, embedded in practice (Clark, 1982, 1997; Giddens, 1981) Clark argues that organisational sociology commonly utilises "time-free" constructs. Where time is considered, it is usually chronological time, which does not allow the recognition of time itself as a socially constructed organising device. Concurrently with the development of capitalism, clock time replaced earlier event-based time reckoning systems. Clark argues for a re-appraisal of the relative importance of the two frameworks. He points out that organisational literature contains longitudinal studies monitoring situations over time, time lags between social sectors and their effect on organisational change, the time-span of the discretion of individuals within an organisation (Jacques, 1957) and planning horizons as well as Taylorist conceptions of time-study. Clark sees the problematic nature of different "sorts of times" as central to the construction of a theory of time as a socially constructed device by which one set of events is used as a point of reference for understanding, anticipating and attempting to control other sets of events. Clark wishes to shift organisational sociology from a claim to be "over time" to be "in times". From such a perspective, time-frames are embedded in practices, and incorporate assumptions about past and future conditions.

Characteristic time-frames can be identified in relation to the design, development and deployment of technologies, the construction of systems, financial and governmental processes and resultant regulations. They may be entirely socially constructed as with government terms or fiscal periods, they may be largely imposed by a specific technology throughout the cycles of its constituent processes or development periods, or they may be derived from seasonal or natural cycles as with agricultural and related activities. Time-frames thus offer a linkage between macro-economic, sectoral levels (Utterback, 1976; Pavitt, 1980) and organisational and project levels (Buchanan and Boddy, 1983; Marschak et al, 1967).

An appreciation of time-frames allows insight into discrepancies between different time-frames and their effect on technical development and design decision-making. Time-frames operate within and beyond organisations and may impose inappropriate decision-making frameworks upon the lower levels of a system. In the context of design and project management the result can be a premature decision based on an immature understanding of a design problem or supporting technology and ultimately, a design or systems failure. At the intra-organisational level these effects are likely to be perceived simply as part of a generalised environmental uncertainty. For a design to be robust in the sense drawn from Gardiner (1984) in Chapter 6, the development process must incorporate some understanding of such externalities. Time-frame difference, if recognised, may stimulate technical innovation.

Scott (1987a) recounts how organisational typologies have been constructed around differences in production technology (Woodward, 1965), variability in organisational inputs and outputs (Thompson, 1967) and types of technology in relation to uncertainty (Perrow, 1986). Indeed, the deployment of technology within a technical organisation can be seen as one means of reducing uncertainty at its operating core (Thompson, 1967). This perspective implies a resource-dependant view of environmental interaction. Buffering the organisation's technical core from external fluctuations becomes a major concern and time-frames offer an additional insight into these fluctuations.

Galbraith's book entitled *Organization Design* (Galbraith, 1977) examines strategies of organisational control in terms of the management of uncertainty through the development of information systems. Scott (1987a) classifies this approach as a rational open systems perspective.

Information systems support innovations at the design and production levels, such as computer-aided design and computer-integrated manufacture. As shown in Chapter 6, this class of information technology can be a means of restructuring time-frames at the product and design project levels. The development of CAD was initially supported in the 1950s by the United States Air Force, as a means of reducing uncertainty in the form of quality variation in aircraft components (Arnold and Senker, 1982). Marschak et al (1967) give an account of several measures to reduce both uncertainty and development time in military projects of that period. The source of their concern was the discrepancy between technical development and project development, and the consequent difficulties for design decision-making.

The work of Rogers (1983), while acknowledging an organisational context, focuses on an individual, entrepreneurial model of innovation. Individual designers, or designs, have likewise been central to many attempts to theorise design history. Rosenberg (1979) talks of the problem of the "heroic theory of invention" obscuring the cumulative impact of small improvements during the life cycle of an individual innovation. A time-frame perspective offers a means of locating the actions of individuals within a systems overview of the design and development process.

Rosenberg draws attention to the importance of technological interdependence in the appearance of successful and wide-ranging innovation. He argues that clustering of both economic and technical conditions precede successful innovations.

Chapter 6 argued both for an understanding of the distinction between incremental and systemic innovation, and of their interrelationship. Incremental strategies allow the variation of significant sub-systems but, as noted, a succession of such incremental alterations may result in unacknowledged systemic change. Similarly it may be argued that time-frame discrepancies can produce systemic effects, the origin of which will not necessarily be recognised. The immediate concern here is with the potential of technical and non-technical dependencies to frustrate the delivery of appropriate technical designs and development policies.

Identifying Time-frames

From a design perspective, the interaction of differing time-frames from several system levels can adversely affect project decision-making. Chapter 6 regarded the motive power policy pursued by British Railways from nationalisation in 1948 as a successful application of an incremental approach to an existing and well understood steam technology. This was not replicated with the newer internal combustion technology because financial pressures led to the abandonment of a pilot diesel evaluation scheme in favour of wholesale and premature construction of almost untried designs. Such premature decision-making is a common difficulty in long-term project management, and can be attributed to discrepancies between the time-frames governing the planning cycles operating at different levels.

A range of predictive techniques has been developed to reduce the uncertainty of long-cycle project and product planning. However, Collingridge (1982) suggests that planning for the development of systems involving extensive lags should be regarded as decision-making under ignorance, rather than uncertainty. He argues that, given the difficulties of long-term high technology projects, the best evaluation possible is rank ordering of alternatives on the basis of the cost of being wrong. He proposes a conservative strategy based not on the identification of the likeliest outcome, but on the route offering the lowest cost of subsequent alteration. His position is that inevitably, at some point in the future the decision will be seen to be wrong, and ultimately an alternative solution will have to be substituted.

Collingridge justifies this conservative strategy with the example of the lead time for large scale power generation. He sets the flexibility of a larger number of smaller units, with a relative diseconomy of scale, against the inflexibility of fewer larger units. This is in effect an argument for a choice of strategy based on time-frame characteristics. Such a strategy may be necessary with very large technical or social systems involving long development cycles, but in less extreme situations, other strategies are available.

However, even short-cycle design takes place in a context influenced by longer cycles at other levels. The design process will therefore be subject to some extent to uncertainty which can be reduced by being allocated to a number of distinct sources, rather than being merely aggregated.

Richard Scott's analysis of systems theory and its contribution to organisation theory allow an understanding of the levels at which time-frames can be seen to operate. Scott (1987a) presents a case for the division of the open system models into rational and natural variants, rather than posing rational, natural and open systems models as alternatives. Galbraith's (1977) view of information systems design as organisation design is placed within the rational systems framework by Scott. Galbraith's concern with task uncertainty and its control as determinants of organisational strategy, together with an orientation to information flows and channels within organisations, provides a context in which to consider communication between decision-making levels. He offers a framework for the consideration of the technical support of design and manufacture. Scott also places Thompson (1967) in the category of rational open systems. Thompson's concern with interdependence and its effect on the structuring of organisations provides an approach to the integrative problems created for design and innovation projects. Such a basis was used to examine the development of computer-aided design systems by one organisation over a period of some fifteen years (Little, 1988). Some aspects of this case-study are examined below.

Scott points out that the open systems approach implies an interactive relationship between organisation and environment. The natural system approach pays some regard to environment, but as a source of uncertainty, rather than as an arena in which uncertainty may be managed or reduced by adaptation or intervention. Natural selection is assumed to determine organisational survival over time.

There is a corresponding difference between a time-frame oriented approach and the concern with organisational lag shown by Mohr (1969), Aiken and Hage (1971) and Damanpour and Evan (1984). Time-frames imply cyclic interdependence, rather than the unidirectional diffusion of influence implicit in the notion of lag.

There is benefit to decision-makers in partitioning uncertainty between different levels by utilising a time-frames perspective. In a systems theoretic framework, each level in a system constitutes the environment for the units comprising the level below, and a rational open systems perspective implies an ability to either intervene in that environment, or to devise internal means of coping with its impact.

Waves, Cycles and Time-frames

Long-wave economic behaviour can be regarded as the meta-level of the cyclic behaviour influencing design decision-making and policy development. Attributed by Kondratiev (1925) to cycles of capital accumulation and interest rate changes, and by Schumpeter (1939) to clustering of technological innovation, it has influenced current discussion of the relationship between design, innovation and economic development (Freeman, 1983, 1986). Rosenberg and Frischtak (1986) examine the evidence both for the existence of cyclic behaviour, and for capital versus technology driven rationales. They argue that while the evident decline of one technology will increase interest in possible successors, the macro-economic environment can be seen to synchronise cyclical change across unrelated technologies, and that ultimately widespread technological change requires favourable macro-economic conditions.

However, long-waves themselves are not simply techno-economic phenomena. Perez (1986) attributes the recurrence of recessions to the differing rates of change of the techno-economic and the social and institutional sub-systems of the capitalist economy. The first is subject to rapid change, the second then has to become re-aligned. Downs and Mohr (1976), discussing a typology of innovation at the organisational level, differentiate between administrative and technical cycles. Both emphasise the same point: cultural and social cycles are longer than their increasingly short technological counterparts. The distinction between technical and social learning advanced by Sproull and Kiesler (1991) fits into this framework at the level of the individual technical project or intervention.

It is a truism to suggest that the time-scales of technological development are shifting from years to months. Kay (1983) argues that in such a situation the universe of the technically feasible will be larger than the economically feasible since the latter will be constrained by the social and institutional setting. This setting will depend upon the perception of a current "techno-economic paradigm" (Dosi, 1986) or "best technological common-sense" (Perez, 1986). This perception will also vary between sectors of an economy. In the extreme conditions of military spending, high costs are accepted for apparently marginal improvements in performance.[2] Elsewhere a different balance of cost and return will be sought.

The role of technology in the determination of the course of an innovation reflects its position in the economic cycle (Perez, 1986) and the next chapter looks at the perceived uncertainty between frames within the organisations and sectors affected by the process in question. As a particular technology becomes better understood, the rate of return on capital invested in it falls. Further investment becomes necessary to restore the pre-eminence of the original innovators over those following (Freeman, 1983; Perez, 1986; Soete, 1986). This pattern is comparable to the life-cycle of an individual product developed within a particular technology.

Roy (1984) demonstrates the ability of a mature industry, bicycles, to counter falling returns with renewed product innovation. Suckling (1986) demonstrates the impact of the cessation of research and development activities by a company dominating its market to stress the need for continuous product development in order to maintain returns by the timely replacement of older products. Initially there is little impact on market share, but once decline sets in no amount of renewed investment can reduce the decade required for even modest recovery.

Cycles can be attributed to other, non-technical aspects of organisations, and these too can be characterised from a time-frame perspective. Organisational cultures can be seen to have life-cycles which must be considered in proposals for change (Boje et al, 1982), these in turn may reflect the time-frame of the careers of key actors or groups as in the Scottish Special Housing Association (SSHA) case study presented later in this chapter. An institution may find its technical resources being applied to greatly changed political and economic conditions as shown by Couto's narrative of the Tennessee Valley Authority presented below.

At the inter-organisational level time-frame differences may reflect core technologies (Thompson, 1967). Stinchcombe (1965) relates the character of organisations to the age of the industry in which they are found. A Schumpeterian approach would relate core technologies to historical periods. Donaldson (1985) relates organisational design to product life cycle and demonstrates a linkage over time between changes in product and organisational structure. The imposition of rigid accounting periods upon public undertakings by a government is an indirect means of external control.

At intra-organisational and technical levels cycles are reflected in coupling (Glassman, 1973; Weick, 1976; Perrow, 1984). Coupling in systems may be loose or tight. Weick (1976) defines loose coupling as implying that events are responsive, but that each retains its own identity, and some evidence of physical or logical separateness. Perrow regards coupling as a critical dimension governing the behaviour of complex systems. He argues that such systems exhibit tight coupling in conjunction with a high degree of complexity.

Chapter 6 suggested that the incremental alteration of a well understood system can take it into the realm of Perrow's "complex systems" (Perrow, 1984). Similarly, environmental change may alter the characteristics of its coupling. Perrow claims that complexity in conjunction with tight coupling must be avoided wherever possible; a time-frame perspective can be valuable in understanding critical temporal features of coupling.

As argued above, in the choices confronting designers, technical possibilities will outnumber economic ones (Kay, 1983). The acceptability and successful development of individual innovations, products or projects will depend upon the outcome of processes mediating between an innovating organisation and its socio-technical setting.

Design and Determination

Time-frame Taxonomies

One objective of the adoption of a time-frame orientation should be the development of a methodology allowing generalisation beyond the context of specific case studies, but retaining the detail necessary to the guidance of individual projects which is so often lost in aggregated material.

Taxonomies could enable the construction of models of design and innovation processes which incorporate both the qualitative insights of case-studies and the analytical insights of quantitative data. Such models assist in the implementation of specific programmes of innovation, and in the analysis and development of design and innovation policy. An effective linkage of disaggregated data with a strategic perspective avoids both the methodological difficulties of the statistical approach, and the limitations of case-study data. The value in the broader development context would lie in the assignment of scarce resources to projects and strategies that could deliver quick and effective outcomes.

Jones (1980) illustrates a hierarchy of system levels from component and product up to community level to suggest that designers need to be able to recognise interactions between levels when they occur. An examination of the effect of interacting time-frames on design and innovation decision-making requires a model of organisational context. The work of Thompson (1967) and Mintzberg (1979) allows consideration of the impact of changing technology on complex organisations. These are regarded as constituencies of interest groups forming coalitions reflecting internal conditions, including technology.

Thompson produces a typology of interdependence. Pooled interdependence allows independent action with overall co-ordination, sequential interdependence requires adjustment between components or parties according to the direction of the relationship and the flow of actions, and reciprocal interdependence requires mutual engagement and adjustment to achieve a satisfactory state or performance (Thompson, 1967, p.55). Time-frame discrepancies can be considered as one form of unrecognised interdependence, the effects of which are often attributed to an aggregated uncertainty.

This rational open systems approach can be supplemented by the work of Gouldner (1976), on the societal implications of dependence upon technology, and Giddens (1979), on the relationship between time, action and structure in social organisms. The consideration of the role of time in the structuring of organisational processes follows from this (Clark, 1982).

A general taxonomy of time-frames could assist in the analysis of the dynamics of globalisation. However, the dynamics of international markets and trans-national organisations described in Part I of this book suggest that a hierarchical distinction between government, market and organisation may be problematic.

Such a taxonomy could, however, differentiate between the time-frames existing within adopting organisations, the sectors and institutions affected, and those implicit in both new and supplanted technologies.

As discussed earlier, Collingridge (1982) gives guidance at one end of a spectrum in which technical development cycles are considerably longer than political time-frames: the construction of large-scale power generation facilities and Perez (1986) emphasises the importance of the disjuncture of institutional and technical change. The organisational context of design and development projects is subject to change at a rate greater than either.

Time-frames which are international in character can be seen to operate at the environmental level of natural cycles. For example, European beet sugar producers have a distinct advantage in competition with tropical cane sugar producers because they rely on an annual crop, whereas cane sugar requires two years to mature, and must be planted on the basis of a two rather that one year forecast of demand. Economic upswings and downswings are increasingly international in character and at the level of national and trans-national government, political and regulatory changes reflect electoral and other cycles. At the level of sectors or industries, markets move towards maturity and require strategies for differentiation. Design decisions at the level of organisations are influenced by accounting time-frames and product life-cycles.

Any taxonomy must distinguish between the effect of time-frames associated with core technologies and those existing in other sections of complex organisations. Identification and consideration of the differing time-frames of alternative technologies would indicate to what extent Collingridge's (1982) conservatism should be heeded.

A useful taxonomy should also relate the trajectory of particular innovations to their position in the economic cycle. This would allow examination of Rosenberg and Frischtak's (1986) suggestion that macro-economic conditions determine the impact of particular innovations, although they themselves regard a causal linkage between both economic and technical variables and economic long waves as essentially unproven.

The best illustration of the analytical value of a time-frame taxonomy, or at least a sensitivity to timer-frames is its application to some longitudinal case-study material. A most dramatic illustration of the potential use of time-frames in analysing the design of complex state-of-the-art technologies can be provided from published material on the Three Mile Island nuclear power plant accident of 1979.

Longer term changes in organisational environment, and their effect on technology policy and design practice are illustrated by accounts of post-war changes in two organisations both of which were created to support economic and social development prior to the Second World War. These are the Tennessee Valley Authority (TVA) as described by Couto (1988) and the Scottish Special Housing Association (SSHA) described by Little (1988).

Three Mile Island Nuclear Power Plant: Technical and Regulatory Time-frames

Perrow (1984) illustrates his term "normal accident" with a description of the sequence of events in the early morning of 28th March 1979, Stephens (1980) provides a wider description of the genesis and development of Unit 2 at the Three Mile Island power station. Between them the two writers provide the following examples of time-frame dependent events at a succession of systems levels.

At an organisational level, Stephens (1980) describes the initial estimation that a single reactor would be sufficient at the Three Mile Island location. In 1967, when the design of what was to become Three Mile Island Unit 2 was completed, it was to be located alongside an existing reactor at Oyster Creek, New Jersey. When it was decided to relocate this unit, from a salt-water river to a fresh-water location, design changes were kept to a minimum because of the expense and delay of alteration and subsequent re-certification. Nevertheless, the delay meant that when the plant was commissioned, the design of the control room was already over ten years old. Another result of the change of location was that the two units at Three Mile Island had relatively little in common, being produced by different contractors, but staffed by the same operators.

Construction work did not begin until 1972, and there were considerable pressures on prompt completion. Stephens points out that, with mandatory overtime, completion was achieved, with power being supplied to the grid on 30th December 1978, some twenty-five hours before the loss of between $37 and $48 million in tax depreciation and tax credits.

At the technical level, both Perrow and Stephens draw attention to design features intended to reduce down-time, by allowing the reactor to run through short transients which would cause rival designs to shut down automatically.

Perrow gives an extended account of the events of 28th March 1979, pointing out that although the first four critical failures in the accident took place within thirteen seconds, relevant information was queued in the computer for some hours before being printed out among a mass of other data. Perrow suggests that the realisation that the pilot-operated relief valve on the reactor was jammed open came after two hours and twenty minutes and a shift change which brought fresh personnel on duty. This particular failure of understanding was a principal component of the accident.

The above account identifies a number of levels across which time-frames created discrepancies in decision-making frameworks. Difficulties in the forecasting of demand are a major concern of energy utility companies. They result from the time-frames implicit in the large scale plant deemed necessary for economic generation of electricity, and from the time-frames implicit in the discovery and development of new sources of energy.

Delays and consequent expense inherent in the certification process for nuclear power stations led to the adoption of an existing design, and the construction of a control room which was a decade behind current practice by the time it was commissioned. This situation was a product of both the long lead time of power station construction which concerns Collingridge (1982) and the requirement of regulatory bodies for early, detailed approval. The needs of regulation are often at odds with a design perspective, since they are geared to the requirements of checking and enforcement, not design decision-making.[3] Decisions on the commissioning of the nuclear plant were strongly influenced by the fiscal time-frames imposed by the U.S. taxation system. Concerns at this level commonly impinge on project decision-making, since financial viability can be considerably affected by accounting frameworks, or tax and investment incentives.

Certain design decisions which resulted in a plant with relatively unforgiving operating characteristics were influenced by the need to minimise down-time and thus safeguard profitability. At this level, the behaviour of the plant in time, and hence the time-frames imposed upon the operators, was itself the product of design decision-making.

Many of the features of the above situation are common to large complex systems, and have led Perrow (1984) to identify dimensions of complexity and coupling as critical to the understanding of their behaviour. Here it is argued that a full understanding of coupling must include a time-frames perspective. A systems perspective is essential to understand the implications of the counter-intuitive impact of the regulatory system, designed to safeguard safety, yet resulting in an obsolete control room design central to the propagation of a major accident.

The Tennessee Valley Authority: Institutional Time-frames

Couto (1988) examines changes in post-war policies of the Tennessee Valley Authority (TVA) from the perspectives of Gouldner's "metaphysical pathos" (Gouldner, 1955). Selznick (1949) had analysed TVA policy in terms of co-optation of stakeholders into decision making as a means of survival in a potentially hostile environment, rather than an altruistic philosophy.

Couto examines the period following Selznick's study of the implementation of the original "New Deal" programme of economic and social development, and reports changes in policy emerging during the 1950s. He identifies unintended consequences reflecting priorities which placed economic development above the needs of the weaker sections of the community. These escalated to the point where the TVA reneged on its commitment to balanced regional development. Instead the Authority pursued a future as a large scale producer of cheap electricity. This led to intervention in the process of coal production in several coalfields, and involvement in the leading edge of technical development of both coal-fired and nuclear power generation.

By the time Selznick's study had been published, the TVA had completed the navigation system for the Tennessee River, and had embarked on its first coal-fired steam-generation power stations. Hydro-electricity had been developed in conjunction with flood control. Cheap and plentiful electricity had become synonymous with development. When it had utilised all potential for significant new hydro generation, the TVA turned to coal. In the ten years from 1949 to 1959 total capacity was tripled, so that hydro-generation provided only a minor proportion of output.

A change in political climate saw the defeat in Congress of proposals for a Missouri Valley Authority in 1948. A Democrat majority, from 1949 to 1952 allowed the TVA to embark upon a programme of seven steam-plants, totalling 8000 megawatts capacity. Each of the first three was in turn the world's largest plant incorporating the world's largest generating unit; each supplied a Federal defence establishment. The Shawnee Plant supplied the Atomic Energy commission at Paducah, the Kingston Plant the Atomic Energy Commission facilities at Oak Ridge, and the Widow's Creek Plant supplied the Redstone Arsenal. The TVA was now firmly located in the Cold War frame.

In the face of growing congressional opposition to the regional development component of its mission, the TVA emphasised the demands of its new customers as the basis of a national mission. Couto argues that a second national mission was rationalised around the role of the organisation as a yardstick of technical efficiency for private electricity producers. Both missions assumed a continued emphasis on low-cost power.

During the 1950s the TVA engaged in a variety of strategies to maintain or lower the cost of coal for its growing number of large steam plants. These included both manipulation of an already depressed coal market and significant technical innovation.

Couto explains that the price of coal represented 80 per cent of the operating cost of the steam plants. The TVA moved from long-term contracting, to an increasing reliance on spot-market buying. By utilising its own navigable waterways the TVA created price competition between physically distant coal fields, and between barge and rail transport. The design of its new plants allowed the use of lower quality coal than with previous technologies. Innovation in coal extraction was promoted, with capital supplied to companies prepared to tackle the new, large-scale strip-mining techniques favoured by the TVA.

Couto points out that the TVA had originally set the price of its hydro power below that of steam generated power, to stimulate the demand necessary for adequate economies of scale. In pursuing a large-scale steam-generation programme, the TVA contributed to the decline of employment in the Tennessee coalfields. The introduction of strip mining caused environmental damage by removing vegetation at high altitude, and contributed to a decline in water quality through run-off from the cleared land.

Following its policy of technical innovation as a stimulant of competition, the TVA became interested in nuclear power generation. The Price-Anderson Act had been passed in 1957, limiting the public liability of electric utilities for nuclear accidents, the TVA attempted to secure the AEC's support for a federally funded programme of reactor construction. The AEC, however, preferred a private enterprise route to a nuclear industry, at least for the domestic market (Pringle and Spigelman, 1982). In 1959 the Authority achieved a capacity for self-finance through bond issues and in 1966 GEC produced an acceptable fixed price bid to construct two 1000Mw units at Brown's Ferry, Alabama. Following the Three Mile Island accident, and an earlier near-disaster in its Brown's Ferry plant, the TVA ran into licensing problems with its nuclear plants. In 1984 work was suspended on the world's largest nuclear plant, at Huntsville, Alabama, comprising four pressurised water reactors. At that point the TVA was generating no electricity at all from a $13bn investment in nuclear plants. Although Brown's Ferry was eventually recommissioned, by the end of the century five of seventeen reactors started by the TVA were operating, with eight cancelled after significant expenditure.

Couto is concerned with the impact of nationally derived policy at an economic periphery, and the effective subversion of an agency charged with the task of addressing regional inequities through economic development. A time-frame perspective can give a different view of the change of organisational objectives.

The policy of the TVA during the 1950s was influenced by a coincidence of time-frames, with the exhaustion of hydro potential coinciding with a change in national political context. Boje et al (1982) cite the TVA of Selznick's period of observation as an organisation able to maintain and conceal political interests through the use of a myth of benevolence. As the power and effectiveness of this myth declined, an alternative was sought.

In pursuing a strategy of organisational survival, the TVA used technical innovation in conjunction with its geographical resources to develop complementary roles as a large-scale supplier of power to the military-industrial complex, and a public sector exemplar of efficient practice. This led to an expensive excursion into nuclear generation during the 1960s, justified in part by the environmental damage wrought by its own coal-fired policies of the 1950s.

The changes imposed on the original direction of the authority reflected the time-frames of national governments and economic cycles. Technical developments in coal combustion, steam generation and finally nuclear reactors were used to pursue ever greater economies of scale. These in turn involved the TVA with longer time-frames at a technical level, with consequent difficulties in responding to changes in forecast demand. This development was also conditioned by an essentially conservative, market oriented view which ignored many of the costs and dis-benefits that the TVA, as a regional development agency, was originally created to address.

Scottish Special Housing Association: Political and Technical Time-frames

The Scottish Special Housing Association (SSHA) was established by the U.K. government in 1937 to assist the Commissioner for Special Areas in his task of relieving unemployment in the economically depressed regions of Scotland. It was established in the same decade, and with a similar remit of economic and social development as the TVA, although on a more modest scale.

For fifty years the organisation existed to provide technical support to local authorities through the construction and management of public sector housing. By the end of the 1980s however, changes in government policy, and the disposal of housing stock through a combination of sales to tenants and transfer to the voluntary housing sector had changed the character of the organisation. In its final incarnation as Scottish Homes, the organisation was absorbed by the Scottish Executive in 2002, following devolution and the re-establishment of a Scottish Parliament within the United Kingdom.

As a housing development organisation, SSHA made recourse to technical innovation at several points, and the locus of innovation shifted across the range of activity, from methods of production towards those of management. Similarly, the focus of the exemplary activity by which the organisation influenced practice in public sector housing moved from production to management of existing stock, and then to the disposal of that stock, reflecting the changing concerns of central government.

The industrial provision of housing is a key distinction between developed and less developed economies. The poorest people on the planet house themselves, while for the richest housing is either a commodity provided by a highly organised industry, or a means of investment and wealth accumulation. The industrialisation of housing was part of the modernist agenda described in Chapter 3 and as a consequence highly inappropriate models of housing provision have been exported to developing countries.

The post-war activities of the SSHA as an organisation committed to the development and management of housing resources coincided with the creation and development of the Bretton Woods institutions. The provision of affordable housing for the industrial workforce is another facet of the "Fordist compromise" (Lipietz, 1992). The period in which the organisation was primarily engaged in the development and management of housing stock can be divided into three distinct phases which reflect changes in government policy and objectives which in turn transformed the environment of SSHA.

PERIOD I: Post-war Reconstruction: 1944-1960

In 1944 the Association's remit was extended from the "special areas" identified as in special economic need to the whole of Scotland. Work began on the infrastructure required for the resumption of peace-time development. A technical policy of "laissez faire" allowed contractors to construct their own house types, or those provided by the SSHA around street and infrastructure layouts provided by SSHA engineers.

General conditions of materials shortage during this period led to frequent substitution of alternative materials during construction, with consequent difficulties in recording such variations. For example, a single development of houses might have begun construction using timber ground floors, switching to solid concrete floors part way through because of a lack of imported timber. Twenty years later such undocumented changes were causing problems for subsequent upgrades, such as the renewal of plumbing or the installation of central heating. This lack of detailed technical control was in marked contrast to the subsequent periods and reflected planning difficulties at a national level.

PERIOD II: Economic Expansion: 1961-1978

The second period emerged around 1960, by which time a concern with closer technical control of design standards had displaced the immediate post-war concern with output.

Closer technical control to ensure a higher quality product involved the development of rationalised procedures to maintain the necessary volume without requiring increased staff levels. The change from the previous preoccupation with numbers above other technical and social issues was associated with policy changes introduced by new staff in senior positions. This resulted in more detailed technical control of design and construction. The technical section was expanded beneath a single head and strengthened. Existing house types were re-designed and co-ordinated into "Suites", each intended to deal with particular site contingencies.

The introduction of mandatory "Parker Morris"[4] standards for space and facilities in public housing from 1966 provided added impetus for a thorough reappraisal of existing house plans. Technical support for staff was developed through the creation of a central library of technical details and a multi-disciplinary technical co-ordinating committee established, with building department representation, to evaluate policy through feedback from contracts and to assess proposed innovation.

A high degree of feedback to designers was possible because during this period the SSHA's own Building Department handled some 50 per cent of the construction workload. Where external consultant designers were used their contribution was guided by the framework of the standard house type range, to which they frequently contributed designs, and by standardisation of specifications and details.

Computerised techniques were introduced during the 1960s, when the rationalisation of quantity surveying procedures allowed computer production of Bills of Quantities which were the contract document specifying the quantities of material and the practices to be used in construction. The rate of change of statutory and technical requirements increased in this period. These all had to be incorporated into the large number of house types in use and computer assistance for this chore was investigated.

Development work commenced, under a series of contracts with the Edinburgh University Computer-aided Architectural Design unit (EdCAAD). However, the prospect of quantification from the information required for the production of drawings led to a more ambitious programme. The advantages of this integrated approach, deriving drawings, specifications and bills of quantities from the same database were considerable. Development was correspondingly more complex, however, and the consequent delay in this pioneering work resulted, in turn, in interim measures being necessary. Meanwhile, metrication of the building industry, completed in 1972, placed additional burdens on the existing manual system.

The division of drawn information into repetitive standard details and relatively simple key drawings for each house type subsequently became a feature of the CAAD system. Once the full system had been tested on a pilot project it was rapidly applied to a large number of contracts. A significant change was already imminent in the character of the Association's workload, however.

PERIOD III: Redevelopment Assistance: 1978-1986

During the late 1970s both the size and character of the SSHA's workload underwent rapid change. With the increasing age of the post-war stock, capital resources were increasingly required for modernisation to current standards of amenity and performance to maintain its viability.

An increasing concern for the general condition of housing in inner-city areas led to the re-allocation of resources earmarked for Stonehouse New Town to the Glasgow Eastern Area Renewal programme in 1976. The Association became one of the participants in what was a precursor of "inner-city partnerships" elsewhere in the U.K. This period was also marked by the emergence of a more central concern for the 90,000 houses in the Association's management as a resource requiring improvement and development.

Much closer cost control, through the introduction of annual cash limits in 1976, meant that the relative priorities of projects had to be more carefully assessed, with some attention paid to the patterns of spending implied, as well as total expenditure.

In addition to inner city Glasgow, the Association's attention was specifically directed to a programme of redevelopment assistance for the other major Scottish cities. New construction projects were frequently concerned with redevelopment sites. These involved complex boundary constraints yet were only a fraction of the size of projects on "green field" sites of between two and three hundred dwellings to which the CAAD system had been tailored.

Consequently, the CAAD system could address only a proportion of new-build work, itself a declining proportion of capital expenditure. Further expenditure on the development of the system became difficult to justify. Although some work was carried out to assess the feasibility of using the system on comprehensive modernisation schemes, the design content of this work was also declining as a result of changing government policies.

As the computing industry as a whole became more mature, the development of sophisticated software for individual users was becoming prohibitively expensive in relation to increasingly available general commercial packages. The close relationship between SSHA and EdCAAD, an Edinburgh University research group, involved interchange of staff and refinement of the software at the Association. This restricted the general commercial appeal of the system, as with the British aircraft designs discussed in Chapter 6. The relatively uncommon hardware on which the system was mounted also frustrated attempts to support the cost of further development through income from sales.

SSHA involvement in the Glasgow Eastern Area Renewal programme led to the establishment of a multi-disciplinary regional office. This enjoyed considerable autonomy to allow the necessarily close liaison with the other statutory bodies involved. It became apparent that the existing management structure of the Association as a whole was in need of examination in the light of the reduced scale of development operations and the increased need to liaise with other bodies.

In 1982 the Association was reorganised as a matrix structure, with the existing functional divisions related to three geographical, multidisciplinary regional units, similar to the Glasgow office. The central technical services became available to Regional Managers while retaining responsibility for standards of professional performance of the technical staff at regional level. In effect the organisation was shifted away from the technical focus that had dominated the first two post-war periods.

The shifts in focus for the Association are equivalent in degree to those of the Tennessee Valley Authority, from a development focused organisation to a management focused organisation, from building housing to be rented and managed to building housing for sale alongside the disposal of existing housing stock. Finally, following devolution, the organisation was absorbed into the Scottish Executive in 2002.

The extensive change across the three major periods described shifted the focus of attention from the production methods used in the construction of housing, via the rationalisation of control over technical standards, to a concern with management information systems, and finally the co-ordination of the resources required to maintain this existing housing stock. This required a fundamental change in organisational culture.

Attention was first drawn to the problem of maintenance of existing stock relatively early in the development of CAAD techniques. Planned maintenance was being adopted, so that all property would be inspected on a five-year cycle. Repairs and replacements would be conducted on the basis of the survey. This cyclic approach represented a considerable advance over the previous method of allocating an annual maintenance budget based on previous average expenditure. The increasing age of the post-war stock suggested that a form of active forward planning would be needed to predict peaks in expenditure as specific sub-systems (e.g. plumbing, electrical wiring) required renewal. Construction information would be required to identify the points at which such work would be necessary to maintain the viability of this stock. The information technology required to sustain such a system was not available when this requirement was first identified, and the quality of recorded information from the immediate post-war period was very variable.

This product life-cycle approach was obvious to organisations responsible for both the construction and management of building stock. Even so, the potential of the reuse of production information for the prediction of life-cycle expenditure could not be realised while priorities concerned the oldest, least well documented stock. The introduction of annual cash-limits ran counter to the requirements of a life-cycle approach, but annual priorities could at least be assigned with confidence.

The support of design computing by a mainframe machine used for normal financial computing and rent collection produced conflicts over resources during CAAD development, both within and between departments. Government financial reporting requirements had to take precedence over refinement of the design facilities in the annual allocations of resources and this source of uncertainty and delay seriously compromised development. Time-frame discrepancies occurred on a monthly basis as payroll and rental processing adversely affected the performance of design software. The eventual phasing out of the mainframe machine in favour of a distributed net of minicomputers provided an opportunity for the co-ordination of computing activities and the development of multi-disciplinary management information systems for the new Regional Managers.

Making Sense of Time-frames

The examination of the Three Mile Island accident offers a bottom-up identification of time-frame discrepancies. This serves to emphasise the significance of interaction between relatively remote levels. Unlike the other two cases, it focuses on a single project, and traces the origins of its failure to a variety of time-frames and discrepancies.

Nuclear power was just one of the technologies utilised by the Tennessee Valley Authority in its attempt to adjust to its changed environment. The redefinitions of organisational mission, identified by Couto, reflect political and economic changes stemming from the Second World War. The core technology of TVA was changing at the same time, here a coincidence of time-frames governing intra- and inter-organisational concerns assisted the substantial change in practice necessary to the change in mission. The life-cycle of organisational myths proposed by Boje et al (1982) can be seen to be derived from changes in their explanatory power within the organisation and its environment. The case-studies suggest that such change reflect in turn national political time-frames.

In the U.S. system, political time-frames are linked to a rigid schedule of elections, so the most regular feature underpinning Couto's account is the succession of changes at a national political level. The successive core technologies exhibit a degree of regularity, however, with overlapping frames of some twenty years each for the dominance of hydro, thermal and nuclear generation.

Just as the events at Three Mile Island can be viewed in the wider context of changes in the power industry, which also affected the TVA, changes in Scottish Special Housing Association policy can be related to post-war changes in the development and construction industry in the U.K. and elsewhere. Russell (1981) indicates a range of pressures behind the move to increase both industrialisation and capitalisation in the building industries of East and West in this period. The factory environment was seen as free from the natural, seasonal variation and disruption of the building site, in effect reducing seasonal time-frame dependence.

As noted in Chapter 3, the theoretical underpinning for designers and architects had been laid in the twenties and thirties, within the Modern

Movement. The ideology was already available when economic and political conditions became favourable. To combine Boje et al's (1982) and Rosenberg and Frischtak's (1986) terms, the myth was in place, awaiting favourable macro-economic conditions.

The notion of cycles of organisational culture must be linked to the life-cycles of individual key actors. The consideration of dominant personalities reflects Rogers' (1995) concern with individual innovators. The tenure of two key individuals, a chief technical office and a chief quantity surveyor, coincides with the key period of technical development at SSHA. A coincidence of changing personalities and conditions enhances the prospect of organisational change. An additional dimension is created, however, through the career progression of other relatively junior actors to more senior positions. Such individuals may form a concealed constituency which could provide a revival, after time, of an earlier cultural orientation.[5]

The SSHA's core technologies changed out of synchronisation with those environmental changes which led to re-assessment of the organisation's task. CAAD technology was not fully available within the duration of the conditions it was intended to address. Nevertheless, with further technical development, the Association was able to facilitate an appropriate change in organisational structure as the basis of a management information system. There is additional evidence, however, that by the time these changes had been accomplished, discrepancies between the internal and external labour markets were creating problems in staffing the new arrangements with appropriately skilled personnel.

In one sense the delay in CAAD development can be explained in terms of straightforward lag. However, the reorientation of the organisational mission of the SSHA around a life-cycle approach reflects an organisational assimilation of the time-frames operating at its technical core. The success of this reorientation reveals the difference between political and institutional change. While political conditions altered for all the case-studies within the time-frame of particular technical project and processes, institutional change, as discussed by Perez (1986) is a different matter. For example, in the 1980s accurate predictions of the U.K.'s national health service building stock maintenance costs for the following decade became available as a by-product of computer-aided design and related databases. These were of no interest at the national governmental level. The problems lay beyond more than one election, and there was no perceived institutional need to plan that far ahead. By the turn of the century, the predicted backlog of maintenance was being tackled by a combination of massive reduction in long-term care facilities and the increasing use of use of controversial private finance initiatives.

Time-frames and Development

The cases presented above provide a range of examples of levels at which differing time-frames can be seen to impact on technical innovation and design policy. The lags and interactions described, and the strategies promoted by Collingridge and others, are relevant to large top-down development projects typified by large scale infrastructure construction. Such projects lock up resources over a long period and represent significant opportunity costs to economies with limited resources. The development of local initiatives and the availability and diffusion of appropriate technologies is also subject to these dynamics.

Innovation policies or specific programmes of innovative design would benefit from an understanding of the dependence of the trajectory of a particular innovation upon its position in the economic cycle. Similarly, both technology transfer and development strategies could benefit from sensitivity to the range of relevant time-frames.

A time-frame approach can assist both theoretical examination of the spatial and temporal aspects of diffusion of innovation and technology, and the implementation of programmes of innovation in complex organisational circumstances. Understanding of the differential between the time-frames existing within adopting organisations, the sectors and institutions affected and those implicit in a technology implies a taxonomy of levels linked to an open systems model.

Just as Perrow (1984) characterises complex systems on two dimensions: low and high complexity and loose and tight coupling, so time-frames might be usefully characterised by plotting them against the dimensions of length of cycle and inter/intra organisational origin. Short, inter-organisational time-frames would contribute to a turbulent organisational environment (Scott, 1987a; Galbraith, 1977). Long intra-organisational time-frames can be argued to contribute to organisational inertia as examined by Hannan and Freeman (1984).

The environmental context of many developing countries includes extremes of climate and the consequent loss of working time. Equally productivity may suffer from seasonal problems of health, particularly in areas where malaria in endemic. The cultural practices that develop in such environments differ from those prevalent in the developed economies, and add a further dimension. Nicholson and Sahay (2001) describe frictions between the work practices of collaborating information technology specialists based in India and the U.K. Significant misunderstanding was attributed to different expectations over the timing and priority given to work tasks.

These broader organisational dynamics and their influence on design cultures and the determination of design outcomes are dealt with in the remaining chapters. Chapter 8 opens this wider consideration with an argument for the notion of "metatechnical" frameworks of understanding.

Notes

* This chapter has been developed from an article published as 'The role of time-frames in design decision-making' *Design Studies*, 8 (3) July 1987, 170-182.
1 Rogers (1962, 1983) provides perhaps the best known overview and explanation of the origins and development of this work.
2 Chapters 8 and 9 will provide further illustrations and discussion.
3 Lawson (1982) gives an account of the impact of such thinking on architectural design processes.
4 See Chapter 3 for a more extensive discussion of the standard and its implications.
5 See Little (1988) for an extended treatment of these issues.

Chapter 8

Finding a Place to Stand: A "Metatechnical" Framework for Development*

This chapter presents an overall framework to encompass the perplexing range of influences both on individual design projects and on the development of the design policies described in the preceding chapters. It provides a socio-technical framework to link national and wider cultural and institutional contexts to the decision-making levels of an individual organisation, or network of organisations where technical tasks are planned. Both task and institutional levels are influenced by the technical dynamics of the emergent economic paradigm discussed in Part I. In this chapter it is argued that conflicts between the rationalities appropriate to institutional and task environments produce inconsistency and suboptimization.

To be successful projects and policies must address both task and institutional orientations. The alternative is to allow the conflict between technocratic consciousness originating at a technical level and overconformity attributable to the institutional level to give rise to pathological outcomes. The development of the space shuttle – the NASA Space Transportation System (STS) – is used to illustrate this argument, and a metatechnical framework is advocated as necessary to the successful linking of task and institutional orientations.

The NASA Shuttle represents the pinnacle of aerospace development in terms of performance and operating environment. At the same time it is a key component of an infrastructure of relevance to the most remote and least resourced regions on the planet. In addition to its scientific and military role it is one of a number of launch systems delivering communications satellites to earth orbit.

While geo-stationary orbit (GEO) satellites serve a specific footprint below their position, middle and low earth orbit (MEO and LEO) satellites provide the same potential of coverage, regardless of per-capita income, to all those who dwell beneath their orbits. Chapter 5 described some of the systems under development with at least the technical potential to eradicate the digital divide by delivering high quality communications infrastructure to previously neglected regions.

Pathological Development

The gap between the levels of performance delivered by complex systems and their designer's expectations or assurances has attracted a range of criticism. There is a popular appreciation that systemic problems occur within complex organisations. These can be regarded as a form of pathology. Evidence of such organisational pathology can be identified in works ranging from *Parkinson's Law* (Parkinson, 1958) via *Up the Organization* (Townsend, 1970) to Brooks' "mythical man-month" (Brooks, 1975). There is a general recognition and acceptance of dysfunction, often as a natural consequence of large and impersonal scales of organisation. Typically, Peter (1986) talks of growth in levels of bureaucratic control as "proliferating pathology".

The concept of organisational pathology has also been used by several organisation theorists to account for unintended outcomes and outputs from organisations. In examining the design process, the concept may be extended to embrace the actions of those designers who appear to make or acquiesce to decisions which frustrate their own overt objectives.

Scott's (1987) analysis of the use of the concept in existing organisation literature. Scott's discussion of organisational pathology yields two key concepts of value here:

Overconformity in an extreme form is exemplified by Milgram's experiments demonstrating the ease with which individuals defer to authority (Milgram, 1974). In a less acute form, insistence on minute conformity to regulations is the "common sense" understanding of bureaucratic behaviour.

Goal displacement is a feature of any complex society, and not necessarily pathological, since generalised goals must be pursued through identifiable sub-goals. Perrow (1986) argues that in practice much apparent goal displacement serves the interests of dominant organisational actors. March and Simon (1958) describe a means-end chain by which general goals can lead to specific sub-goals. Typically, however, goal displacement results in survival becoming the principal concern of an organisation, as shown in the analysis of the Tennessee Valley Authority in the post-war period by Couto (1988) described in Chapter 7.

There is ample evidence of the existence of pathologies in complex projects and design decision-making processes, despite attempts to facilitate effective communication and decision-making. The crossed fingers of the engineers at the Marshall Space Flight Center, cited in McConnell's (1987) account of the background to the fatal STS mission 51-L or their attempts to use an auditor as a channel through which to communicate their concern with the technical shortcomings of the solid rocket booster field joints, are particularly striking evidence of failures in management information systems. The development and operational failures of NASA's Space Transportation System reveals how a changed environment can lead to suboptimisation which effectively reverses the function of critical components of a management information system.

If a systems perspective is applied, the impacts of these conflicts may be considered as *suboptimisation.* Any decomposition of a complex system offers the possibility of suboptimisation, and to that extent it may be regarded as a normal consequence of the division of intellectual labour required by complex organisations. The danger is that suboptimisation may only be revealed by an attempt to re-assemble the outcomes of delegated decisions. The narrower viewpoint of a subsystem level can lead to apparently sound local solutions which create problems for the system as a whole.

Designers are familiar with the concept through their experience with conflicting requirements which can only be satisfactorily resolved at the level of the project as a whole. Technology in the form of computer-aided design (CAD) has been used as a means of avoiding sub-optimisation across the disciplines within a design team by providing a global real-time data base on to which all design decisions are mapped (Little, 1988).

The notion of suboptimisation implies a supervening rationality by which the system as a whole can be judged. The implications of a distinction between the rationality applied at the level of the task with the rationality developed at an institutional level are discussed below.

Thompson (1967) sees the purpose of much of the structure of a complex organisation as the protection of its technical core so that it can achieve efficient operation. Boundary-spanning sections of an organisation therefore achieve influence because they can mediate transactions with the external environment and minimise perturbations at the core. In Thompson's terms, suboptimisation is the result of the penetration of the technical core by environmental and external influences. He argues that technical rationality can only suffice at the core of an organisation if it is adequately buffered from environmental influences.

The concept of an organisational core buffered from and linked to the organisation's environment is a key to understanding the impact of external contingencies on the design process. Time-frame discrepancies between areas affecting or affected by design decisions are one source of core penetration, and the imposition of inappropriate decision-making frameworks reflects the discrepancy of time-frames linking the different levels between core and environment.

The significance of time-frames for design projects was touched upon in the analysis of British Railways modernisation strategy in Chapter 6, and in the description of the Scottish Special Housing Association in Chapter 7. Here it is argued that these differences are symptomatic of the varying orientations of actors at different levels and that any design team must fulfil a critical bridging role between the concerns of the task environment at the technical core and the wider environment.

Task Environments and Institutional Environments

Scott (1987a) distinguishes between the *task* environment of organisations and their *institutional* environment. He points out that the latter is a relatively recent concern of organisation theorists, and requires very different responses from the better understood task environment. Institutional theory gained interest among organisation researchers in the nineteen nineties, since it addresses very different concerns from the task oriented views commonly incorporated into management science.

The two principal concerns of task environment management are the protection of the central work processes, principally through "buffering" strategies and the management of the relationship with the task environment as a social and political system, dealt with through "bridging" strategies. The task oriented view sees the environment as a source of inputs, markets for outputs, competition and regulation.

However, the demands of institutional environments require a different mechanism for transactions from those demanded by task environments. The institutional orientation seeks to build bridges into the environment by conforming to expected categories of staff and structure. Scott argues that organisations *exchange* elements with their technical environments, but are *constituted by* elements from their institutional environments. These elements are not transformed by the organisation as are technical elements and inputs. Instead they are made visible to outsiders with their distinctive features remaining intact. The purpose is to legitimise the organisation and to reassure clients. Bridging, not buffering, is the key strategy with regard to institutional environment.

Within business and industrial sectors, organisations will become more alike over time, as they draw upon a common institutional framework. This view goes some way to explaining Stinchcombe's (1965) finding that the age of an industry was a much better predictor of an organisation's characteristics than the age of an individual organisation within it. Organisational culture can be seen to be as closely associated with institutional choice as with technical choice and task environment.

Scott describes these mechanisms for bridging into the institutional environment in terms of conformity:

Categorical conformity in which institutional rules provide guidelines which can pattern structures.

Structural conformity in which environmental actors may impose very specific structural requirements upon organisations as a condition for acceptance and support.

Procedural conformity resulting from the pressures from institutional environments to carry out procedures in a particular way, and again, under uncertainty familiar and accepted procedures may be adopted by an organisation, such as those commonly used in accounting systems.

Personnel conformity arising within the complex, differentiated organisations likely to contain large numbers of educated, certified workers who assume specialised roles within them.

Following Peters and Waterman (1982), many writers have looked at these institutional arrangements in preference to task oriented variables, as an explanation of organisational performance. Thus they promote, among others, the model of Kelly Johnson's "Skunkworks", the independent and secret development team within Lockheed Aircraft responsible for the U2 and SR-71 spy planes, as a successful institutional model for highly uncertain tasks. However, the need to mimic the secrecy of a military "black project" (that is one beyond the scrutiny of the U.S. government's General Accounting Office) can be regarded as evidence of organisational weakness, if not outright pathology (Brown, 2001).

A developmental perspective might suggest that early in their existence, organisations would be more dominated by technical processes and that over time they may come to reflect institutional processes. Selznick (1957) accounts for the institutionalisation of organisations in terms of organic growth and the emergence of distinctive "character" or culture over time.

Parsons (1960) identifies three levels of organisational structure: the bottom level is the technical system; above this is the managerial system which mediates between the organisation and the task environment. At the top is the institutional system which relates the organisation to its function in the larger society. Parsons sees a clear analytical distinction between technical, managerial and institutional levels, arguing that there is a qualitative break at the interfaces of the three. The systems views of organisations described by Scott (1987a) can easily be related to these levels. However, it can be argued that although task and institutional environments require the different strategies enumerated by Scott, these overlap in some cases, and the two areas are less easily separated than is implied by Parsons.

Influences from different levels encompassing institutional and task environments coexist in the decision-space of project managers and designers, Chapter 7 suggested that these can be understood in the form of conflicting time-frames imposed upon their decision-making. However, interaction with the two different types of environment also makes very different demands on the skills and attention of actors.

According to Thompson (1967), the technical core strives for technical rationality, even though it exists in an open, natural system requiring environmental transactions. Managers and departments in an organisation exist to buffer the technical core and work at the managerial level requires an appreciation of conflict and motivation given by a natural systems approach. This involves an appreciation of the variety of human resources as an essential ingredient. The institutional level of the organisation must deal with external relationships with other organisations in the environment, so it must embrace an open systems view.

All the above indicates that, in the design of complex systems, the character and dynamics of transactions at the institutional level are very different from those of the technical level at which information technology design decisions are traditionally made. Conflict may develop between the technical requirements of this support technology and the objectives it is intended to serve at the institutional or organisational level. If such technical considerations prevail, an elegant system may gather dust because it does not address an organisation's perceived problems. If institutional concerns overwhelm technical capabilities, over-ambitious projects may be tackled with inadequate resources.

The reconciliation of technical and institutional orientation is the key to the success of complex design projects. An effective design project or intervention must address both levels of analysis and the implications of the different orientations which exist at each level.

From Challenger to Columbia: Developing the Space Shuttle

To achieve a robust outcome, technical design must address both task and institutional environments. There are ample examples of technical success which yields no effective outcome, and of institutional constraints giving rise to inadequate technology. The space shuttle programme provides a striking demonstration of the difficulty of changing the institutional dynamics of complex organisations. Between 28th January 1986 and 2nd February 2003 the U.S. Space Shuttle Program completed 87 successful missions. However, on the first of these dates the *Challenger* shuttle was lost on take-off following failure of an O-ring joint in a solid rocket booster. On the second the *Columbia* was lost during reentry owing to damage sustained during take-off by collision with insulating foam shed from the main propellant tank. Despite the intervening fifteen years, the organisational context of these accidents displayed striking similarities, with many of the recommendations implemented after the first accident inquiry having been quietly reversed in the intervening period.

The crossed fingers of the engineers at the Marshall Space Flight Center while observing shuttle launches, or the attempts by desperate designers to use an auditor, Richard Cook, as a channel through which to communicate their concern with the technical shortcomings of the solid rocket booster, give ample evidence of the impact of pathologies on design and project decision-making within an organisation of the quality and track record of NASA. A complete failure of formal mechanisms was evident. The very committees which were established to share critical information and to identify problems became arenas in which various groups sought to disguise their own problems. Each hoped that some other constituency would reveal a problem to which any delay could be attributed.

Magnuson (1986a) graphically indicates the interface between technically and institutionally oriented actors within Morton Thiokol, the sub-contractors responsible for the solid rocket boosters. He shows which individuals responded to the request of Marshall Space Flight Center to "put on their managerial hats". At the notorious teleconference held the night before the fatal *Challenger* launch, a clear division emerged between engineers still oriented to the task environment, and aware of the potentially catastrophic consequences of a booster joint failure, and managers, many with engineering backgrounds, who were aware only of the institutional consequences of a delay attributable to their company or division. The task oriented engineers were challenged to demonstrate that a launch was unsafe in the prevailing conditions. This represented a reversal of established practice in which the onus was to demonstrate safety and a triumph of procedural conformity over technical analysis.

The complex reporting structure of NASA's organisation was effectively inverted. Nodes in a communication network became the mechanisms for a massive gate-keeping exercise which prevented the communication of technical problems to the institutional level of the organisation.

McConnell describes how launch constraints were placed on the solid rocket boosters when it was realised that the designed redundancy of the O-ring seal system was not reliable. Despite the criticality of these components, however, the constraints were routinely waived before each mission. The Presidential Commission on the Space Shuttle Challenger Accident (1986), known as the Rogers Report, discovered documentation on the problems with the booster joints dated 21st October 1977, almost a decade before the *Challenger* accident. O-ring erosion appeared on the second orbiter mission in 1981, but was dealt with within the confines of the Marshall Center. McConnell also describes the autocratic management style of this division of NASA in contrast to the overall culture of the organisation. No problem or delay was permitted to be attributable to Marshall. By the eve of the final *Challenger* mission, Thiokol's representatives were claiming that there was no clear relationship between launch temperatures and the severity of the well established O-ring erosion. They were only able to do so because they had not attempted the simplest numerical analysis of the relevant data.

The situation which emerged at the Rogers Commission enquiry is in stark contrast to that recounted by Sayles and Chandler (1971) in explaining the success of NASA's organisation in the 1960s. One major difference between these two periods of activities is the loss of a single integrating objective for manned space flight provided by the *Apollo* programme, and a consequent increase in environmental uncertainty for the Agency.

Following the loss in flight of a second shuttle on 1st February 2003, the Columbia Accident Investigation Board (CAIB, 2003) pointed out that may of the organisational changes introduced following the Rogers Report hade been undermined. This was either through simple reversal, as in the return of control of the overall programme to the Marshall Space Flight Center, or through further reductions of resources and the outsourcing of critical aspects of the safety programme. One of the members of the second board, John Logsdon, had provided some of the most trenchant criticism of NASA after the *Challenger* accident (Logsdon, 1986) and the 2003 document contains many of the same criticisms.

An Institutional Narrative

The uncertainty extended to the institutional environment in which the agency had to operate, and involved the U.S. Congress, the industries involved in the space programme, institutions competing for public resources, and the public itself. As Couto (1988) has shown with the TVA, it can be argued that attention given to the management of the institutional environment was ultimately at the expense of the task environment.

Uncertainty is seen as the enemy of rationality within organisations in the systems context constructed by Scott (1987a). From this perspective, environmental and task variety will lead to asymmetric distribution of power, which may not correspond to the formal or nominal hierarchy within an organisation. This asymmetry leads in turn to the displacement of the organisation's goals in the direction of the interests of the constituencies to whom power accrues. Unfortunately, much organisation literature ignores the issue of power. The socio-technical approach (Mumford and Weir, 1979) attempts to account for the incorporation of technology by organisations, and to provide appropriate prescriptions for its deployment. It fails in this respect by incorporating uncritically the dominant managerial rationalities.

NASA and Government

The fact that approval to proceed with the space shuttle programme was given on 5th January 1972, at the outset of a presidential election year, leads Logsdon (1986) to argue that the "normal" party political bargaining process among coalitions had impinged on what should have been a long range national commitment. By 1972 the Deputy Administrator of NASA was talking about "multiple use, standardized systems" and the myth of the "space truck" making routine trips into space was in the making. This view survived for fourteen years, to be shattered in January 1986. However the CAIB reports that by 1995 the system was again being described as routine and mature.[1] On this basis cost savings were sought through the outsourcing to commercial organisations of safety-critical activities previously kept within NASA itself.

Fries (1988), in an analysis of NASA's changing proposals for a manned space station, argues that Kennedy's famous political commitment to a manned lunar mission during the 1960s disrupted an emerging technical programme which involved the development of orbiting research and development facilities. The lunar mission was accomplished without any earth-orbit assembly or supply requirements, but with lunar orbit rendezvous. As terrestrial concerns began to impinge on the prospects of post-*Apollo* activities, during the Johnson administration, a scientific role emerged for manned space flight.

Fries points out that both the Johnson Space Center and the Marshall Space Flight Center enjoyed the support of powerful industrial and political constituencies which were committed to the continuation of manned space activities. She argues that two separate orbiting space stations were proposed in 1966 in order to serve the requirements of a sufficiently broad section of the scientific community and thus to ensure funding. Even within NASA there was a lobby for unmanned scientific research and no single orbit could have served the full range of proposed research. However, because of budget constraints, the actual outcome of these ambitious plans for the post-Lunar period was the Apollo Applications Programme, utilising *Apollo-Saturn* hardware from the lunar programme, and achieving the relatively successful *Skylab* missions, launched in May 1973. By 1968 it had been decided to phase out the expendable *Saturn* system in favour of a Space Transportation System utilising a reusable orbiter and boosters.

The shuttle concept was formulated in terms of the supply requirements of permanently manned low-orbit space stations, but the White House had rejected these proposals. McConnell (1987) argues that there was a further hidden agenda of manned Mars missions beyond the establishment of orbiting stations, and that the capacity of the earliest shuttle proposals only makes sense in this full context.[2]

In order to secure funding for what was seen as the most promising manned programme, NASA had to embark upon a series of compromises to achieve a programme capable of occupying its development engineers. Routine low-cost access to low orbit was attractive to the Department of Defense and replacing all existing launch systems for unmanned military satellites locked in the DoD as a supporter. This led NASA to resist both the development of less ambitious systems and the maintenance of back-up resources. The Shuttle became an omnibus design, as defined in the next chapter.

The lack of alternative manned space-flight systems led to a five-year gap in U.S. efforts following the completion of the essentially political *Apollo-Soyuz* mission in 1975. Delays in shuttle development and the inability to mount a re-supply mission also led to the uncontrolled reentry into the atmosphere of the massive *Skylab* structure in 1979, an event of relevance to those currently responsible for maintaining the International Space Station.

While pursuing the stringent requirements of the Defense Department, however, NASA had to deal with the criterion of cost-effectiveness imposed by the Office of Management and Budget (OMB). Logsdon (1986) argues that the outcome of a series of budget-driven design changes was approval in 1972 for a system which was unlikely to be able to meet the wide range of requirements it attempted to address. The shuttle was the first space programme subjected to formal economic analysis, and the early and optimistic claims of cost-effectiveness became a further burden.

It became essential to NASA to capture all military missions proposed for the eighties, yet the military requirements, particularly those relating to cross-range maneuverability, that is the capability to significantly alter course in flight, were adding to the weight, complexity and cost of the orbiter. Despite their considerable impact on the shuttle design, Logsdon suggests that the military clients were not particularly committed to the concept. The Air Force, in particular, had access to the substantial capacity of the *Titan III* rocket. Nevertheless, in spite of an October 1971 offer from the Secretary of Defense to modify the stringent cross-range requirements, James Fletcher as head of NASA insisted that the agency would meet all military requirements.

Logsdon plots the evolution of the shuttle configuration, from a fully reusable system of a manned winged booster plus orbiter, burning in series, to the current parallel-burning reusable solid rocket boosters and orbiter, with disposable external fuel tank. Removing the shuttle fuel-tanks from its airframe made the use of an expendable booster system possible. The design changes were prompted by a five-year budget profile imposed by the OMB, and concentrated on the reduction of capital cost with less concern for operating costs. Eventually solid rocket boosters were chosen over liquid fuel because of their lower development costs.

Unfortunately the range of alternative configurations investigated by NASA, coupled with scepticism about cost projections, led some OMB staff to conclude that the imposition of an even lower fixed total cost limit would still produce some form of reusable spacecraft. NASA was preparing to compromise on its preferred 15x60ft by 65,000lb capacity cargo bay when the White House gave the go-ahead for the full size proposal. According to Logsdon, the grounds included the greater military capability and job-creation potential of the full proposal.

NASA's Wider Environment

The potential scope and influence of space exploration has been likened, in NASA sponsored research, to that of the railroad industry in North America (Mazlish, 1965). The scale of this potential impact meant that as well as balancing the requirements of their military customer with budgetary constraints, NASA has had to consider wider industrial and political constituencies. The discourse involved went beyond agency and government to broader industrial and political concerns. The ultimately fatal solid-rocket booster field joint only existed because NASA were concerned to allow tenders from contractors remote from the Florida launch site, despite the fact that the Aerojet company could have provided monolithic rocket casings transported by barge. Management of such interplay between industry lobbies, employment considerations and sensitive Congressional constituencies has become a key feature of the military-industrial complex in the United States, and is described at length by Coates and Kilian (1986) and Franklin (1986).

The Thiokol Corporation won the massive booster contract, with the overt support of James Fletcher, the director of NASA. By 1985 Congressional pressure had prompted NASA to consider the competitive award of a further billion dollar extension to the contract. Negotiations with Thiokol were proceeding right up to the accident. A teleconference was scheduled between Marshall Space Flight Center and Thiokol for 28th January 1986, the day following the fatal launch decision. This context suggests that the graphic division between the attitudes of engineering and management participants plotted by Magnuson (1986a) represents the interface of institutional and task environments.

As the commercial use of space expanded, so NASA's environment expanded to include competition for non-military payloads from the European Space Agency ESA, the Soviet Union and China. Australia, for example, has launched domestic satellites with the Shuttle, the European *Ariane* booster, and the Chinese *Long March* system. Among these competitors, differing task and institutional environments have resulted in greater flexibility.

McConnell (1987) and D'Allest (1988) both describe the Ariane family of launch vehicles developed by the ESA in terms of the incremental design development examined in Chapter 6. Vallerani (1988) evaluates space station experience and proposals and comes to similar conclusions about the development of the Soviet *Salyut* and *Mir* systems.

The *Mir* permanently manned space station was the result of an incremental development of the earlier *Salyut* series and the Soviet Union maintained a continuous presence in space from the seventies to the nineties through the success of this incremental policy. The success of the U.S. *Skylab* was undercut by the phasing out of the Saturn system in favour of the shuttle. The *Saturn*-derived elements were also phased out in favour of a new booster system. The consequence, as predicted by Vallerani (1988), was that the U.S. space station, now the International Space Station, was ten years behind *Mir* in deployment and flight experience.

During this period the Soviet Union had tested its *Buran* shuttle and the ESA had developed detailed proposals for its *Hermes* space plane. Despite aerodynamic similarities, these systems are both in marked contrast to the U.S. design. Each utilised a much simpler reusable orbiter, with no main engines, although the Soviet version had air-breathing engines for landing and, as a consequence of military competition, was clearly intended to match the U.S. shuttle in overall performance.

Alternative expendable systems continue in use for non-manned satellites. The U.S.S.R. developed *Energia*, a *Saturn* class expendable booster capable of lifting 100 tonnes into low Earth orbit, but retained a development of the SS-6 missile, first tested in 1957, and used to place Gagarin in orbit in 1961, for both routine unmanned payloads and ferrying cosmonauts to orbit. China's initial entry into manned space flight has followed the Russian route, with a low-cost expendable vehicle delivered into space by the *Long March III* system.

If the less safety-critical tasks are uncoupled from manned space flight, then the manned systems can be deployed for highly specialised tasks such as recovery and repair, and maintenance of space platforms (Feustel-Beucht, 1988). Perrow (1984) presents the notion of uncoupling as a crucial tool for the development of manageable high-risk technologies. If a system must be complexly interactive in order to achieve its required performance, then the introduction of redundancy and substitutability can reduce the risk of catastrophic failure.

Technical versus Institutional Fixes

NASA's strategy with regard to its institutional environment actually increased the tight coupling and complexity in its task environment. The combination of a complex and tightly coupled technical system and the increasing launch schedule pressure originating with the early and over optimistic payload cost estimates for the mythical "space-truck" led to what Perrow describes as a "normal accident": one which is the inevitable result of system characteristics. Here the system characteristics must include those of the institutional environment. Technical mechanisms which were intended to monitor and control the development and deployment of a complex and high-risk technology came to serve a largely symbolic function in the institutional environment. In the post-*Apollo* period the staff responsible for monitoring safety were drastically reduced in number and buried within the operating divisions.

In addition to a restructuring of the safety programme to achieve much higher visibility, the Rogers Report on the Challenger accident (1986) recommends attention to a range of safety critical items, ranging from tyres and brakes on the orbiter to flight rates. Immediately after the accident there was speculation about direct pressure from the White House to have *Challenger* in orbit during President Reagan's State of the Union address. The existence or absence of such overt influence was irrelevant, since NASA had thoroughly absorbed the concerns of its institutional environment. Despite a backlog of critical issues, and increasing pressure on resources, Trento (1987) describes fraught negotiations over whether Pepsi or Coca Cola should be the first carbonated beverage in outer space (both had to be carried to placate their respective manufacturers).

NASA's goal was displaced from a technical mission, with an explicit concern for safety, to a classic organisational concern with survival in an increasingly uncertain institutional environment. This can be compared with Couto's narrative of the TVA in Chapter 7. Between the two shuttle accidents came the end of the Cold War and this led to further reductions in overall resource levels for NASA, who themselves diverted money for the shuttle to other programmes. From 1991 to 1994 Shuttle operating costs were reduced by 21 per cent (CAIB, 2003). As part of these savings control was returned to the Marshall Space Flight Center, triggering the resignation of the head of the Shuttle programme.

Both technical and institutional fixes can be seen in NASA's actions. Alongside the implementation of the Rogers Report recommendations, the canonisation of the STS 51-L crew, described by McConnell in the 1988 appendix to his book, indicates that the organisation continues to regard the institutional arena as the effective route to resources. The Agency incorporated its own failure into its organisational mythology, turning it into a resource for the continuing pursuit of its mission at an institutional level. Unfortunately the success of this tactic resurrected some of the problems which led to the original disaster.

Conflicting Rationalities in Technical Development

The distortion of normal technical reasoning used in NASA's Flight Readiness Reviews and revealed by the Rogers enquiry raises the issue of the conflicting rationalities applied by task and institutionally oriented actors. Richard Feynman, a Nobel laureate and Commission member, suggested that the reasoning applied to the growing evidence of O-ring erosion was the opposite of what was required: "It flies, and nothing happens, then it is suggested that the risk is no longer so high for the next flight, we can lower our standards a bit because we got away with it last time" (Magnuson, 1986b). In fact, the 53°F minimum launch temperature for which the rearguard of task-oriented Marshall engineers were pressing had produced by far the worst erosion experienced prior to the *Challenger* accident.

The 2003 accident report describes a similar history of the loss of insulation foam during launches, much of it documented by visual recordings. Again the full implications of the issue were not understood. Clearly, any understanding of such pathological outcomes from a complex design system requires an examination of the rationalities adopted by the actors involved.

Selznick (1957) distinguishes between administration as a rational, means-guided process, and institutionalisation, which he sees as value-laden and adaptive. Thus goal-displacement might be regarded as a symptom of institutionalisation. In one sense organisations are seen to become institutions when they develop distinctive characters, or cultural values. Other writers distinguish institutions from organisations. Douglas (1983), in discussing "how institutions think", suggests that they play a key role in establishing and maintaining rationalities by providing cognitive economy and removing larger contextual issues from the arena of discussion. This analysis of rationality acknowledges that the "bounding" of rationality described by Simon (1957) is an understandable consequence of human attempts to deal with too great a range of interdependent variables. It corresponds to the strategies enumerated by Jones (1980) as means of reducing extensive design solution search spaces.

The restriction of a decision space, whether in terms of time or information resources, may also be part of a deliberate strategy to pre-empt the range of possible outcomes of a design or management process, as with the manipulation of decision time-frames discussed in Chapter 7. Such strategies may serve the interests of particular constituencies, but if the process is viewed from outside the perspective of Thompson's (1967) dominant coalition of constituencies, they will be seen to lead both to goal displacement, and to problems with effectiveness.

Arriving at a single rationality for any significant undertaking remains problematic. Brubaker (1984) points out that Max Weber utilises no fewer than sixteen apparent meanings of "rational" in his writings. There is, nevertheless, a central concern with the irreconcilable tension between formal and substantive rationality:

> "The distinction between formal and substantive rationality implies that what is rational from one point of view may be non-rational or irrational from another, and vice versa... ...to the extent that people share beliefs they can agree in their judgements of rationality and irrationality; but to the extent ends and beliefs diverge, so too will judgements of rationality and irrationality." (Brubaker, 1984 p.4)

According to Weber, the modern economy has a double rationality: *subjectively* rational, and thus purely instrumental, market transactions guided by *objectively* rational, and thus purely quantitative calculations. *Formal* rationality is concerned with calculability of means and procedures and ultimately with *efficiency*. *Substantive* rationality addresses the value of ends and results and is ultimately concerned with *effectiveness*.

Brubaker (1984) argues that for Weber formal rationality rests on institutional foundations that are morally and politically problematic: unrestrained pursuit of formal rationality will produce substantive irrationality. This is one analysis of pathology in organisational action, which is reflected in Scott's (1992) definitions of overconformity and relentlessness through which the internal objectives of constituencies are pursued with disregard for the consequences elsewhere.

Brubaker is principally concerned to establish the limits to rationality, as set out by Weber. For Weber, ultimately the choice of values which underlie substantive rationality (*Wertrational*) can only be chosen by non-rational means. Only formal rationality (*Zweckrational*) may be analytically examined in its own terms. The ultimate choice of which values to accept must be criterionless. The problem is that the separate "value spheres of the world stand in irreconcilable conflict with each other" (Weber, 1947, p.147).

It must be emphasised that much prescriptive advice offered by management literature, and which may influence designers, simply adopts what is seen as an unproblematic managerial perspective towards rationality in organisations. The evidence above from the Shuttle case-history, and studies by Kaldor (1976) and Coates and Kilian (1986) of the inefficiencies of the military-industrial complex reveals the inadequacies of such an approach in practice. Coates and Kilian in particular are criticising the defence industry of the United States from a technical perspective which examines its institutional dynamics from a task orientation. They reveal how irreconcilable this can be with an instrumental managerial concern with institutional issues.

Design and technical development are engrossing activities. Creativity and innovation require an immersion in process, but there is an ever present danger that the intrinsic challenge of a particular technical sub-goal may loosen the designer's grasp of the overall implications of their technical decisions. The sub-optimisation identified by Scott (1987a) and Galbraith (1977) must be overcome through a framework which can assess effectiveness over the range of rationalities operating at task and institutional levels.

Scott points out that conceptions of organisations and goals, participants and constituencies have become progressively more complex. Complex organisations are composed of subgroups with different social characteristics, social locations and views and interests. External constituencies can form part of the political system of the organisation, by holding goals "for" it. The output of a design coalition can only be evaluated by its impact beyond the boundaries of that coalition. Any evaluation implies some target against which performance can be measured, by definition such measures must transcend the design coalition and its members.

Design Objectives and Development Goals

Goals are used both to motivate and direct activity, and to evaluate it. However, the criteria developed to direct organisations are not always the same as those employed to evaluate them. Motivation may utilise broad and vague goals, but evaluation requires specific goals. Since evaluation goals are often quantitative and limited, goal displacement can arise when actors realise the limited range on which they themselves are likely to be assessed.

Varying goals will also be used by different types of participant: top management, middle-level personnel, performers, or external constituencies. Scott reminds us that researchers also fit into a framework of interests and objectives, and must be aware that their own criteria will influence not only the interpretation of data, but the identification of situations of potential interest. By extension, designers will also have a set of criteria for effectiveness related to their technical expertise which equally may serve the interests of some groups rather than others. Scott presents three predictions to guide investigation:

1: Criteria proposed by each group will be self-interested
2: They will be presented as universalistic and objective
3: There will be little commonality or convergence between groups, and some conflict.

(Scott 1987, pp.324-325)

Any assessment of effectiveness requires the selection of standards, indicators and an appropriate sample. Cyert and March (1963) attempt to adapt the psychological concept of "aspiration level" to the setting of standards, arguing that current goals reflect the organisation's goals from the previous time-period, organisational experience with those goals and experience of comparable organisations. Thompson (1967) constructs a more complex model of standards and beliefs about cause and effect relations in which he relates beliefs about cause and effect to standards of desirability.

Where cause and effect and desirable standards are clear, efficiency tests can assess whether the desired end was reached with the minimum use of resources. Where cause and effect relationships are only partially understood, instrumental tests can determine whether the desired end has been reached, but if required standards and/or cause and effect relationships are ambiguous, social tests must be used. These can only assess the validity of an organisation's efforts by consensus or by authority.

Difficulties in the evaluation of any design process start with the problem of an appropriate metric. A successful metric must address adequately both the task requirements of appropriateness and adequate sensitivity and the institutional requirements of perspicuity and ease of application. If these frameworks are neglected, then in effect, overconformity and technocracy meet at the level of codified design constraints. Examples from architectural design can illustrate the difficulties.

As noted in the previous chapter, Lawson (1982) examines the relationship between building codes and design decision-making. Overconformity or goal displacement may be attributed to the application of rules which are designed for ease of enforcement, not for ease of incorporation into the design process. However, this in turn reflects the necessity of enforcement, and may not constitute a pathology in itself. A more extreme outcome of the need to comply with regulation and inspection was seen in Chapter 7 in the impact of delays in certification which led to the design of the control room at Three Mile Island Unit 2 being ten years out of date at the commissioning of the station.

Edwards (1974) analyses the difference between the furnishing of houses indicated on British local authority architects' plans with that subsequently carried out by householders. This is presented as evidence of a predictive failure on the part of the designers. However, as noted in Chapter 3, the furniture placing on architects' house plans reflected the requirements of the mandatory Parker Morris standard, as much as any predictive activity on the part of designers. These specific items of furniture had to be indicated in each room of a house plan to qualify it for government finance.

The impact of such codified design constraints means that under everyday production pressures, meeting quantified requirements becomes a substitute for fresh analysis and solution. Richard Feynman's description of the logic implicit in Flight Readiness Reviews for the Shuttle missions (Magnuson, 1986b) suggests that such procedural conformity became a ritual which precluded any proper evaluation of the situation.

Inappropriate criteria for assessment may be selected simply because of their relative ease of use and communication. Jay Galbraith (1977) points out that any increase in information capacity brought about by the formalisation of communication channels must be offset against a loss of qualitative information. In conditions of high task uncertainty, irrelevant quantitative measures are likely to enjoy an edge over relevant qualitative ones. In addition, commissioning clients are likely to have little expertise with which to judge choices made on their behalf at a subsystem level.

Dreyfus and Dreyfus (1986) emphasise the predominance of quantitative methods in much management and decision theory. They argue that such "calculative rationality" is likely to degrade expert performance by focussing on quantitative criteria at the expense of experientially based qualitative understanding. McConnell (1987) quotes the complaints of engineers chastised in Flight Readiness Reviews at the Marshall Center because they used terms such as "I feel" and "I expect" which were dismissed as "not supported by engineering evidence". In contrast to the low value placed on experiential assessments, Dickson (1976) describes the deferential treatment of the output of a formal information system. He describes the deployment of sophisticated computer-based information systems during the Vietnam War, contrasting the lack of quality control over the information fed in at the bottom of the system with the importance accorded the aggregated and transformed results, an institutional example of the *garbage in - garbage out* phenomenon.

A "Metatechnical" Framework

The evaluation of the outcome of large-scale technical projects is likely to require social tests. Even if clear criteria are available for identifiable sub-systems, the issue of the effectiveness of any remotely complex system will impinge on a range of potentially conflicting values. The next chapter looks at the source of cost overruns and technical deficiencies in the products of the military-industrial complex. The proponents of what has been described as military Keynsianism (Coates and Kilian, 1986), may attribute higher priority to broad economic objectives than technical performance.[3]

The evaluation of design outcomes requires a framework that acknowledges the coexistence of technical and institutional dimensions to organisations by presenting the task of design and management as a dialectic. The design process cannot be isolated from the everyday concerns of organisational survival without compromising its product, nor can managers and clients expect a free technical fix for institutional problems. The term "metatechnical" is intended to avoid the implications of a technical versus non-technical dichotomy. It implies that managerial and institutional concerns are also technical and therefore any framework embracing both design and its organisational context is *meta*-technical. It presupposes a systems view of design and its place in the organisation, but not a consensual one.

Open systems theory argues that explanatory variables must be as varied as the phenomena they seek to explain. The contingency approach to organisation theory argues that organisations whose internal features best match the demands of their technologies or their task environments can be expected to be most effective. However, contingency models can overlook the issue of equifinality: different conditions and causes may give rise to the same outcomes. It should be remembered that "the effectiveness of an organisation is a socio-political question" (Pfeffer and Salancik, 1974). Nevertheless, little is said about real interests of participants and groups. There may be real benefits for actors in the sub-optimizing decisions which we are trying to eliminate in the pursuit of our understanding of efficiency and effectiveness. Power relations may be well entrenched and difficult to counter, extending to the institutional level of cognition.

Douglas (1987) argues that the high triumph of institutional thinking is to make the institutions appear invisible and this invisibility can compound the difficulty of getting an expanded context accepted within any established institutional and organisational framework.

Clegg (1987) makes an important distinction between the established view of uncertainty as a contingency and the use of uncertainty in support of the exercise of power, illustrating the point with the ambiguity evident in the interpretation of building contracts by the actors involved in the construction process. It may be argued that the former understanding is apparent in a task orientation, the latter in an institutional orientation. Clegg indicates the way in which uncertainty may offer a resource with which to resist the control implicit in the constraints to action from the institutional.

As suggested in the previous chapter, production pressures may be deliberately manipulated through such devices as accounting time-frames, where budgets are confirmed at the latest possible date for full expenditure within a fixed time. In such circumstances a constituency will have little time for forward planning or coalition building. Even without any deliberate exacerbation such pressure will be present in complex technical systems, as shown by Stephens' (1980) account of the commissioning of the Three Mile Island nuclear power plant. In such circumstances it is hard for actors to take a sufficiently broad view of their situation. However, to be successful, the design activity must bridge the discontinuity between task and institutional orientation. Designers must balance both technical and institutional considerations even though the design coalition is pulled in both directions. The OMB squeeze on NASA's 1971 shuttle design proposals represents an institutional approach with little or no concern or understanding for technical difficulties. This typifies the "black box" view of technology evident in economic theory (Rosenberg, 1982).

Attempts to incorporate such considerations in the design process are problematic, given the existing technical complexities and uncertainties which must be addressed. If a formal system of design control and accountability is perceived as cumbersome by its intended users, it may be subject to by-passing with informal and undocumented decision processes, just as production pressures lead to by-passing of physical safety features in processing and manufacturing. The critique implicit in McConnell (1987) must be addressed at an organisational and a societal level if measurable improvements in the performance of high risk systems are to be made. This is the ultimate implication of a metatechnical framework for the consideration of systems development.

Conflicting Cultures, Conflicting Rationalities

The practices and expectations established within organisations over time acquire a cultural dimension. Selznick (1957) invoked notions of culture in his explanation of the emergence of institutionalised organisations. The concept of organisational culture has been invoked to explain the relative success of individual organisations and entrepreneurs (e.g. Peters and Waterman, 1982). It is by no means a new concept in organisational sociology, but has been used in a variety of ways.

Some writers refer to culture in terms of national differences in social and economic organisation. Latin and Anglo-Saxon and traditional cultures are reflected in distinctive organisational types identified in studies examined by Lammers and Hickson (1979). In this context it is as well to remember that U.S. President Truman thought it unlikely that the Soviet Union would develop nuclear weapons, since they were an Asiatic nation (York, 1976).

Turner (1971) describes industrial subcultures which can be identified across individual organisations, and are distinctive from the larger society, Eldridge and Crombie (1974) define organisational culture as a characteristic of individual organisations while Strauss et al (1973) describe a range of cultures within a single organisation. Thompson (1967) utilised the concept of an organisational constituency capable of entering into coalition with other constituencies in order to promote its interest. Such a conception allows the formal elements of an organisation to be related to the informal communication and negotiation which often modifies, or in extreme cases frustrates, the intention of management. It also allows consideration of intra-organisational variations in culture, arising from these differences of interest and experience.

Part I discussed the differences in institutional culture between Western and Asian forms of capitalism. Johnson (1983) defines a "market rationality" as seen in the U.S. where the state is interested in maintaining, through regulation, the mechanisms of competition in order to maximise efficiency. He contrasts this with a "plan rationality" as seen in Japan where a close working relationship exists between industrial sectors and government departments such as the Ministry of International Trade and Industry, and its successor the Ministry of Economy, Trade and Industry (METI), in order to pursue common goals with maximum effectiveness. He argues that this essentially different view of the role of public institutions in the economic arena accounts for a great deal of misunderstanding between these trading partners over what constitutes "fair trade".

The cultural dimension may be regarded as mediating between technical and institutional orientations. The next chapter introduces the notion of distinctive design cultures as reflections of the institutional framework in which technologies are developed. The example used is the difference between American and Soviet military design philosophy and their differing institutional environments.

The work of Elliot Jaques, initially with the Glacier Metal Company (Brown and Jaques, 1965), led him to the formulation of a relationship between the hierarchy of bureaucracy and the time-span of control of actors. From these empirical observations Jaques develops an argument that a *natural* metric based on time-span of discretion may be used to ensure that an organisation is appropriately divided into efficient decision-making levels. Jaques promotes the levels of his hierarchy as the foundation of an empirically based general theory of bureaucracy, which encompasses the qualitative difference between tasks. While it offers a valuable adjunct to Thomson's (1967) constituencies and coalitions, it cannot address the critical assessment of the calculative rationality deriving from the increasing abstraction implicit in its levels in the terms defined by Dreyfus and Dreyfus (1986).

Thompson's model of standards and beliefs about cause and effect relationships is echoed by Perrow's discussion of rationality in the context of risk perception. Perrow (1984) suggests that the difference in outlook between risk assessors and "public" and the conflicting perceptions of risk we display as individuals can be attributed to differing frameworks of rationality.

"Absolute" technical rationality is attributed to engineers and economists by Perrow. In technical rational terms, nuclear power generation can be demonstrated to cause less loss of life and disablement than coal-fired generation, taking into account the risks of coal mining, transportation and sulphur emissions etc, provided the prevailing assessments of level of risk are accepted.

"Bounded" rationality, after Simon, can be used to account for the different assessment made by individuals using their experiential heuristics. Perrow argues that heuristic, rule-of-thumb judgement appears to work because the world is relatively loosely coupled and approximations can be absorbed by slack and buffers. Unfortunately decision-makers may find themselves outside the familiar context they had assumed, and may apply an inappropriate interpretation and rationality to a new situation needing to be approached from first principles.

This is the principal danger of an otherwise robust incremental strategy of development, which, by its success may take a system into a new performance environment as in the case of the Comet airliner described in Chapter 6. In 1988 the inability of the crew of the U.S.S. Vincennes to alter their initial identification of an Iran Air A-300 passenger plane as an F-14 fighter-bomber indicates the danger of established heuristic behaviour. A psychological set can be created in which additional evidence is either used to confirm the original judgement, or is simply ignored.

The difference between the above positions is illustrated by Perrow through possible reactions to the Three Mile Island nuclear power plant accident. For absolute rationalists, the fact that a one in three hundred year event occurred less than a year after start up was of no significance, they did not revise their assessment of the reliability of the system. For users of bounded rationality, the rapid failure is valuable evidence that there may be a problem with the risk estimates. Bounded rationality is efficient, according to Perrow, because it leads to pointed questions being put to the engineers, it examines the outcome of a serious accident and judges its acceptability, without massive technical evaluation.

"Social and cultural" rationality departs further from absolute rationality, but argues that the consequences of human cognitive limits are less consequential than usually assumed. Social rationality emphasises the complementary nature of social decision-making. Individuals have different interests and abilities, an expert has useful analytical skills, but needs some cultural guidance to ensure that appropriate problems are addressed. Individual limits on cognitive ability provide the motivation for social bonding and consensus.

Perrow suggests that the public emphasises social rationality over the absolute rationality of the technician and the bounded rationality of the economists and risk assessors. He regards social rationality as an extension of the "garbage can" theory (Cohen et al, 1972) which grew out of the work of Simon and March: a range of approaches and options are generated by organisations, and alternatives are drawn upon as and when they seem useful or appropriate. However, Perrow suggests that cognitive psychologists still see their task as one of reconciling the heuristic reaction of the general public with the absolute rationality of the experts. Douglas and Wildavsky (1982) demonstrate the degree of social selection involved in the identification of risks, and attitudes towards them. Their position could be regarded as linking Perrow's conception of social/cultural and cognitive rationalities. It should be evident that any attempt to link institutional and task orientations must also be capable of accomodating and interpreting between these rationalities.

Design Paths for Development

The design activity has been identified as linking two very different spheres, the task and institutional environments of organisations. Examples of each have been examined in terms of existing literature and the concept of a "metatechnical" framework introduced to indicate the breadth of view necessary to encompass both.

An awareness of a hierarchy of rationalities relating to the hierarchy of task and institutional environments allows an understanding of the implications of the term "metatechnical" as a replacement for "socio-technical" or "non-technical" aspects of design. However, technical and contextual issues are inextricably linked, and task and institutional concerns may not always be clearly distinguishable. Metatechnology is necessary to counter goal displacement, which may arise as a defensive response to institutional uncertainty, and to counter overconformity reflecting the relative power of the institutional level. There are very real dangers in pursuing pathological or suboptimized goals with the increasingly powerful tools and technologies now available to designers. Either allowing the institutional environment to overwhelm the task environment or allowing technical rationality to ignore institutional concerns will result in outcomes such as the space shuttle accidents, or in attempted technical fixes for political and diplomatic issues such as the Strategic Defense Initiative.

The design process inevitably bridges the technical and institutional spheres and the metatechnical framework provides the starting point for the development of methods to avoid design pathologies. However, the design coalition can also be seen as the meat in the sandwich, with little power to influence those decisions at an institutional level which may severely impact on its freedom of action.

Their education and training may give designers an exaggerated view of their power over the material world. Among designers, architects are particularly prone to volunteer responsibility for the outcomes of institutional influences. Chapter 3 contrasted the narrative of the genesis and development of industrialised building provided by Russell (1981) with the post-modern narrative which ignores the networks of interest which produced this phenomenon, instead ascribing it to the hubris of individual modernist architects.

Scott (1987b) speaks of the "adolesence of institutional theory", suggesting that it has not yet reached maturity, but is becoming more established and developed. In effect this chapter draws upon the cutting edge of organisation theory. It is unreasonable to expect working designers to maintain such a level of sophistication in conjunction with their technical skills. A metatechnical approach is proposed as a framework for the solution of the problems identified in the case studies in this and the preceding chapters. The postmodern approaches to design such as Actor-Network Theory, introduced in Chapter 3, offer a means of creating a collectivity which could hold the range of skills necessary for a reasonable resolution of complex design problems at a metatechnical level.

The next chapter extends the examination of the metatechnical framework of technical development. It analyses the nature of the broad determination of high technology design and application by the dominance of military technology in the Cold War and post-Cold War periods.

Notes

* This chapter has been developed from an article published as 'Task Environments and Institutional Environments: understanding the context of design decision-making' *Design Studies*, ISSN 0142-694-X, 11 (1) January 1990, 29-42.
1 See Chapter 5 of the Board's report which deals in detail with the relationship between pre-and post-*Challenger* activities, structures, funding and the situation prevailing in February 2003.
2 In the run up to the 2004 U.S. presidential election, the manned Mars mission was resurrected.
3 Chapter 9 examines the implications of Coates and Kilian's position in detail.

Chapter 9

Cultures, Designs and Design Cultures*

Perry Morrison with Stephen Little

Military equipment accounted for much of the advanced technology transferred to developing countries during the Cold War period. These technologies offer clear examples of differences reflecting institutionally varied frameworks of invention and innovation. Their performance driven extremes also reveal characteristics that are less clearly exposed in the development and deployment of more mundane and robust technologies.

This chapter continues the examination of design processes though the notion of "design cultures" as an explanation of distinctive outcomes from processes addressing essentially the same technology in different social and cultural settings. Chapter 3 looked at continuities in technical understanding and motivation through the Cold War period and Chapter 6 provided case studies and examples which included military technology. The complex socio-technical systems described here also illustrate the assertions of the Actor-Network Theory set out in Chapter 3. The artifacts encapsulate the values and objectives of the actors who created them and the setting in which they were created, and in turn influence the further development of their context.

While design processes and their outcomes can be seen to reflect their cultural setting, a simple invocation of the role of culture may become a means of avoiding further exploration of difference. National stereotyping gives associations such as style and capability which are of value in branding and marketing, for example, German or Italian automobiles. However, such "national" characteristics reflect distinctive outcomes based on differing priorities among designers in different settings. Culture must therefore be disaggregated into a constellation of tradition, ethnicity and organisational and institutional frameworks.

This chapter explores major differences between the U.S.A. and U.S.S.R. in their design of military equipment. Following the end of the Cold War, Western observers often explain away these differences simply in terms of the West's manifest technological superiority. However, this is an insufficient explanation for the stylistic, doctrinal, economic and social influences embodied within the design of Soviet and American weapons systems. A distinction must be drawn between the task environment in which a weapon exists as a destructive device and the institutional environment which spawns it. In the case of the U.S. in particular, a large array of institutional factors, fallacious arguments, assumptions and assorted sophistries have combined to produce a design culture – a constellation of design characteristics – which produces weapons that are often dysfunctional at the level of the task environment. In contrast, the Soviet Union often developed reliable, cost-effective armaments under the influence of different institutional influences, including compulsory military service and ultimately unsustainable levels of arms spending.

Deconstructing Culture

The key technologies underpinning globalisation have been modified by cultural orientations and preferences which are in turn incorporated into popular accounts of difference in organisational practices. Such accounts themselves may carry a significant emotional charge reflecting anxieties played out at a national level (e.g. Lewis and Allison, 1982; Isahara, 1991).

O'Hara-Devereaux and Johansen (1994) argue for a distinction between work cultures, both professional and corporate, and the primary culture in which an organisation is embedded. For them the synergy between levels is a potential resource, but the tendency towards a convergence determined by the primary culture is seen as an obstacle to cross-cultural working. Kaplinsky and Posthuma (1994) map cultural dimensions of industrial innovation onto the micro and macro layers of economic analysis, offering one way to achieve an overview of a highly complex area.

The macro level view is represented by writers who refer to culture in terms of national differences in social and economic organisation. Latin, Anglo-Saxon and traditional cultures are reflected in distinctive organisational types identified in studies examined by Lammers and Hickson (1979), or the broad groupings of cultures arrived at by Hofstede (1980) and considered in specific national contexts in Part III.

Unfortunately, simply to ascribe differences in outcomes to "cultural difference" between adopters offers little guidance for either potential adopters or for policy-makers. Additionally, regional variations, often reflecting divergent historical and institutional traditions make the notion of a homogenous "national" culture problematic, even in relatively small countries. Culture can be de-composed into issues related to the historical, geographical and institutional setting in which organisation and individual must operate. For example, Selznick (1957) invoked notions of culture in his explanation of the emergence of institutionalised organisations, and differences in institutional culture can be identified at national and regional levels. As noted in the previous chapter, Johnson (1983) identifies the U.S. state as "market rational", relying on the regulation of competition in order to maximise efficiency in contrasts to "plan rationality" developmentally oriented states, like Japan with close working relationships between industrial sectors and the relevant ministries in pursuit of common goals with maximum effectiveness.

Both these approaches have historical roots based in nineteenth century technical and economic developments.[1] Johnson (1983) argues that this essentially different view of the role of public institutions in the economic arena accounts for a great deal of misunderstanding between these trading partners as to what constitutes "fair trade". U.S. inspired reforms after World War II modified business relationships, but much of the economic friction evident in the global economy reflects differences in accepted institutional relationships and expectations.

The micro level of cultural variation is represented by writers such as Eldridge and Crombie (1974) who define organisational culture as characteristic of individual organisations or by Strauss et al's (1973) description of a range of cultures within a single organisation. Morgan's (1986) paradigm of "organisation as culture" is incorporated into popular texts which promote the notion of organisational culture as a variable amenable to management intervention (Peters and Waterman, 1982). Thompson (1967) supplies the concept of an organisational constituency capable of entering into coalition with other constituencies in order to promote its interest. This emergent 'dominant coalition' would then be in a position to determine overall corporate culture.

However, Turner's (1971) description of industrial subcultures which can be identified across individual organisations implies a meso-level of culture. Such inter-organisational cultures which are distinctive from both primary culture and individual corporate cultures add considerable complexity. As noted in the previous chapter, Stinchcombe (1965) argues that the industry to which an organisation belongs is a strong determinant of organisational structure and culture. Comparison of the age of an industry with its technological base suggests a related argument that core technologies reflect the age of an industry rather than that of any individual enterprise within it. This technically determined line of argument would suggest that industries would retain key features, even as they diffused across very different cultural and social settings. The business recipes and frameworks grounded in these differences offer a meso-level view of "culture" of more direct value to actors (Marceau, 1992).

Framing Culture

The theme of this chapter is that it is possible to identify and describe cultures of design. Weapons are designed to function in the most demanding and extreme circumstances. As Kaldor (1981) points out, the argument for additional functionality and performance can always be made on the basis of literal "life or death" importance, and on the assumption that failure is unacceptable. Cultures which are distinct in terms of the values and ideologies that are brought to bear in the design process produce weapons systems that have identifiable characteristics and capabilities that derive from these same values and ideologies. This theme is both specific and general, relating at once to popular beliefs about high technology that have important consequences in the very expensive business of equipping armed forces, while at the same time providing an analysis of the systemic nature of the differing weapons design processes in the U.S. and U.S.S.R. as they existed during the Cold War period.

The analysis presented here requires a differentiation between task and institutional environments as set out in Chapter 8. The former refers to those features of an environment that are relevant to an organisation as a production system. In the case of weapons manufacturers this involves the transformation of design research and materials inputs into working weaponry. Hence, at this level, the organisation is concerned with the task in hand (an attack helicopter or tank for example) and the design, performance and materials decisions that will determine its utility as a destructive engine.

On the other hand, at the institutional level, the organisation is concerned with the political, economic and competitive influences that will affect its continued existence in the marketplace. These levels are obviously mutually interactive since, in the case of weapons manufacturers, political and economic considerations determine to a large extent the designs they create (task level), while these designs in turn help determine the political, economic and strategic agenda that the organisation must face (institutional level).

This chapter presents evidence of inconsistencies and fallacies at both levels of the arms development process. On the one hand, the institutional environments in which competing arms manufacturers find themselves result in designs that are often defective, even in the narrow performance sense applicable to the task environment of the arms designer. On the other hand, such defective designs serve as indictments of the institutional aims and agenda of arms developers and arms development itself.

This constitutes the higher level framework within which a further argument pertaining to the factors that influence the nature of arms developers' institutional environments can be developed. In the U.S. and U.S.S.R., differences in the mix of institutional factors spawned different task environments which in turn resulted in stylistic differences in weapons design – patterns of design that here are termed "design cultures".

Weapons Design Cultures

By the last decade of the Cold War, operational inadequacies and questionable cost-effectiveness of modern hi-tech weaponry were well recognised. Widespread criticisms were being levelled at the U.S. system of weapons development and procurement. These views were promulgated in publications such as Mary Kaldor's *The Baroque Arsenal* (1981) and James Coates' and Michael Kilian's book, *Heavy Losses* (1986). The picture emerging from such publications is one which characterises the American defence industry in particular, as corrupt, inept, inefficient and incapable of producing functional weaponry at reasonable cost.

A specific focus of Kaldor's work has been her thesis that despite the massive investments made in their continued development, modern Western weapons systems reached a point of diminishing returns in terms of their functional capability. She also notes that this situation has existed previously, most clearly in the British shipbuilding industry near the turn of the nineteenth century, when the dreadnought was regarded as the principal weapon of its era. Here, the escalating costs of dreadnought development remained secondary to the national prestige and security that a fleet of dreadnoughts was believed to bestow. In particular, the establishment of an industry that required continuity of orders to maintain employment levels and its multiplier effect on other, dependant industries, contributed to the need to establish a dreadnought export industry, as well as a sustained internal demand for new warships.

It is this situation that Kaldor terms *baroque*: a direct feedback loop between weapons supply and demand, a demand that is sustained by arguments of increased capability in the face of escalating costs, and in the absence of evidence of either improved capability, or even the need for it. Furthermore, this process is augmented by the symbolic power that such weapons have and the ideological role this plays in procurements for national defence.

The dreadnought case history is particularly illuminating in that it depicts an arms industry that was insulated from what are generally understood as market forces. The proxy "market" was driven by particular military and technical ideologies and, for its maintenance, consumed a massive amount of domestic capital. Moreover, it is one which has strong parallels with the American situation in the closing stages of the Cold War. It may be argued, the U.S. national economy was being strained to produce the equivalent of a new generation of dreadnoughts with the development and prospective deployment of the Strategic Defense Initiative (SDI). It is a tribute to the durability of the institutional environment that ten years after the removal of its raison d'etre, SDI is being promoted in a revised form as Ballistic Missile Defense, necessary for security against rogue states and terrorists.

Kaldor's criticisms have targeted the existing Western system of weapons procurement and development and culminated in a plea for greater numbers of cheaper, simpler and basically effective weapons. The list of weapons systems castigated by Kaldor and other critics includes the M1 Abrams tank, the Bradley Fighting Vehicle, the Aegis fleet defence system and the *Sergeant York* air defence system, among others. Their shortcomings can be summarised generically in terms of the problems that very complex (and, potentially, very capable) systems of any sort experience; namely, a tendency to chronic unreliability, a tendency to fail in complex, unpredictable ways and a tendency for their operators and buyers to overestimate their operational capabilities. Of these systems, only the *Sergeant York* was abandoned (Wilentz, 1985). Over time the others were brought to a degree of functionality which justified their presence in the inventory of the armed forces.

This perseverance mirrors the Cook-Craigie recommendation of the 1950s that aerospace design and development should overlap by progressively modifying production aircraft (Marschak et al, 1967). However this tactic was a technical response to the newly discovered discrepancy between the performance of hand-built prototypes and aircraft built on expensive production jigs. Kaldor and other critics are describing an institutional system for creating early lock-in to escalating commitment. Discrepancy between the lengthening technical development time-frames and institutional decision-making and budgeting frames made commitment at an immature stage of development necessary in order to secure the resources needed for completion.

In the West, the Cold War period saw an alarming, exponential growth in the per unit cost of modern, complex weapons, and publications of the *Baroque Arsenal* type have emerged as one form of response. A rather graphic illustration of the literally exponential growth in the per-unit cost of U.S. aircraft was given by Augustine (1975), beginning with the first Wright Brothers' machine sold to the U.S. army and ending with the F-15. His graphs show that if such trends continue, then in the year 2054, the projected U.S. defence budget would be able to afford a single aircraft- shared between the Air Force and Navy. The current B-2 strategic stealth bomber fleet of just twenty-one aircraft certainly fits this trajectory.

Such escalations in cost has been justified in terms of the increased functional capabilities of these weapons; that is, more money for fewer units with greater capabilities. Their proponents argue that these capabilities compensate for both increased cost and diminished numbers. However, it is not merely that the actual effectiveness of these weapons can be severely criticised, or even that their exponential costs have not provided concomitant exponential growth in effectiveness. It is that there are a variety of factors, ideological, historical, economic and political, that have led to this situation and which maintain it in the face of severe criticism and condemning evidence. These institutional factors find their expression at the task environment level to form a weapons design culture. In the West, this is distinctive in terms of the characteristics of the weapons it creates. In particular, the values embedded in such weapons are starkly different from those produced by the design culture of the Soviet Union. In the post-Soviet period, however, Russian designers are beginning to address export markets beyond the old spheres of influence which were required to follow their approach.

Design cultures, as described above, are the result of a myriad of factors and influences which occur at the level of the institutional environment. Indeed, a weapons design culture can be defined in just these terms: the systemic combination of a hierarchy of factors on the design commonalities that can be seen to exist in a nation's arsenal. These factors range from political and economic dispositions to military strategic objectives, historical factors, the availability of capital and even national manpower and education levels. It is precisely because of the difficulty in teasing out the separate influences of such factors and their relative magnitude, that a design culture must be viewed in systemic terms.

Nothing Personal: Men, Machines and Smart Weapons

In a very crude sense Western, and in particular U.S. built weapons are the result of a complex, profit-driven set of relationships first characterised as the military-industrial complex by President Eisenhower in his retirement address (Eisenhower, 1961). Clearly, the ideologies concerning technology which are a part of Western culture are key components of this system. The ideology of technocracy (and its manifestation in the economic/political process of arms manufacture in the U.S.) and the West's cultural technological imperative.[2]

In addition, there was a clear difference between the Soviet Union and the U.S. in terms of the extent to which they succeeded in using technology as a potential substitute for human operators or soldiers. Although this may be due at least in part to differences in technological capability and sophistication, this remains an incomplete explanation. Certainly the U.S.S.R. had considerable strengths for example in the development of automatic resupply rockets for its space stations and has the capability to develop complex remotely piloted vehicles, yet it largely refrained from developing military systems with remote operators or with semi-autonomous sensor based intelligence. In terms of the United States however, one can trace a trend, most clearly evident in the Vietnam era, in which the withdrawal of manpower from the battlefield, and its replacement by ostensibly more efficient technology, has been looked upon as a more than favourable development.

This removal of humans from the trauma of combat by using increasing amounts of long range firepower, long range sensors and electronic replacements for the surveillance, reconnaissance and combat functions of soldiers, airmen and sailors, has been in evidence from at least the Vietnam era, if not before. Certainly, the Vietnam conflict acted as an enormous incentive to the development of electronic sensors and data collection devices such as sniffer aircraft and motion and heat sensors for example (Dickson, 1976). Moreover, in more limited engagements, or in covert activities, the removal of the possibility of the death or capture of personnel offers a political benefit. recognised in the West since the 1961 destruction of Gary Power's U2 aircraft. The human cost of the surveillance activities of that period has only been verified with the ending of the Cold War (e.g. Burrows, 2001).

By the Vietnam War period pilotless reconnaissance aircraft and satellites were replacing the more dangerous reconnaissance missions formerly flown in secret by crewed aircraft (Wagner, 1982). These aircraft, developed from target drones, are the ancestors of the current generation of Global Hawk, Raptor and Predator surveillance and strike systems (Streetly, 2003). In the post-Cold War period, there is considerable political advantage in being able to conduct hostilities with minimal or no exposure to harm for military personnel.

In the last decade of the Cold War a generation of "smart" munitions emerged (Perry and Roberts, 1982). These included autonomous, intelligent mines and torpedoes that "pattern match" tank or submarine heat signatures or noise emissions to their stored memory of enemy targets These represented the fruits of more than 20 years of continuous military funding of artificial intelligence research. These were followed by "intelligent", man-portable surface-to-air missiles and anti-tank missiles, as well as intelligent anti-armour weapons. Skeet and SADARM (Search and Destroy Armour) are launched from artillery or mortar tubes to search for tanks while dangling from a parachute and then pierce their thin, uppermost armour with an explosively formed projectile (Jackson, 1985).

The Defence Research Projects Agency (DARPA) sponsored research into the development of intelligent, autonomous reconnaissance vehicles, and intelligent "pilot's assistants" as well as knowledge based tactical assistance systems (Stefik, 1985). Indeed, the terrain-following capabilities of cruise missiles rely heavily upon the incorporation of intelligent pattern matching procedures to assist their inertial guidance systems.

In essence, these efforts converge in their attempts to incorporate a spectrum of intelligence into weapons systems; this spectrum ranging from simple detection of a laser target designator or the use of other forms of sensor, to intelligent target recognition and autonomous control of an attack sequence and even artificially intelligent fleet defence systems or battle control assistants. It was initially on the grounds of cost-effectiveness that this replacement of human intelligence with limited machine intelligence was supported. That is, the price of such systems relative to their targets, or (for defensive systems) their defensive concerns (aircraft carriers, aircraft or tanks), is such that an advantageous economic tradeoff can be achieved even if several such weapons are needed to disable the target, or, in the case of a defensive system, if the defended entity such as an aircraft carrier, can be made to survive a sustained attack. However, it must also be acknowledged that the automation of almost all processes whether industrial, professional or military, is clearly manifested at almost all levels of Western society and has precipitated similar outcomes in the removal of high levels of human involvement from the decision loop.[3]

These ideologies re-embedded in the design of modern Western weapons and the escalating costs of their development and manufacture can be contrasted with the Soviet characteristic of relying heavily on manpower equipped with cheaper, less sophisticated, and more reliable weapons in greater numbers. From this one can denote a central ideological difference which has a number of facets, including a schism in the envisaged role that technology may play as a replacement for human presence, decision making and risk.

These differing emphases on the relative capabilities and deficiencies of machines versus humans are an important distinction between U.S. and Soviet weapons design cultures and the weapons they have traditionally produced. That is, in American weapons systems, humans are deliberately being phased out as an essential part of the decision loop.[4] This is not only because the United States has the technical expertise to do so, particularly in the context of serious manpower shortages in its defence forces, but also because the West's technological and economic imperatives have traditionally automated all specifiable processes and this history supports the belief that such systems are actually more effective.

In addition to these different histories and motivations for deskilling and automation, the sources of such ideological differences may very well have reflected the different levels of available manpower in the U.S. and U.S.S.R. and different cultural values and powerful, even militarily traumatic historical experiences.

Cold War Practicalities: Sophistication and/or Functionality

The potential economic efficiency of precision guided munitions and other intelligent weapons that are the products of Western weapons design culture must be acknowledged. However, their functionality in environments or under conditions that are less than optimal for their performance must be questioned. The susceptibility of these weapons or defensive systems for instance, to adverse weather or battle conditions such as fog, dust, smoke (deliberately laid smoke screens or the incidental outcome of combat), snow, or rain, the distracting effects (for the weapons operator) of enemy fire, as well as rather simple enemy countermeasures, is now a matter of public record. For instance, a constant research effort is conducted to provide software that allows air-air missiles to "filter" infrared or radar data supplied by their sensors, so that spurious sources of heat (flares, fires, the sun etc.) or false radar returns, can be distinguished from the heat emissions, or radar returns of real targets. Despite these efforts, even very simple countermeasures, decoys and sub-optimal conditions continue to be problematic for many modern missiles and smart munitions. Snow, for instance, is a hazard that the topology matching algorithms of the cruise missile find difficult to handle, as are the changing densities of leaves throughout the seasons.

A number of video recordings of the successful use of precision guided munitions were released for television broadcast during the 1992 Gulf War against Iraq. These were widely considered to represent the total of successful deployments in a bombing campaign that was conducted ninety percent with World War II munitions technology. This was despite the environment being much closer to the desert proving grounds in which the weapons were tested and developed than the theatres for which they were originally intended.[5]

There is a belief, peculiar to Western modes of thinking, that a weapon's performance is something that stands in isolation; that whether a weapon is effective or not depends on its technology alone, not the environment in which it finds itself. Hence, for Western weapons manufacturers and purchasers, there is a tendency to confuse sophistication and technological complexity with actual functionality. This in turn leads purchasers to an assessment of sophistication and apparent capability rather than actual capability when making their decisions. In other words, the issue here is the difference between efficiency within essentially hypothetical system goals and actual effectiveness in a realistic environment.

The significance of this point may be better clarified by an example. The F-15 fighter for instance has a radar system that allows it to simultaneously track up to 24 targets and simultaneously engage any six of them. This remarkable apparent capability is permitted by the complexity of the radar and avionics systems. However, this capability is not only bought at a price in real dollars terms, it is bought at a price in terms of reliability, maintenance time, spare parts, and training of pilots and maintenance personnel, not to mention the possibility that this capability, even when it is working, may be irrelevant.

Cold War preparations focussed on the standoff between NATO and Warsaw pact forces in Western Europe. NATO's defence was based in part on a belief that their fewer hi-tech weapons would be more than adequate to meet the greater numbers of less sophisticated Soviet weapons. In any outbreak in Western Europe, the favoured scenario in the anticipated air conflict, was that the opposing airforces would meet en masse and Western fighters would achieve air superiority by picking off Soviet aircraft at long range (out of sight) with their very accurate, long range air-to-air missiles. Hence, it was believed that the Warsaw Pact's numerical advantage would be whittled away by superior Western capability.

However, if one considers the more realistic situation involved in such a full-scale aerial conflict, then this view becomes much less convincing (see Coates and Kilian, 1986, pp. 256-257). In a situation where hundreds, perhaps thousands of objects (if one considers missiles, drones, remotely piloted vehicles and other miscellania) would have been airborne over the middle of Western Europe at any one time, where both enemy and friendly squadrons were taking off, carrying out, or returning from airstrikes, where high and low speed aircraft were providing tactical fire support for ground forces, where others were performing forward air control or reconnaissance missions and where Electronic Counter Measures, jamming and chaff had created widespread confusion in radar, radio and satellite communications, then the convenient opportunity for an F-15 to pick off its targets may never have appeared.

In such circumstances, even an Airborne Warning and Control aircraft (AWAC) may be hard pressed to assist in vectoring friendly forces or processing target data, even if it was able to divert attention from its own immediate survival. In support of this, Coates and Kilian (1986) recount the case of an A-6 Intruder accompanied by two F-106 fighters making a successful sortie against an AWAC in an exercise off Hawaii by jamming the modern aircaft's radar with their 1960's technology.

Moreover, NATO's assured superiority involved a situation that so far has never actually happened on any scale in aerial warfare; the situation where large numbers of targets are identified as enemy and then attacked, solely on the basis of electronic data. Given the total pandemonium of the first few days of a NATO-Warsaw Pact conflict, it seems very unlikely that this procedure would actually have been followed. After all, the fact that an aircraft, or even groups of them, do not respond to radio or electronic "Identification Friend or Foe" (IFF) procedures may merely be the result of damage sustained in returning from enemy territory. It may be the fault of a communications anomaly or dead spot, broadband jamming, even radioactive fallout or the effects of Electromagnetic Pulse.

It seems highly unlikely that mass engagements would have proceeded without visual identification, both because of the extensive electronic and physical confusion involved in such a conflict and the susceptibility of complex weapons (as described above) to "spoofing" by even simple countermeasures. Indeed, the difficulties of beyond visual range identification in even very simple scenarios can be seen in reports that, during the 2003 war in Iraq, anti-aircraft missiles were "ripple fired" against single targets to improve the probability of hits. A British aircraft, along with its crew, was destroyed in an environment of very limited opposition monitored by a system described as delivering "network centric warfare" (Brookes, 2003).

In the circumstances likely to have prevailed in a full scale Western European conflict the apparent capabilities of the F-15 would not have been converted into actual capabilities. Aircraft would be forced to close to visual ranges at which, experience has shown, the numerical superiority of even quite unsophisticated aircraft is the deciding factor in most aerial engagements (Miller et al, 1981).

There is a tendency to equate apparent capability – that which has not been tested in real circumstances – with actual capability. Since it is the sophistication of the technology that denotes the apparent capability of modern weapons, then this is what most purchasers tend to buy. The comments of the MIT computer scientist Joseph Weizenbaum are most apt in this regard. He calls the rampant pursuit of high technology the "pig principle" – the notion that because some is good, then more must inevitably be better (Weizenbaum, 1976). Yet in the context of a heavily armed Europe, it is important to note that not only was the pig principle rigidly adhered to, but it was also made more ludicrous by the illusory military capabilities it provided.

Bangs and Bucks: Quality, Quantity and Asymmetric Warfare

Within Western design culture there has always been a constituency interested in quantity traded against quality, and indeed, as has been illustrated by the above discussion, this ideology has held an enormous amount of sway in projections of the effectiveness of high technology weapons against more numerous, but less sophisticated weaponry. In effect, as discussed above, this is a position that Western powers are forced to take if they are to justify the ballooning costs associated with the development of sophisticated weapons systems.

It is interesting and appropriate at this point to recount some of the historical evidence which contradicts the claimants for quality. In the Korean War for instance, the MiG-15 was seen by U.S. pilots to be an effective, although relatively crude weapon, while these same pilots had very few good words for many of the supposedly advanced features of their own aircraft (Marschak, Glennan and Summers, 1967, p.111). The veteran

Russian pilots now known to have piloted the MiGs were restricted in their area of operations to so-called "MiG Alley" by the need to avoid capture or identification if shot down and this reduced the effectiveness of their operations.

The history of the Northrop F-5 and its application also yields much that is disconcerting for the supporters of quality versus. quantity in weapon evaluations This aircraft, a lightweight, cheap, yet effective and extremely reliable tactical fighter was intended for the export market to match the MiG-21 which itself was being exported by the Soviets in what became known as "MIG diplomacy" (Sweetman; 1985). In terms of export volume, the F-5 was a remarkable success, but its application in the U.S.A.F. has been confined to training and especially to the emulation of the MiG-21 in training exercises (the "aggressor" role), a task to which it is eminently suited because of its similarities in size and handling characteristics. In this application however, and in the numbers expected of MiG-21 formations, its performance gave rise to considerable concern when it carried out visual attacks from low level utilising cheap heat-seeking missiles, even against aircraft with sophisticated "look-down, shoot-down" capability, such as the F-15 (Coates and Kilian, 1986).

A further concept that underlies Western adherence to advances in quality at the expense of quantity is the notion of the "force multiplier". This is the expectation that superior communications and force co-ordination, earlier warning, and better intelligence – all qualities that high technology weapons systems are potentially able to provide – have a multiplying effect on any given force, so that numerical inferiority can be multiplied into a superior position.

Perhaps the most highly regarded example of such a force multiplier is the Airborne Warning and Control aircraft or AWAC. Yet, despite the anticipated multiplier effects of such systems, Ford (1985) argues that their effectiveness is often downgraded by the demands on resourcing actual weapons hardware, which is often deployed with inadequate spares because of unit cost inflation during development. The force multiplier argument can be seen to reflect the need to justify such high unit costs, and derives in turn from the quantity versus quality position taken by the West.

The flaw within the multiplier argument, is that the cost involved in the loss of force multipliers may also have a multiplicative effect, but in a negative sense. Consider for example, that while a single AWAC may genuinely have the capacity to monitor the airspace of the entire Middle East, its loss would be prohibitively expensive not only in dollar terms, but in terms of the effectiveness of the highly expensive fighters that would be reliant (in a tactical sense and in a design sense) upon its targeting data. This is precisely the situation in which the British found themselves during the Falklands War, when they desperately shielded their two aircraft carriers from Argentinian attack, since the loss of either ship would almost certainly have ended their campaign's chances of success. This multiplicative loss effect may also be the reason why U.S. naval computerised combat simulations reputedly do not provide for the loss of Nimitz class aircraft carriers, regardless of the amount of damage sustained.

Each B-2 Stealth Bomber deployed in Kosovo in 1999 operated with a minimum of fourteen combat air patrol and escort aircraft, electronic counter measures and other support requiring eighty-five aircrew, not counting the overall AWACS control (Brookes, 2003). As noted, the B-2 fleet itself has been restricted to 21 aircraft and the bulk of bomb delivery will continue to be undertaken by the aging B-52 fleet. This is currently scheduled for service until 2040, that is 88 years after the first flight of the prototype aircraft.

Another problem with an argument for weapons quality at the expense of quantity is that once the difference in sophistication between combatants becomes very great, then much of the sophistication of one's high technology systems may actually become useless. For example, the encounter by a U.S. taskforce of 1908-vintage Russian mines in the Persian Gulf, during the Iran-Iraq Gulf war, illustrates how a technology, so unexpected in its primitiveness, could create distinct problems. A similar argument can be applied to the irregular and open-ended "War on Terrorism" in which the West's opponents deploy the civilian infrastructure as weapons of mass destruction. Together with many of the still unlearned lessons of Vietnam, this represents a difficulty that remains unaccounted for by the supporters of quality.

Even the "Rolling Thunder" bombing offensive which led up to the Paris peace talks of 1968, while thought capable at the time of destroying North Vietnam's war effort, actually appeared to have little effect upon an economy that was already quite rudimentary in terms of its technological basis. Yet it was this same economy which nevertheless had successfully opposed U.S. forces in South Vietnam for a number of years (Dickson, 1976, p.20) and which ultimately brought about the frustration of U.S. military intentions, a point which should inform current policies in Afghanistan and Iraq.

Forty Years On: The Military-Industrial Complex in the Twenty-first Century

One component of U.S. weapons design culture involves the nature of the relationship between American arms manufacturers and the military itself; Eisenhower's military-industrial complex of 1961. The intimacy of this relationship has been identified as a profound handicap to the development of weapons that at least meet the technical specifications demanded of them.

In Coates and Kilian's terms, the almost incestuous relationship between these two entities, whereby personnel routinely move from one camp to the other, (the "revolving door" as it is termed by these authors) eliminates the separation between arms manufacturer and arms buyer, so that the normal benefits of the market, such as open competition and impartial evaluation, cannot prevail. The result is a system of weapons development in which kickbacks and bribes continue to play their part, where the confidentiality or secrecy needed for fair competition can be breached by the free trade in personnel between contractors and the military, and where the general market requirements of cost-effectiveness and quality have not always received a reasonable share of attention.[6]

In addition to this, there is the continuing institutional process in the U.S. military, whereby promotions are increasingly offered to those involved in administrative, political or bureaucratic roles rather than to those tasked with combat or operational commands. On top of this rush to bureaucratic duties by the highly ambitious, it has been shown that the system of promotion in the American military forces, works to deny advancement to those individuals whose project cost-cutting exercises reduce their staff and budgetary requirements.[7] Indeed, because of the military bureaucracy's steeply tapering pyramid at its highest echelons, those who are promoted beyond their colonelcys (or equivalent) are generally those who have shown an ability to conduct a large and expensive project, rather than the ability to administer within budgetary limits. This tendency can be observed well beyond the military sphere. Even universities are routinely ranked by equivalent input measures such as the consumption of research funds.

According to Coates and Kilian's evidence, by equating size and cost with project importance and by downplaying outcomes such as cost-effectiveness and role capability, inflation of project costs can be regarded as a desirable goal for ambitious individuals, and military careers are thereby allowed to flourish in an environment that has been almost freed of real accountability. It is in this environment that cost-overruns, shortfalls in anticipated performance, reshaping of original specifications and indeed even complete rethinking of weapon roles has become endemic and almost expected as a matter of course.

The most striking example in this regard was the DIVAD system, or *Sergeant York* air defence gun, where the intended targets changed from high-speed low-flying fixed wing aircraft, to helicopters taking evasive action, to helicopters in level flight as continued development revealed the difficulty of reaching the original specification.

However, that the nature of this relationship between weapons users and developers serves not only to preserve a commercial system that has mutual internal advantages for those who are members of the club, but also acts as a filter or gatekeeper to those that are not already part of it. Armacost (1985), for instance, recounts how Chrysler received a great deal of interference from the existing aerospace companies when it became interested in missile development at the beginning of the "space race".

Clearly, the preceding discussion does not concern itself directly with the larger issues of what purpose military budgets actually serve and how measures of "effectiveness", success or failure can be attributed to activities which are essentially wasteful of resources and skills. Yet it does illustrate that even within the narrow definitions of success and failure that permeate the U.S. arms industries and military establishments, by the end of the Cold War the domain of arms procurement and purchase in the United States was corrupt, inept and in terms of its own "rationality", verging on dysfunctional.

Eggs and Baskets: Omnibus Designs

One major consequence of cost increases in the West, has been a diminishing variety of weapons and the tasking of individual weapons systems with a greater range of combat roles. The European Tornado aircraft for example, the F/A-18 and F-111 were all touted as being capable of fulfilling attack/interceptor/bomber/fighter roles, a burden now passed to the new generation of technology represented by the Eurofighter and U.S. Joint Strike Fighter (JSF) programme. Such "mission creep" has been a means of achieving commitment to a specific design project. Chapter 8 describes this aspect of the Space Shuttle programme but the approach dates back to Robert MacNamara's tenure as U.S. Secretary for Defense in the 1960s.

The TFX fighter-bomber project was extended to reduce cost by delivering a common design to both the Air Force and Navy. The winning variable geometry ("swing wing") design by General Dynamics promised 91 per cent commonality between land and ship-based versions compared with only 44 per cent in the rival Boeing proposal. Because of the variance in performance requirements, however, the Navy was able ultimately to make its case for a separate aircraft from what was essentially an Air Force design. The surviving Air Force version was ultimately produced in a variety of versions and in numbers that achieved little economy of scale (Gunston, 1983). Ironically in June 1973 the Wall Street Journal claimed that the eventual termination of F-111 production was intended to ensure commitment to the next generation Rockwell B-1 bomber by removing a fall-back alternative (Levine, 1973).

The F-111 showed that success in achieving a range of demanding requirements is likely to be elusive. Even more than with naval versus land-based aircraft, the design requirements of defensive fighters and attack bombers are in conflict. Indeed, they are essentially incompatible in that while one role may demand low level stability for weapons delivery, another demands high level maneuverability; while one sacrifices fuel capacity for the haulage of large amounts of ordnance over short distances, another demands long range and large internal fuel capacity.

The result of this multitasking requirement where designs are asked to perform every conceivable role, is the production of smaller numbers of more costly, complex aircraft that are possibly less capable in any individual role than the aircraft they replace. The Tornado aircraft for example, the outcome of the European Multi-role Combat Aircraft project and once called "the milk giving, wool growing, egg laying sow" (Kaldor, p.142), proved too expensive to be used in its ground support role. Its losses were the highest suffered in the 1992 Gulf War, leading to an abandonment of the Royal Air Force's low-level bombing tactics. By 1999 the R.A.F. was dropping guided munitions from 13,000 feet in Kosovo, in one instance leading to the misidentification and destruction of a civilian refugee convoy.

The omnibus aspect of Western design culture may be regarded as the institutional outcome of the technology driven approach on sophistication and unit cost aiming to lock-in the institutional customers to a single solution. It represents a political response to budgetary restraints which produce a downward spiral of fewer units, which therefore need greater capability, which means greater unit cost and fewer units. As a consequence, new economies of scale are sought by addressing an ever wider range of tasks, thereby continuing the spiral.

There are signs that the ambitious omnibus design is under reconsideration with the F-35, winner of the JSF design competition, being offered in significantly different forms allowing a short take-off and vertical landing version alongside simpler, more conventional variants. This is a move from a single type towards achieving economy of scale through commonality as understood by the designers of civil aircraft. The Eurofighter Typhoon and the Saab/BAe Gripen, however, offer conversion from fighter to bomber at the touch of a button while Soviet designs, such as the Sukhoi Su-30 fighter are now being offered to export markets as multi-role aircraft in the Western tradition, with mixed results (Lake, 2001).

Weapons Development and Application: The Soviet Experience

The essential culture of weapons design and development as it still exists in the West contrasts with the culture of weapons development as it existed in the Soviet Union. The differences highlight key advantages and disadvantages of the two systems, as well as the persisting characteristics of the weapons they produced.

Although Cold War accounts credited the Soviet Union with being technologically backward and possessing large numbers of crude weaponry, the technology of which has been stolen or copied from the West, such an account hides much that is fascinating about the Soviet's historical and cultural values toward weapons and the processes by which they are developed. A crucial difference is that while the Soviets traditionally considered technology as important, for them it was only relevant to military matters in so far as it can help achieve particular tactical or strategic goals. Indeed, whereas there remains an implicit assumption in the West, that if it can be made, it should be, and implemented as well, on the whole, Soviet planners often ignored technological potentialities unless they represented a means by which their military objectives could be assisted. The MiG-25, for instance, involved design compromises that were virtually unthinkable in the West, in order to achieve a specific mission – neutralising the threat from the proposed B-70 supersonic bomber.

> In spite of Soviet appreciation of the importance of technology, the weapons produced for the Soviet forces often lack refinement. Their ruggedness and simplicity, often mistaken for crudeness, is the result of a deliberate design policy which eschews all unnecessary complexity. A Soviet weapon, whether it be an assault rifle or an air superiority fighter aircraft, is designed first and foremost to carry out a military task. However, ease of production and ease of maintenance are also important requirements, the latter especially so in a

largely conscript-manned service. Therefore, new technology is only introduced when it provides the sole solution to a designer's problems. Otherwise, existing equipment will be modified to undertake new tasks.

(Robinson, 1985)

This tendency to refine existing designs rather than incorporate new technology, can be seen in a number of major Soviet weapons systems, and it is the extent of this refinement and the longevity of many Soviet designs that acts as a significant counterpoint to U.S. technology driven design strategies. The MiG-21 aircraft for instance, has seen a series of dramatic refinements since its inception in 1959, remained in front line Soviet service for almost forty years. The MiG-27 "Flogger" as well, originally designed as an interceptor, has been incrementally developed into a ground attack aircraft, the "Flogger-D", by redesigning its engine intakes, armaments and avionics. Yet, while such incremental refinements do occur with Western aircraft of a similar vintage allowing them to serve in the twenty-first century, such upgrades tend to be performed only by secondary military powers.[8] American military forces characteristically pass their older aircraft on to reserve units and re-equip their front line forces with the latest designs. As a consequence, the Air National Guard generally achieves a greater level of combat readiness than equivalent front line units.

The longevity and extensive reworking of Soviet designs had the major advantage of allowing production runs to continue with minimal disruption, certainly without the level of disruption that the frequent introduction of new designs would cause. Secondly, this continuity of production permitted larger production runs and lower per-unit costs, with the costs of initial development being written off quite quickly. This emphasis on volume can be seen to be reflected in the selection of single engine aircraft designs, which allow high volume production and simplified maintenance at the expense of redundancy and some reliability in use. It is interesting to note for example, that Robinson (1985) quotes an increase in maintenance man hours per flight from 22 to 45 when the Egyptian Air Force replaced MiG-21 and 23 aircraft with U.S. F-4s following a change in political alignment.

Furthermore, it is clear that Soviet factories, unlike their Western counterparts, have tended to be more adaptable to wartime needs, partly as a function of the lower complexity of the products they manufacture and partly through deliberate provision for conversion. For example, in the 1930s Stalingrad and Chelyabinsk, two of the world's largest tractor factories, produced only half of the output of comparable U.S. factories, yet their conversion to tank manufacture at the outbreak of war was achieved almost instantaneously (Cooper, 1976).

Although this convertibility has declined, nevertheless the doctrinal commitments to simplicity, commonality and design inheritance are important advantages in Soviet utilisation of commercial facilities for weapons production, as discussed in the context of Western military specifications. The existing gap between these and commercial quality requirements represents not only a barrier to Western exploitation of commercial facilities in the event of need, but also supports a small cadre of specialist arms suppliers and manufacturers whose relationship with the military is based purely upon satisfaction of these needs in a restricted marketplace.

Systemic Robustness

A significant advantage of the Soviet system was that weapons and indeed, most technological efforts, such as space exploration, tended to be subsumed under a broader national purpose. When allied to a constancy of funding that the West would find difficult to justify, this resulted in a degree of systemic functionality that was at least impressive. That is, while individual units or weapons were, in general, less capable than those of the West, they possessed a greater measure of reliability and a more clear-cut and achievable role. This resulted in a military system, which, as a system, was more integrated and robust to individual weapons system failures.

That is, as we have seen, one of the effects of increasing costs in Western weapons development, has been the production of fewer ostensibly more versatile designs. If we contrast this with the more specific design targets of Soviet weapons and their numbers, it is possible to assess the robustness of the respective defence systems to the total failure of individual designs. In other words, in the event of an important weapons system failing disastrously, for example, if American F-16s and F-15s had been swamped by Soviet MiG-29s in Western Europe, or American carrier battlegroups had proved more vulnerable to anti-ship missiles than had been thought, then the systemic consequences of such failures would have been much more problematic for the U.S. than for equivalent failures in the Soviet system. This is because the overlap of weapon roles in Soviet weapon systems, as well as redundancy in the designs that perform these roles, made the Soviet system more robust to individual design failures.

This notion is strongly related to the negative force multiplier discussed above. Due to their unit cost, highly complex weapons take upon multiple roles and hence, role overlap of weapons diminishes so that design failure produces a negative multiplicative effect both because of fewer absolute numbers and because a catastrophic design failure simultaneously eliminates many roles from the weapon spectrum.

Bureaux and Bureaucracies: Soviet Research and Design

As would be expected, the Soviet system of weapons development and procurement was inevitably highly centralised. In many ways, the relationship of Soviet industry to the Warsaw Pact members avoided the difficulties experienced by Western nations in their attempts to co-ordinate international procurements. In the Warsaw Pact, the Soviet design became, with few exceptions, the de facto standard. This advantage was increased however, through the relationship between research, design and production organisations.

Sweetman (1985) and Robinson (1985) both give accounts of the different way in which competition was introduced into the Soviet system. While NASA, like its predecessor NACA, provides scientific and design data to both civil and military aviation companies, the centralised Soviet system ensured that innovations which were judged appropriate by TsAGI, the central aeronautical research institute, were adopted by the relevant design bureaus. In turn, the bureaux were required to evaluate alternative features within the same basic design programmes. This was the case with the MiG-21 for which prototypes were produced with both swept and delta wings. Thus, fly-offs and competitive evaluations occurred within the bureaux rather than between them, thereby producing competitive designs with minimum resources. Production runs were then assured for selected designs, handled by separate GAZ factories. It is interesting to contrast this approach with the intense profit-oriented rivalry occurring in the U.S. and which introduces cost considerations into a design's earliest moments.

Because of the features of the Soviet process, innovations proceeded in a more incremental fashion; first being evaluated by the research agencies, from which appropriate selections were passed on to the design bureaux for incorporation into prototypes, and eventually, production models. This preselection process met the criterion of choice of technical alternatives identified in Chapter 6 as a key to successful incremental innovation and robust design. Preselection in the Soviet system also reflects military doctrine and the spectrum of existing deployed systems, rather than pure technical feasibility alone. Thus the basic airframe of the MiG-25 has been utilised for a different role as the MiG-31, while the MiG-29 and Su-27 families share the same basic configuration.

At the same time, particular design bureaux might produce relatively few production designs, or only small volume production models, yet would deal with a generally higher level of innovation which was fed back to the research institutes, eventually to emerge in the large volume designs of other bureaux. As an illustration, the Kamov helicopter design bureau performs a role in redressing the generally conservative trends of Soviet designs by pioneering technical developments which may not be justifiable for general adoption without further investigation or refinement.

Lastly, a feature of Soviet weapons design was the political enmeshment of successful designers and the wielding of their political authority to secure favourable conditions for their activities. Well known examples of this include Academician Paton and the aircraft designers, Antonov, Ilyushin, Tupolev and Yakovlev (Cooper, 1984). It remains debatable whether this political involvement was counterproductive to competition and innovation in the manner that Coates and Kilian's revolving door operates, or whether it was beneficial in terms of allowing those best qualified to judge designs (namely designers), better access to the resources they need for efficacious development. Certainly though, this smoother discourse between technical and institutional environments appears to have been less destructive than U.S. inter-service rivalries which have often terminated or delayed promising joint projects and common purchases, such as the Boeing-Bell JVX troop transport discussed by Coates and Kilian (1986, p. 140-141). This ambitious programme is still under development as the V-22 tilt-rotor aircraft while the ageing CH-46 helicopter it was intended to replace is exhibiting increasing unreliability, including a fatal accident in Iraq in March 2003.

Reliability and Availability

An important difference between Soviet and American designers lay in their differing conceptions of reliability, and the differences between longevity of individual weapons and weapon availability. That is, for the Soviets, weapons reliability occurred when the weapon was functional whenever needed. It was of little consequence that the period of availability of the weapon, or its durability was limited, since these factors were taken into consideration when planning equipment rotation, overhaul and replacement. What mattered to the Soviets was not how long the period of high availability lasted, merely that such a period existed and was reliably known, so that planners could consider resource estimates as accurate. In contrast, the Western military concept of reliability is that a weapon remains constantly serviceable until it is effectively made obsolete, destroyed, or worn out. Highly reliable weapons in this view have extensive service lives and during this lifetime, malfunction infrequently until eventually they are no longer serviceable as a whole. Hence, for the West, it is the durability and availability of individual weapons that defines the concept of reliability, and it is this that must be maximised. For the Soviets, it was merely the known availability of the weapon and the period for which this could be guaranteed, regardless of how long or short this period was.

This difference in the concept of reliability can even be seen in the manner in which American and Soviet airforce units were committed to combat. For example, U.S. tactical strike units were expected to sustain heavy losses and perform indefinitely with the assistance of replacement aircraft and pilots, until they either prevailed or were effectively destroyed. Soviet units were expected to perform at a frantic pace for very short periods (generally five days) after which they were retired, refreshed and re-equipped before returning to combat status (Robinson, 1985).

It is probable that Soviet procedures were ideologically grounded in the experiences of the Great Patriotic War (WWII) where the source of victory lay in the consumption of enormous amounts of unsophisticated ordnance and weapons. Longevity was never important so long as the great factories of the East were churning out materiel.

It is interesting to note that the influence of these views in their respective design cultures appears almost paradoxical. While U.S. designers strive for high weapon availability in combination with maximum longevity and often fail to achieve either of these goals due to the complexity of their designs, Soviet designers on the other hand, while not being ideologically committed to the production of durable weapons, generally succeed in producing longer lasting, less failure prone designs by virtue of their simplicity and the extent to which they were incrementally developed.

Learning from Extremities: The Post-Cold War Design Environment

The purpose of this chapter has been to provide an account of the differing institutional influences in Soviet and American weapons design, the systemic combinations of which result in stylistic patterns of design decisions termed "design cultures", and which, in turn, manifest themselves in weapons characteristics that are distinct and identifiable.

A distinction has been drawn between the task environment in which a weapon exists and the institutional environment which spawns it. In the case of the U.S. a large array of institutional factors, fallacious arguments, assumptions and assorted sophistries have combined to produce a design culture which produces weapons that may be plainly dysfunctional at the level of the task environment. That is, if one accepts that weapons systems are engines of destruction whose performance in this capacity can be rigorously evaluated, then it is evident that factors operating at the institutional level in the U.S. have prevented the production of weapons that are effective in this most primary of senses.

At a superficial level, this analysis of weapons design cultures may be said to contribute nothing more than a listing of factors that distinguish between the economies and political systems of the United States and Soviet Union, and it is these that determined the form that weapons design took. Such a view is both naive and simplistic. It is not merely the capital available to weapons designers that determines the form their designs will take, nor is it merely the influence of the military or political systems. In essence, it is a dynamic combination of these and other influences, including prevailing ideologies and dominant values and even historical lessons and geographical realities. Moreover, the complex interaction of these influences represents an identifiable culture of weapons design in much the same way that we regard different architectures of the world as stemming from a cultural basis that is comprised of economies, values, politics and world views.

The arguments here call into question the rationality of Western, and particularly U.S. design culture which emerged during the Cold War and to contrast it with that of the Soviet Union. While criticisms of the Soviet Union at the level of the task environment have been somewhat less severe, this is not to say that Soviet design culture should be regarded as a model for technological development, or that the process of arms development in the U.S.S.R. was a more rational one.

The Soviet system tended to produce weapons systems which have an identifiable set of properties: reliability, maintainability, integration into a weapons spectrum etc., and in many circumstances these properties are more than a match for the West's expensive, high tech, unreliable gadgetry. However, while at the task level the U.S.S.R. can be accorded certain advantages and disadvantages, this is not to say that at the institutional level, it was not guilty of equal or even greater irrationalities. After all, although ease of maintenance may be regarded as a desirable quality of weapons, such a requirement is derived from the institutional level where compulsory military service limits the technical training and experience of the users of the equipment. The institutional rationality behind conscription as an appropriate and productive application of a nation's youth may be questioned, but the estimated 10 per cent to 14 per cent of Soviet GNP (Holloway, 1983) committed to the development and production of weapons has proven ultimately unsustainable. While the post-Soviet system still produces significant designs, these are generally poorly resourced and developed, with current government priorities lying elsewhere than in defence.

The U.S. design culture impacts in turn upon the institutional environment. Assumptions of technological superiority and a technicist perspective determine the advice given to political decision makers by military advisors. This is evident at macro and micro levels. At the micro level the results are tragedies such as the inadvertent destruction by the U.S.S. Vincennes of an Iranian A-300 airbus, referred to in the previous chapter, resulting from the deployment of complex and unreliable systems in crowded international corridors, ostensibly to protect the right of free passage. The deaths of 3-400 people in a Baghdad (Amaria) air raid shelter identified as a command and control centre and the deaths in the Chinese embassy in Belgrade resulted from out of date target data. The deployment of guided munitions from 13,000 feet in Kosovo was claimed to be for the restriction of civilian casualties; the unintended destruction of a refugee convoy demonstrated that the real concern was in fact with military casualties. Similar destruction of civilian life and property in Afghanistan during 2002 demonstrates the consequences of an ideology combining remote delivery of weapons with limited presence in the area of operations.

At the macro-economic level the military-industrial complex has dictated the direction of development of a significant proportion of research and development, not just in the United States but also in the economies of Cold War allies. In the United Kingdom the defence sector has controlled a significant proportion of high technology through out the Cold War period and beyond. Lovering (1988) argues that this military near monopoly of high technology from the Korean War onwards is a striking feature of Britain. As a consequence an export industry has developed across the developed Western economies beyond that required for mutual defence during the Cold War confrontation. Pythian (2000) argues that this has consistently constrained British foreign policy decisions and the international arms trade generally is seen increasingly to have constrained progress in developing countries.

In turn foreign policy in the United States seems to be driven by the capabilities of weapons systems rather than the longer term interests of that country and its allies. In the post-Cold War environment, U.S. military investment has continued at levels far higher than those maintained by other nations. The Project for the New American Century[9] is an influential think-tank which premises a global role for the United States based on unassailable military might. However, the post-Cold War period changed its character after 11th September 2001. The unchallenged military superiority of the United States was in effect circumvented by the "weaponisation" of the civil transport infrastructure. The response, in both Afghanistan and Iraq has been shaped by the characteristics of the very weapons systems that offered no defence from the 9/11 attacks. A "war on terrorism" has quickly shifted to a recognizable high-technology conventional conflict against those targets that are suited to the application of such measures.

The scale of the U.S. military-industrial complex creates and supports technologies which other nations can only emulate through collaboration and consortia, either with U.S. companies, as is increasingly the case in the United Kingdom,[10] or with others former Western allies, as with Eurofighter and the military Airbus design A-400M.[11]

The post-Cold War reconfiguration of Europe, as foreshadowed by Delamaide (1994) is now under strain because the expansion of NATO and the demands for regional security beyond its traditional sphere are placing a burden upon economies seeking to close the gap between East and West Europe. European and U.S. manufacturers compete for sales to the new NATO members, while both former Eastern bloc and Western countries vie for up-grade contracts for the surviving Soviet era hardware.

Elsewhere developing countries are similarly distracted. The Republic of South Africa retains significant human and technical resources in infrastructure developed to ensure military self-sufficiency during the isolation of apartheid. In a post-apartheid context there are both actual costs and opportunity costs to be addressed.

India and Pakistan pursue nuclear technology and delivery systems development. India is a customer for the Russian Su-30 fighter-bomber and both nuclear and conventional warships.

Military technology is an extreme case, but the examination of extreme situations reveal issues that may not surface in an environment in which elements can be seen in the transfer of technology more directly useful for development The account presented in this chapter provides a number of cautions. It reinforces the points made in earlier chapters about the nature of designed artefacts and the need to pursue design policies that are sustainable in terms of the human and material resources that they require. It also places design and deployment of artifacts and systems in a technical and institutional context and argues that the technical drivers of advanced weapons are shaping global strategies, to the detriment of broader views of the priorities of global development. This is typified by the gulf between the level of funding available for the application of military force and the funding available for the amelioration of the consequences of that application of force. This has been detailed by Monbiot (2003) in the current case of Iraq.

It has been necessary to examine in detail the complex interactions between the constraints and opportunities presented by the development of high technology systems. The final section of this book examines the decision space available to developing regions and communities in which to develop an appropriate response to the determination created by the interests and actions of their developed counterparts.

Notes

* This chapter has been developed from an article published as 'Technological cultures of weapons design' *Science as Culture*, 2 (2) (Number 11) 1991, 227-58.
1 See Chapter 10 for a more detailed discussion of the development of Japan.
2 See Chapter 3 and Morrison (1986).
3 The automated battlefield along with the workerless factory and the paperless office forms a technocratic triptych at the centre of Western technological aspirations in the Cold War period.
4 See for instance Morrison, 1984; Parnas, 1985 and Mosco, 1987 on the autonomous nature of SDI.
5 Ironically, the U.S. White Sands testing range bears more resemblance to the Iraq desert than to the North German Plain, the assumed theatre for many of the weapons developed there. The shift from a ten percent to a ninety percent proportion of smart weapons between the 1991 and the 2003 Iraq wars reflects both growing maturity and declining costs in the technology, and the similarity between the test and deployment environments. The reported failure rate remains at around ten percent however.
6 See for example, Tyler (1986) and Franklin (1986) on the history of General Dynamics - a history of extensive bribery, corruption and the source of the largest cost overruns in U.S. military history.
7 See for instance Coates and Kilian's account of the A-10 aircraft project, pp.154-155.
8 Laureau, (2003) describes the upgrade option for the F-4 Phantom adopted by Greece.

9 See http://www.newamericancentury.org/ for their clear explanation of the underlying philosophy.

10 British Aerospace Systems is in partnership with Lockheed Martin for the F-35, the successful bid for the JSF programme, a member of the Eurofighter consortium and a partner with Saab in the design and production of the Gripen fighter.

11 There is clearly an agenda within Europe to maintain independence from U.S. technology, and this extends to military satellites and global positioning technologies, which deliver both civil and military functions and which will be examined in the concluding chapter.

PART III

FROM GEOGRAPHY TO HISTORY: DESIGNING A PLACE IN THE WORLD

Chapter 10

Development by Design: Two National Development Paths

Melih Kirlidog with Stephen Little

Part I set out the parameters of an emerging global system of design and development, dominated by a triad of developed regions (Ohmae, 1990). Part II looked in detail at the dynamics of the complex socio-technical innovations essential to this system. Part III looks at the consequences for decision-making in relation to development strategies.

This chapter compares the historical conditions and the reform processes of two countries committed to development towards a Western model since the nineteenth century. The two countries are not comparable in current technological development, although such a review suggests some measures of success from their development strategies. One of them, Japan, is often taken to represent the modernisation of all East Asian economies. This book points out in several places the significant differences in development paths and outcomes in that region. The second country, Turkey is often neglected as an example of modernisation, in part because of the relatively less successful results. However as a secular, predominantly Islamic state bridging between Europe and Asia, it merits attention in the opening decade of a century characterised so far by the threat of the replacement of political division with religious division.

The Western understandings of modernism and development described in Part I date from the middle of the last millennium, derived from the renaissance and related scientific and social developments. For Max Weber, the roots of this revolution lay in the reformation and the emergence of a "Protestant Work Ethic" which facilitated an unprecedented transformation of the production of materials and of culture. It was inevitable that this transformation would affect all the peoples of the world.

Many non-European cultures found the shock waves of Western influence shaking their very existence. Although Turkey and Japan had very different historical and social settings, by the middle of the nineteenth century they both found themselves in a situation where radical transformations were necessary. Each country accelerated the design of its own reform processes in that period with the aim of matching the contemporary (i.e. Western) level of development. Seen from a distance of one and a half centuries, one nation appears to have been more successful than the other. These countries are worthy of detailed consideration as prototypes for the successful development states which appeared in the second half of the twentieth century.

The preceding chapters have been concerned with the myriad constraints on design outcomes. Viewing national development strategies as a problem of design does not imply a view that the designers had a free hand. Nevertheless, it must be argued that both attempts at social engineering produced significant outcomes of their own. An obvious aspect of the Turkish and Japanese modernisations was that, unlike the West, their leaders had a concrete target for the modernisation process. In consequence the strategies selected to achieve development were the result of a conscious design process for the development of catch-up strategies aimed at the early adopters and pioneers. Unlike the Western countries where modernisation reflected internal dynamics, Turkish and Japanese modernisation sought to reflect these external influences.

Development creates profound effects in the social and economic lives of societies. It also intensely influences and is influenced by the production and usage of technology. The close interaction between social processes and technological outcomes has been described by numerous writers (Mackenzie and Wajcman, 1985; Bijker and Law, 1994). As shown in Part II, technology is not socially neutral and can carry traces of the culture and values that produced it (Latour and Woolgar, 1979; Callon and Latour, 1992). Its usage is also affected by specific cultural settings. The information technologies that underpin the emerging global system are no different. They are products of a Western sensibility, but they are increasingly used in different cultural contexts, as discussed in Parts I and II.

Unlike Japan, where military and economic expansion was abandoned in the seventeenth century, the Ottoman Empire was in close contact with Europe from its foundation at the beginning of the fourteenth century. It was one of the cultures most severely affected by the Western enlightenment. The dominant ethnic group in the Empire were Turks who were originally from Central Asia, although all Ottoman Sultans were of Turkish origin, their mothers were overwhelmingly from other ethnic groups. They had been migrating to the West en masse since the eleventh century. With the foundation of the Ottoman Empire in the Anatolian peninsula, their westward advance continued until the end of the seventeenth century. By that time the entire Balkan peninsula and parts of Austria and Hungary were under Ottoman rule as well as Northern Africa, the Anatolian and Arabian peninsulas, the Eastern Mediterranean, and the Northern Black Sea.

The fall of Constantinople to the Ottomans in 1453 ended the Byzantine Empire and according to some authors, the Ottoman Empire became the third and the last of the classical empires by succeeding Rome and Byzantium (Ortayli, 2001).

By contrast, Japan was able to control contact with the West until the middle of the nineteenth century. Unlike the Ottoman Empire which covered a vast geographical area and several ethnic groups, Japan's population was ethnically almost homogenous and it had natural boundaries which allowed outside contact to be minimised. These two facts were advantageous for Japanese rulers who held deep reservations over the impact of foreign influence and had banned foreign travel in 1633 and, six years later, restricted contact with the outside world, expelling foreigners and eventually abolishing the firearms they had introduced (Perrin, 1982). Trade relations were limited to contacts with China and the Netherlands, conducted through the port of Nagasaki.

Although contact was eventually forced on Japan by the West in the person of Commodore Perry in 1853, Japan's modernisation process evolved in a more controllable fashion than that of the Ottomans. The related characteristics of clear natural boundaries and a homogenous population seem to be the key to the controllable nature of Japanese modernisation. Indeed, Japanese rulers were highly proactive in designing their reform process in line with their culture in the second half of the nineteenth century. During that time the Ottomans had to concentrate on endless wars with neighbours, fire-fighting the rebellions of various ethnic groups, and pursuing a balance between the often conflicting demands and interventions from the foreign embassies in Istanbul.

Ottoman Modernisation

The Ottoman Empire reached the peak of its power in the sixteenth and seventeenth centuries. Being the "soldiers of Islam against infidels", they felt that their might was not restricted to the battlefield, they also felt that they were culturally superior to any other civilisation in the world. They regarded the European civilisation to be culturally and spiritually inferior. Muslim armies were driving into India to convert the "infidel and backward" population to Islam, and little was known about far away and confined China. During that time Ottomans were also not on good terms with the neighbouring Islamic states.

The Memluk state in Egypt was toppled in 1517, but the victory won against the Persian state was not enough to eradicate it. Subsequent hostile relations with the Persians led to long wars at the beginning of the seventeenth century, which diverted attention from the West. Thus, after a long history of military victories against Western powers, the Ottomans had to sign a peace treaty with Austria in 1606 with problematic terms. Up to that time it was the Ottomans who had dictated the terms of the treaties in Istanbul. However, the Treaty of Sitvatorok had to be negotiated between peers on neutral ground on an island in the Danube. Even worse for the Ottomans was the recognition of equality between the Austrian Emperor and the Sultan who, until that time, designated other rulers in official documents by subordinate Ottoman titles (Lewis, 2002).

Although the Ottomans did reasonably well in the seventeenth century, they had to face some setbacks in their quest for maintaining superiority against the West. Like the first siege of Vienna in 1529, the second one in 1683 was also unsuccessful, Buda of Hungary was lost in 1686, and Azov on the Black Sea had to be surrendered to Russia in 1696. These failures were followed by the Treaty of Carlowitz with the Holy League in 1699 through which substantial territory was lost. According to many historians, the importance of the Carlowitz peace treaty to the Ottomans went beyond territorial losses. Many believe that this treaty marked the beginning of the decline of the Empire and it was a clear indication of the end of Ottoman superiority over Western powers.

Alarmed by these developments, the Ottomans started to think about remedies. On their side not much change has occurred; tools, techniques, and the organisation of the army and navy was mainly as before, so, the West must have changed. They reluctantly concluded that the Western powers were no longer the "inferior barbarians and infidels" who previously had had little to offer culturally, technically, and spiritually. On the contrary, their obvious progress on the battlefield compelled Ottomans to start a long history of attempting to adapt Western tools and techniques. However, this adaptation process had a crucial flaw which continued in the eighteenth century and beyond: since the only objective comparable measure of superiority was military power, the Ottomans concentrated their efforts on strengthening the military directly rather than strengthening the economic and social progress that supported military innovation in the West.

Over the following two centuries, Turkish modernity meant only the modernisation of the military. During the eighteenth century, still firmly believing in their own social and religious superiority, the Ottomans made several attempts to reorganise the military. Many of these initiatives suffered strong opposition from the military itself as well as religious scholars. This opposition sometimes became so intense that the reformist Sultan Selim III, who endeavoured to establish a new and modern army corps, was overthrown and killed by rebelling Janissaries in 1807.[1] Eventually, one of his successors, Mahmud II, who was a resolute reformer, had to abolish the Corps of Janissaries through a major annihilation in 1826 in order to establish his new and modern army corps.

Unlike the Western world which had a keen interest in the Orient, the Ottomans initially neglected civil contact with the Occident. While both Christians and Muslims had to travel to the Middle East for pilgrimage, there was little motivation for Ottomans to pursue civil contact with the Westerners. Although increasing numbers of travel books and accounts of the Westerners in Ottoman territories were published from the beginning of the second millennium, the opposite was not true. Only during the eighteenth and nineteenth centuries did the Ottomans develop a genuine interest in the Western world. The state sent resident ambassadors to Western capitals, Christian minorities sent their children for education, and Ottoman merchants established trade contacts. Increasing civil and commercial contacts in the nineteenth century clearly showed Ottomans that they lagged not just in the military field but also economically and socially. Nevertheless, subsequent reform attempts continued to be mainly in the military area.

Two major trends emerged among the Ottoman intellectuals. The first line of thought blamed the society for not correctly practising their religion, therefore being punished with backwardness. Proponents of this view were mainly the religious scholars who urged a return to tradition. The second line, which endorsed modernisation and Westernisation of the society, was promoted largely by the military and civil bureaucracy who were relatively open to new ideas and practices. However, due to the extremely complicated structure of an Empire that had subjects from three major religions and more than fifty ethnic groups, their suggestions for modernisation were highly diverse.

One of the key departments of the bureaucracy was the Translation Office, founded as a result of increasing contacts, both peaceful and hostile, with the West. Initially the main body of staff was drawn from Greeks in Istanbul, but after the Greek insurrection in 1821 they were replaced by Muslim ethnic groups. As the most significant window to the outer "developed" world the Translation Office acted in effect as a Ministry of Foreign Affairs. It became so important that by the second half of the nineteenth century the higher state posts were filled by its bilingual or trilingual staff rather than other departments of the bureaucracy and military.

Although Ottoman leaders could not anticipate the consequences, the French revolution had a profound effect on the Empire. Like most other empires of the time, the subjects of the Ottoman Empire consisted of several ethnic groups and religions. The non-Muslim ethnic groups also had a hierarchy among themselves: Greeks were regarded as a higher rank than Armenians who were in turn in a better position than Jews. Each ethnic and religious group was headed by a member from their community who officially represented the group in the Empire. Although subject to some constraints, they were allowed to practise their religion freely. Above all these groups stood the Sultan with his unchallenged authority.

Understandably, this model did not fit well with the *liberté – égalité – fraternité* motto of the French revolutionaries which was passionately propagated by their embassies in all countries. Although these slogans were dangerous for all empires, they were even more so for the Ottoman Empire with a very heterogeneous population and dwindling power. It didn't take much time for the waves of nationalism to reach the Empire, and the Ottomans saw in despair that most of their subjects were no longer prepared to be subordinate to the Sultan. The situation was exacerbated by the fact that the world powers started demanding more rights for the Christian population of the Empire. As an important consequence, the Greek uprising in 1821 led to the establishment of the Greek state in 1829.

The Greek uprising took place during the reign of Mahmud II who had been in a very weak position when he ascended the throne in 1808. As a result of intense internal unrest, mainly stirred up by local lords, he had to sign an agreement *(Sened-i Ittifak)* in 1808 with them for "consultation against threats to the Empire". However, when he established the order, the copy of the document simply disappeared from the Ottoman archives (Ortayli 2002) and everything continued as before. Nevertheless, Mahmud had to endure a humiliating defeat against one of his subjects, the ruler of Egypt Kavalali Mehmet Ali Pasha and his son, and even had to call upon his arch enemy, Russia, for help.

Mahmud was one of the most Western oriented Sultans, and he firmly believed that many things were going wrong in the Empire and something had to be done. This view was shared by everyone in the Empire except die-hard traditionalists. The problem was what and how to change. Should the modernisation mean Westernisation, or should a new way be found for modernisation?

Mahmud's solution was to adopt Western methods and organisations eagerly and to the extent that he could. To this end, although he himself was a composer of Ottoman music like many of the sultans, he invited Giuseppe Donizetti, brother of Italian composer Gaetano Donizetti, to establish a Western style orchestra in the palace, set up new army corps with Western uniforms and he himself wore Western-like clothing. This was too much for conservatives who called him "the infidel Sultan".

In 1838 with an economy close to bankruptcy, Mahmud had to sign the Baltalimani Trade Treaty with the British. This treaty commanded even more privileges for British merchants in addition to existing ones. One item in the treaty was the abolition of internal customs for British merchants, while these continued to be applied to Ottoman merchants (Aksin, 1988). As a result, imported manufactured goods flowed into the country, strangling a large part of local manufacturing that had no means to compete. According to many historians, the Baltalimani Treaty completed the course of Ottoman economic, and thereby political, submission to the West.

After Mahmud's death in 1839 his son Abdulmecid became the Sultan at the age of 17. He had had a Western oriented education along with a traditional one, probably a good command of French to the extent that he subscribed to several Parisian magazines, and was fond of Western classical music. Unlike his father who had ordered the last open political executions in the Empire and thereby slaying most of the Janissaries and several rebels, he did not have to order executions, the order that he hated.

However, everything seemed to be in a terrible mess in the Empire. The new army was defeated, the navy was hijacked to ex-subject and new rival Egypt, and rebellions were common in the Balkans and the Arabian peninsula. In this environment he defended Mustafa Reshid Pasha, former ambassador to London and Minister of External Affairs, against conspiracies in the palace and commanded him to proclaim the Edict of Reorganisation *(Tanzimat Fermani)* on 3 November 1839. This was a key event in the Empire, occurring in very turbulent times. The situation was so tense that the Pasha, unsure whether he would be able to return home, is said to have said farewell to his wife and children on the morning of the proclamation (Turkone, 1998).

The Edict started the period known as *Tanzimat* (reorganisation) in the Empire. The 17-year old Sultan's contribution was limited; in that it is widely accepted to be the design of the bureaucracy, notably Mustafa Reshid with the "assistance" of the British embassy. It was mainly a document of the Sultan's pledge to limit his power and to reorganise the state. It started with a statement that "the debility of the state and its subjects in the last 150 years is the result of deviating from Islam and its holy law *sheria*". However, there was no doubt that in a matter of "five to ten years" the Empire could start another epoch of glory and might, provided that it adhered to Islam as before. This must have been to soften what followed: the non-Muslim population would be granted equal rights with Muslims.

The Sultan went on to pledge that there would be no more arbitrary use of power, no political executions, and no confiscations without a court order. The effects of the edict went beyond its contents. Together with the 1856 *Islahat Fermani* (*Edict of Reform*), the quest for change paved the way to a limited modernisation and modest Westernisation in the Empire.

Perhaps the most important statement of the edict was the pledge that there would be no more confiscations without a court order. Unlike Western feudal lords and the newly born class of bourgeoisie who were able to accumulate capital, Ottomans regarded this potentially too dangerous for the state. Thus, getting rich was not safe for the subjects of the Empire who might see their wealth confiscated at any time. This was one of the most important differences between the West and Ottoman Empire where Western style feudalism and capitalism could not flourish. With profound effects towards the end of the millennium, obstruction of wealth accumulation by tyrannical means and the resulting lack of capital seem to be the key to understanding the decline of the Empire.

The period of *Tanzimat* covered most of the nineteenth century, leading to important changes in the state and the society. Traditionalists opposed and ridiculed it for creating rootless admirers of the West, while supporters of modernity backed it in the hope of progress in the quest for a route away from backwardness. In line with the *Edict of Reorganisation* a Criminal Code, partly inspired by the French code, was issued in 1840. In 1850 a commercial code, also partly inspired by the French, was issued.

During the reign of Abdulmecid (1839-1861) and his successor Abdulaziz (1861-1876) two important issues became institutionalised in the country. Firstly, the chronic shortage of finances forced the state into ever increasing external and internal debt often on very unfavourable terms. This reflected both frequent wars and the extravagance of the palace. In the draft budget for years 1861 and 1862 education and investments for civil works accounted for 0.3 percent, while 24 percent was for debt payments, with the palace getting 8.5 percent for its expenditures (Aksin 1988). Secondly, it was becoming increasingly difficult to keep non-Turkish ethnic groups in the Empire voluntarily. Sometimes encouraged by world powers such as Russia and influenced by Greek independence and the French Revolution, both non-Muslim and Muslim subjects started several rebellions to gain their sovereignty, and many of these were successful. Nevertheless, nationalism also affected the Turks, who were regarded as the main ethnic group in the Empire.

Three main views emerged among the Ottoman intellectuals who were desperately seeking a way out. The first view was to transform the Ottoman Empire in such a way that the ethnic groups would "melt in the pot" like the United States. In the course of the century, however, it became obvious that increasing national-consciousness meant ethnic groups were striving to gain their independence rather than yield to assimilation. The second view was to call all the Muslim subjects for an Islamic revival under the leadership of the Sultan as *Calif*, "God's shadow on the earth". This view also seemed to be unfeasible with the frequently rebelling Muslim Arabs. The third view built on Turkish nationalism: national unity for the Turks. However, perhaps reflecting their position as the main element of the Empire, the national awakening of the Turks would have to wait until the first quarter of the twentieth century, only after the Empire collapsed along with its counterparts in Russia and Austria-Hungary.

Political and social unrest led to the overthrow of Abdulaziz in 1876. After the brief reign of Murad V who was understood to be mentally unhealthy, Abdulhamid II rose to power the same year and stayed there for the next 33 years. He had promised to give more freedom to his subjects, proclaim a constitution, and establish a parliament with elected members from all ethnic groups. He kept his word; the first Ottoman constitution and parliament were declared. In 1877 the parliament assembled after the elections and an atmosphere of freedom prevailed in the country. However, Russia's declaration of war on the Empire in 1878 became the excuse for Abdulhamid to abolish the parliament immediately. The Ottomans lost the war and the Russians advanced as far as the suburbs of Istanbul before retreating back to the Balkans.

Draining resources to the end, the war exacerbated the financial situation. Repayment of internal and foreign debts became impossible. Abdulhamid was obliged to establish an organisation *(Duyun-u Umumiye)* in 1881 with the authority to sequester some of the state's income at source. It had administrators and representatives from Britain, France, Germany, Austria-Hungary, and Italy along with Ottoman members. It marked a further stage in the financial bankruptcy of the state.

Over the subsequent years Abdulhamid's stringent administration led to the constitution of opposition in the country. In 1889 five students of the Military Medical School formed a clandestine club which became an active dissident organisation in 1895. Named *Ittihat ve Terakki* (Union and Progress), this organisation had the objective of saving the state from total collapse. Since the Sultan's detectives made any kind of activities difficult to conduct domestically, many of its young and ardent members had to flee overseas. Known as Young Turks in the Western capitals, they were influenced by the secular and emancipatory ideas of the age.

One of their leaders, Ahmed Riza, became a passionate positivist. His bold opposition to religion was not uncommon among his fellow Young Turks. In the first decade of the twentieth century opposition from the young officers led Abdulhamid to appoint them to posts far away from the capital, mainly in Seloniki. However, in the cosmopolitan atmosphere of this city young officers and bureaucrats joined *Ittihat ve Terakki* in increasing numbers. Determined to save the country, their fight against the rebel Bulgarian guerrillas in the Macedonian mountains sharpened their patriotic feelings. However, deciding on what exactly to save was a bit problematic. Although they were military and civil bureaucrats of the Empire, they were increasingly convinced of the difficulty of keeping many reluctant nations in the Empire and the necessity of a homogeneous population and the ideology of nationalism to motivate it.

As a result of increasing unrest, Abdulhamid reluctantly declared the second constitution and reopened the parliament in 1908. The next year a revolt erupted in Istanbul. The rebels supported the Sultan and demanded a return to the roots of the empire and abolition of the "infidel" practices and institutions which they believed as the chief reason for the rotten situation of the Empire. With the main body of the officers *Ittihat ve Terakki* members, the army in Seloniki advanced to Istanbul and suppressed the revolt. One of its members was a young officer named Mustafa Kemal. Abdulhamid, suspected of organising the revolt, was overthrown and expelled to Seloniki. Although *Ittihat ve Terakki* placed Mehmed V on the throne at the age of 65, it retained the real power.

The Balkan war which erupted in 1912 ended with another defeat, this time resulting in the loss of the entire Balkan territories. The Empire was also on the losing side in World War I, this time resulting in the occupation of the heartland of the Empire, the Anatolian peninsula, by the victors. In 1918 Mehmed V died, and *Ittihat ve Terakki* leaders had to flee from the country. Mehmed VI, the last Ottoman Sultan, ascended the throne which was by then little more than symbolic.

After the occupation of the Ottoman capital Istanbul by the victors, Mustafa Kemal started a campaign in Anatolia with the objective of expelling the occupation forces and founding a new state. The war against Greece which occupied inner and Western Anatolia was won in 1922. The same year Mehmed VI had to flee from the country and this event marked the end of the six century old Ottoman Empire. The decline of the Empire in the last few decades was so dramatic that across three continents around two million square kilometres of territory was lost over which 24 states were subsequently established.

The new Turkish Republic was declared in 1923 and the difficult task of nation building started.

The Balkan war, World War I, and the war against the occupation forces had resulted in huge loss of lives in the eleven years prior to 1923. Even worse, the most valuable and the scarcest resource, the educated workforce, was almost completely lost. Industry was almost non-existent and the new

Republic, being regarded as heir to the Empire, had to pay the Ottoman debts.

Mustafa Kemal, who took the surname Ataturk, became the first president of the republic. He was determined to design a new society and modernise the nation through Westernisation. Unlike the Western oriented Sultans who had to carry the unbearable burden of the past, he had the advantage of starting with an empty white page and a fresh design process. Using this opportunity, he initiated many reforms to transform the society towards West: the Gregorian calendar was brought in, the Latin alphabet was adopted instead of Arabic, a new dress code was introduced for both sexes, the institution of the *califate* was abolished and the last *calif* Abdulmecid was expelled from the country. Perhaps the most important reform of all was the adoption of a new constitution in 1924 which emphasised the secular nature of the new state.

Most of these reforms are now deeply rooted in the contemporary Turkish society, the key secular state in the Muslim world. However, unlike the West where such transformations have occurred usually over very long time frames and through the internal dynamics of the society, Turkish reforms were undertaken over a short period and imposed on the society by an intellectual elite, sometimes by force. There was also another important difference with the West: Super-structural institutions such as secularism are the products of a particular economic order, namely capitalism. There is no guarantee that the reverse process can succeed; official secularism in Turkey did not create a robust working capitalism in the eight decades of the Republic.

Although reduced in size, a large percentage of the population still lives in rural areas striving to earn a livelihood with inefficient agricultural methods. The relationship between the state and religion is also still somewhat uneasy. At the beginning of the new millennium dispossessed masses tend to perceive their plight as a consequence of retreating from religion, whereas the state sees the "backward interpretation of the religion" as the source of most of the ills in the society and a threat to its very existence.

After the foundation of the republic it was obvious that the capitalist way of development was not possible due to the lack of capital, therefore a protectionist development path was preferred. Nevertheless, the creation of a capitalist class was a priority for the republic's government. With hindsight it could be said that over the course of eighty years, such a class was indeed created, but with the major flaw of direct dependence on state funds, incentives, and custom tariffs. As the most important controller of resources, the state had and still has the power to determine "who will get what". This applies not only to the classes in the society, but also to individuals or groups of capitalists who had to develop good relations with the bureaucrats. As could be expected, this is a situation which provides a fertile ground for corrupt practices. To some extent, this resembles the practices of the Ottoman State that also strove to be the sole controller of the economic resources of society.

The Key Philosophical Debate

Religion has always been a very important factor in the social life of Ottomans. After the defeat of the Memluks of Egypt by I. Selim in 1517, the Ottoman Sultans became *calif*, the shadow of God on earth. Although the sultans did not emphasise this appellation until the nineteenth century, it could be regarded as a strengthening factor on the role of religion in the society.[2]

Two debates of the same nature, one before and one after 1517, seem to be decisive in Ottoman history and in the history of Islam. The debates were about the nature of philosophy and the role of belief and intellect. In fact, the discussants were continuing the debate of several centuries earlier between two Muslim scholars, Al-Ghazali (1058-1111) and ibn Rushd (1126-1198) who is known as Averroes in the West. Although both were devoted Muslims, Averroes was more open to new ideas and schools of thought than his predecessor, possibly due to the high level of Andalusian civilisation in Spain where he spent most of his life. A closer look to their teachings would be illuminating:

Al-Ghazali started his scholarly life as a sceptic but later stood rigorously against all schools of thought other than one strict interpretation of Islam and he is regarded by many as a scholar whose works have been influential in closing the door to philosophy and other schools of thought in the Muslim world for centuries.

As a reply to Al-Ghazali's book *Tahafut al-Falasifa* (The Incoherence of Philosophers) in which reason is criticised as opposed to pure reflection from scripture, he wrote *Tuhafut al-Tuhafut* (The Incoherence of Incoherence) where Averroes criticised Al-Ghazali's orthodox interpretation of the religion. In his books his main point was that philosophy and religion do not need to contradict to each other. He argued that if there is an obvious conflict between Holy Scripture and demonstrative reasoning, then the source of the conflict must be the metaphor in the scripture.

This debate, which took place more than three centuries prior to Galileo and Bruno, continued in the Ottoman period. In the reign of Mehmed II (The Conqueror 1451-1481) and Suleiman I (The Magnificent 1520-1566) the debate was mainly whether to teach the "reason" of Averroes and his commentaries about the thoughts of the ancient Greek philosophers along with Al-Ghazali's "pure reflection from the holy scripture" in educational institutions. Averroes lost. As the highest authority in religion and related sciences, Al-Ghazali's victory closed the door to critical thought in the Islamic world for centuries. However, as the re-discoverer of Aristotle after centuries, "The Commentator" was taught extensively in the Western universities after his death. According to many people including some Muslim scholars, the Ottoman way of interpretation of religion and denial of philosophy carried the seeds of the later decline of the Empire.

However, it must also be noted that not every historian agrees with this causal explanation. While orthodox Muslim scholars maintain that all ills are the result of retreating from religion, there are also some researchers who argue that Islam had little to do with the decline. Karpat (2002) contends that the Ottoman elite constructed a modernisation theory to protect their position and maintain themselves as architects of the transformation.

This theory was based on the argument that all flaws of the state resulted from the weakening of the authority of the centre. As usual in such cases, the proposed remedy of modernisation was to strengthen the authority which resulted in unanticipated consequences within the fragile and delicate social structure and this in turn laid the foundation of the collapse of the state. He further maintains that although the conditions for Ottoman modernisation were very favourable in the sixteenth century, that opportunity was wasted due to several factors. These included the heterogeneous and partly nomadic population, extreme central control of economic resources, and the birth of a new bureaucratic social class whose attention focussed on wealth rather than the process of wealth production. The main concern of this new bureaucracy was to sustain its very existence and maintain strict control of central authority over economic resources.

Unlike the Japanese and Russian modernisations where bureaucracy was seen as a service provider for the needs of the greater society, Ottoman bureaucracy became the major consumer of resources with little contribution to the modernisation process of production and wealth creation. Thus, according to Karpat, the role of Islam was marginal in the decline of the Empire. It became the scapegoat for the intellectuals who were unsuccessful in establishing a genuine ideology and who failed spiritually, humanly, and intellectually.

Japanese Modernisation

Unlike most of the empires of its age, the Emperors of Japan had only a minimal involvement with political affairs during the second half of the previous millennium. As "Heavenly Sovereigns" they were believed to descend from the Sun Goddess and had a semi-divine status with symbolic authority. Political power moved to court officials and, by the twelfth century, to the *shogun*, military lords who governed the country with excessive power. The *shogunates* were dynasties in which a family member succeeded the *shogun* on his death. There were three *shogunates* between 1192 and 1868: Minamoto (1192-1333), weakened after successfully repelling two Mongol invasion fleets, Ashikaga (1338-1573), which degenerated though internal squabbles into civil war, and Tokugawa (1603-1868) which achieved two and a half centuries of stability at the cost of national seclusion.

As the foremost authority in the political issues, the *shogun* had the ultimate authority over *daimyo,* the territorial rulers who controlled a specific area for agricultural production. *Daimyo* also had to provide military and financial support to the *shogun* when requested. Numbering between 250 and 300, the *daimyo* also had ranks, the highest being those having kinship with the *shogun's* family.

With the Ashikaga *shogunate* unable to control the country, Japan was in political turmoil in the middle of the sixteenth century. Bloody wars among the *daimyo* for territorial control resulted in the victory of a few, notably Nobunaga. With the help of locally produced copies of Portuguese firearms, he gained control over a large area and installed Yoshiaki as the last ruler of the Ashikaga *shogunate* in 1560. After overthrowing Yoshiaki thirteen years later he extended his power and controlled increasingly more territory. After his assassination in 1582, power was grasped by one of his generals, Hideyoshi, who continued his master's work and completed the military unification of Japan in 1590.

Before his death in 1598 Hideyoshi named five major *daimyo*, one of them Tokugawa Ieyasu. Although all five *daimyo* had pledged to make Hideyoshi's infant son *shogun* when he became an adolescent, they soon became rivals in pursuit of power, the result being a major battle in 1600 which ended in victory for Ieyasu. Three years later he was appointed as *shogun* by the Heavenly Sovereign and the last *shogunate* dynasty started.

The Tokugawa Shogunate

The Tokugawa house, which reigned for over two and a half centuries, began by securing its position in the country through the subordination of the *daimyo* and the remaining warlords. Unlike the previous two *shogun* dynasties, they asserted the right to levy taxes and proclaim laws. After tranquillity and national unity was totally established in the middle of the seventeenth century, Japan began a long history of economic and social development.

Rural communities initiated small scale enterprises for producing agricultural goods for the market, and a merchant class emerged which enjoyed the quickly developing infrastructure such as roads. Due to the peaceful environment, some of the *samurai,* the professional warriors, became competent professional local administrators under the authority of the *daimyo*. Ever increasing trade and a quest for a high living standard resulted in the rapid urbanisation of the country. Thus, by the end of the Tokugawa period Japanese living standards were among the highest in the world, comparable to England and U.S.A. according to some estimates (McClain, 2002).

Japan's traditional Shinto religion peacefully coexisted with Buddhism, an import from the Asian mainland. Religious shrines usually contained chapels of both religions. As long as the social order was maintained, *shogun* and *daimyo* had nothing against either religion. Neo-Confucianism, another import from Asia, also found its way to Japan in the seventeenth and eighteenth centuries. Its emphasis on obedience to authority was exactly what the *shogun* needed after centuries of chaos and turmoil.

However, the Tokugawa rulers were not prepared to welcome all religions. Western traders and seamen brought not only goods and technology with them, but also Christianity. By the beginning of the seventeenth century it is estimated that around 300,000 Japanese had converted to Christianity. This alarmed the rulers who were confident that the new religion with a "jealous God" would in no way coexist peacefully with the existing ones. It was also regarded as foreign and pernicious with little or nothing in common with Japanese traditions and way of life. Consequently they banned Christianity in the country and initiated a repressive campaign resulting in its eradication from Japanese soil during the first half of the seventeenth century. In addition, foreign trade was strictly regulated, foreign travel was prohibited, and foreign ships were barred from Japanese harbours. The only exceptions were Dutch and Chinese ships which could only visit Nagasaki, with the Dutch traders confined to a small artificial island in the harbour.

Unlike the Ottoman Empire where the rulers mistrusted subjects who became wealthy, Japanese rulers had nothing against the accumulation of capital in private hands. On the contrary, they actively supported the well-off *daimyo*, merchants, and peasants in the hope of collecting more tax. Thus, pre-capitalist forms of production blossomed in Japan during the

Tokugawa period. Mitsui is a good example of the course of the economic development in Japan. After a long history serving their *daimyo* as *samurai*, the Mitsui family opened a sake brewery house after the Tokugawa rulers established tranquillity in the country. Encouraged by the profits, the family started another business in money lending. In 1673 they decided to invest their money by establishing a drapery house which after a few decades became Japan's largest store. Mitsui Trading Company and Mitsui Bank were founded in 1876 and the next year the trading company established its first overseas office in Shanghai. Before World War I it had dozens of offices in Asia, Europe, and America (Mitsui, 1977).

This pattern of development resulted in the emergence of Japan's *zaibatsu*: groups of companies owned and operated by single families, as key players in the modernisation process. Such a move would have been unthinkable for the Ottoman companies which commanded neither capital nor know-how of production and trade in such proportions.

Morris-Suzuki (1994) argues that the Tokugawa period saw the development and consolidation of a wide range of craft skills which proved of great value in the assimilation of foreign practices in the nineteenth and early twentieth centuries. The foundations laid during the late Tokugawa and early Meiji periods created an absorptive capacity (Cohen and Levinthal, 1990) which was lacking in the Ottoman empire.

Thriving trade and artisanship together with increasing living standards led to a flourishing cultural life in Japan. By the beginning of the nineteenth century there were hundreds of bookstores and rental libraries in the country and each year thousands of new titles were produced, ranging from serious works of scholarship to travel guides. Burgeoning curiosity about other locations in Japan, the ancient history of the country, the strange habits of bizarre barbarians, and countless other topics produced a strong demand for books which were affordable to the general public (McClain, 2002).

The books were not only of local origin; some were translations from Chinese and Western languages. The prohibition of foreign books was abolished in 1720 except for books on Christianity. One of the first books to be translated was about human anatomy, previously a proscribed topic. Upon studying dissection of the body of a criminal who had been executed, it was observed that the Dutch translation of a German medical book correctly described human anatomy. This led to an increased appreciation for Western science and medicine and more translations from the West as well as producing dictionaries.

The Ottoman situation was very different. Although the non-Muslim minorities had established their printing houses as early as the fifteenth century, they were allowed to print only in their own language. Muslims had to wait for a printing house until 1727. However, after printing a total of 17 titles this house was closed in 1743, only to be reopened in 1784 (Aksin, 1988). The reason for its closure seems to be manifold: some religious devotees did not want the Holy Scripture to be affronted by an infidel invention, and more importantly, there was not adequate demand for reading other than the Holy Koran which was hand-written (Ortayli, 2001). The resistance of the calligraphers is unlikely to have been a significant factor, a strong demand for reading and curiosity would have been reflected in levels of demand which would be difficult for calligraphers to obstruct. It is striking that the total number of titles in the entire Ottoman period printed up to the collapse in 1922 is between thirty and forty thousand, many of which were religious texts (Ortayli, 2001). Books of a scientific or practical nature were a small fraction in that amount.

Although the Tokugawa period provided tranquillity and economic growth for some, not everyone was happy with the rule of the *shogun*. Some *samurai* successfully transformed themselves into prosperous merchants or local administrators. However, others of lower rank were distressed by diminishing stipends and declining importance in society. Poor rural families were also distraught by high levies, low prices of their products, and occasional famine as a result of climatic circumstances. Thus, the number and intensity of peasant rebellions gained momentum in the first half of the nineteenth century.

Encouraged by the British victory in the 1839-42 Opium War against the Chinese who wanted to prohibit the free trade of opium by the British in their own territory, the Western powers started to press the *shogunate* to end its policy of isolation. In 1853 Commodore Perry delivered a letter from the U.S. president requesting an end to economic seclusion and the start an era of "peace and friendship" by opening Japanese harbours and soil to free trade. Perry left Japan indicating that he would come again soon with a larger force if the request was not fulfilled.

As promised, Perry arrived next year again in line with the rules of the gunboat diplomacy of the era. Anticipating bitter criticism from traditionalists but having little option other than yielding to the Americans which could easily overcome the Japanese defences, *shogunate* rulers reluctantly signed the treaty of "peace and amity" between the U.S. and Japan. Within a few years similar treaties were concluded with Britain, Russia, and France.

As expected, yielding to foreign demands led to an uproar of criticism in the country. Under pressure the *shogunate* decided to get the support of the Heavenly Sovereign for the new policy of opening harbours to foreigners. However, this proved to be a severe mistake: Emperor Komei was decidedly against the new policy. The only option left to the *shogunate* was the ruthless suppression of the dissidents. Several of them were arrested and some were executed. In the course of the 1860s, Japan was again in turmoil with the suppression of dissidents and assassination of *shogunate* officials. Destabilised by a series of severe riots and civil unrest, the Tokugawa *shogunate* collapsed in 1868, ended by a decree of the 15-year old emperor Meiji who had ascended the throne in 1867.

The Meiji Restoration

The long reign (1867-1912) of Meiji, the so-called Meiji restoration, turned out to be an extraordinary example of modernisation which created contemporary Japan. For many, the 1868 Meiji Restoration marks the birth of modern Japan, but the change was neither a Norman Conquest nor a French Revolution. As dominant groups in the old regime weakened, subordinate or similar elements moved into their place (Mason and Caiger 1972). Under the slogan *fukoku kyôhei* (rich nation, strong army) the Meiji government sought to establish a prosperous country that remained free from colonisation by any Western power. In practically all major industries the Meiji Government took the initiative (van Wolferen, 1990).

This epoch became a model for many nations with a strong desire for modernisation, but sceptical of Westernisation. Its appeal to many conservative movements in the less developed world is the concept that Western science and technology could successfully be adopted without substantial change in the traditional values and without embracing the Western way of life and customs. This argument is problematic for two aspects: firstly, it assumes that Japanese society has not changed much during the period of modernisation. This is not true, because although the difference between Japan and a Western society have always been and will always be greater than, say, that of France and the U.S., Japanese customs and traditions have also changed substantially during the course of and as a result of modernisation. Secondly, it implies that science and technology can be independent from their cultural setting and that they have little power to influence the culture of a society. This is also not true when one observes the rapid diffusion of real virtuality tools such as multimedia, video games, karaoke, cable television, and computer mediated communication in Japan and the resulting cultural transformations (Castells, 2000).

The year the last *shogunate* was toppled, Meiji proclaimed the *Charter Oath* which showed some similarity to the Ottoman *Edict of Reorganisation*. Both decrees were indications of a new era and sincere attempts to modernise Eastern societies to catch up with the West which was clearly understood to be way ahead. With this disparity in mind, both empires sought to develop good relations with Western powers and pledge to uphold the rule of law.

Radical reorganisations were realised in Meiji's first few years. The Confucian-based social classes were reordered by redefining the rights and duties of *samurai*, peasants, merchants, and artisans. The *daimyo* and their domains were abolished in 1871, replaced by prefectures. In 1873 Land Tax Reform was proclaimed with the objective of a "burden to be shared equally among people". Students and several missions were sent to Western countries with the objective of learning about society, science, and technology. Most significant of such expeditions was the Iwakura mission in 1871 where government leaders visited the U.S. and Europe for a systematic investigation of the West, its institutions and technology. The mission and its successors recruited Manchester-based engineers to establish British style industrialised textile mills in Osaka, sought medical and pharmaceutical technology from Germany, and agricultural innovations from the United States.

In 1872 a Code of Education was issued which mandated four years of compulsory primary education for both sexes. Inheriting the robust education infrastructure of the Tokugawa period with abundant teachers, schools, and textbooks, the Meiji administration made reasonable progress in its first years, providing primary education to 60 percent of boys and 20 percent of girls by 1880 (McClain, 2002). This contrasted with the Ottoman Empire where, according to Karpat (2002) during the 1870s only 15 to 20 percent of Muslim children attended schools, many of which had closed by the end of the century. The reason for closures was, as usual, shortage of funds. In 1894-95 education expenditure was less than 0.05 percent of the total income of the state while the army and navy got 70 percent. Although primary education was made compulsory from the beginning of the nineteenth century, the statute was neglected and the number of schools and teachers were nowhere near adequate.

It must also be stated that during that time Ottoman rulers had to deal with different problems from their Japanese counterparts. The establishment of a high school in Istanbul is an example of the difficulties facing modernisation in the Empire. The Ottomans had several education systems in which each religious and ethnic community had its own schools. When the shortage of educated people reached alarming proportions, Sultan Abdulaziz founded a high school *(Mektebi Sultani – Galatasaray Lisesi)* in 1868 which was to have a secular education system and teach French along with Turkish and other community languages.

The school was also supposed to unite subjects from all ethnic groups under the banner of Ottoman ideology and it was intended to be an important milestone in the modernisation process. However, upset by the idea of secular instruction and feeling threatened by their loss of control of education, Catholic, Orthodox, Jewish, and Muslim community leaders protested against the new school and prohibited their community members from attending it. Even Pope Pius IX in the Vatican threatened to excommunicate Catholic parents who sent their children to the new school and the Russian Tsar demanded the school be closed without delay unless a similar Russian-teaching one opened immediately. Indifferent to the protests that decreased over time, the Sultan eagerly supported the school and *Mektebi Sultani*, which remains a distinguished institution today, became a very successful establishment that provided elite cadres to the Empire as well as religious leaders to some Christian communities. However, economic, social, and cultural conditions in the empire were far from ideal to establish many such institutions in the country. It was too little, too late.

Government influence was evident in Japan's moves to establish universities (starting with the University of Tokyo in 1877), which were essentially agencies for training bureaucrats and not properly equipped to conduct research (Itakura and Yagi, 1974). Gooday and Low (1998) describe how the carriers of the foreign employees were used to instruct Japanese scientists and engineers in the Imperial College of Engineering which took a more practical approach than the universities. At this point, the only foreign equivalent was the Zurich Polytechnic Institute. Despite the trauma of the arrival of the "Black Ships" of Perry's naval squadron, the late Tokugawa period had seen the refinement of indigenous technologies with input from Dutch and other foreign sources (Morris-Suzuki, 1994).

It was understood by the Japanese and Ottoman rulers that one of the key characteristics of Western societies was the abandonment of the arbitrary use of power. They carefully observed the governance of society according to rational and secular laws. Considering this an important step in modernisation, Meiji proclaimed the Japanese constitution, written with input from Western consultants in 1889. The constitution stated that although the emperor had the utmost and sacred authority with power to declare war and peace, he and other rulers had to govern the country according to the laws. In Japan these tentative steps towards parliamentary democracy also echoed bureaucratic imperatives. When the National Diet opened in 1890, Meiji rulers created a weak parliament and sought to counterbalance it with a strong bureaucracy, staffed by their own supporters. The parliament became concerned with ratifying rather than initiating policy (Johnson, 1983). In contrast, the Ottoman constitution was abolished immediately after its proclamation.

Thus, unlike the Ottoman Empire which was doomed to an inevitable collapse, the Meiji restoration had successfully transformed Japan from an agrarian country to one on the path of industrialisation by the end of the nineteenth century. The war with Russia in 1904 and the subsequent occupation of Korea led Japan on a path of mimicking the colonial expansion that had underpinned the economic development of the Western powers in the previous century.

Cultures and Consequences

One and a half centuries after the Ottoman *Edict of Reorganisation* and the Japanese *Charter Oath* one can retrospectively evaluate the success of both modernisation attempts. The Ottoman modernisation endeavour did not bring success, even in terms of the survival of the Empire. The sixteenth century superpower failed to compete with Western rivals that produced an unprecedented achievement in social and economic development.

A comparison between Japan and Turkey in one key area of nineteenth century technology – railways – is instructive.

Railway development under the Ottomans involved either government sponsorship of strategic lines, such as the Hedjaz and Baghdad railways, or privately sponsored lines in areas of high demand. As a result the national network was far from complete, with large areas of population still without rail access when the new Turkish Republic founded a state railway company in 1927. The process of buying out the surviving private lines was not completed until 1948. British interests in particular were ambivalent towards the development of overland routes towards India in competition with the Suez Canal. German assistance was used to develop lines in Anatolia and the Baghdad Railway, from which British investors were barred.

In Japan the government was keen to see the rapid development of railways, whether in government or private ownership. The importation of the latest Western technology was encouraged, with little resistance from the British, German and American suppliers. Development took place quickly, with Tokyo and Osaka being linked in 1872, the equivalent link in Turkey, between Izmir and Istanbul was only completed in 1912. Domestic manufacture of railway equipment including locomotives and rolling stock was well developed by the time of nationalisation of the majority of railways in 1906.

The extension of government ownership from 30 per cent to 90 per cent of the railway network and the direction to favour private Japanese manufacturers over foreign sources for locomotives led to the rapid development of a bulk building capacity and associated standardisation by the Japanese industry (Ericson, 1998). In 1911 treaty revisions allowed the re-introduction of domestic tariff protection, and from 1913 Japanese railways were able to source all their standard locomotives from domestic manufacturers.

The modernisation efforts of the new Turkish Republic that inherited meagre infrastructure and an almost non-existent educated workforce from the Empire, were only moderately successful during the course of the twentieth century compared to Japan. As a consequence, contemporary Turkey is still a developing country with abundant social and economic problems ranking eighty-fifth in the Human Development Index (HDI) of the United Nations Development Program (UNDP, 2002). There is a similarity with the problems encountered by the Soviet Union which sought parity with the Western powers, but pursued the military and security issues ahead of broader economic development. Although performing better than many comparable Middle Eastern countries, the Turkish Republic, heir of the Ottoman Empire, now competes with a post-communist Russia that occupies sixtieth place in the HDI.

Meanwhile Japan has become the world's second largest economy, and as a world class production base and a good example of a post-industrial society, Japan ranks ninth. According to the same report Gross Domestic Product per capita for purchasing power parity of the two countries are US$ 6,974 and 26,755 respectively. In the more commonly used Atlas method, the World Bank Gross National Income (GNI) figures for Turkey and Japan in 2001 are US$ 2,540 and 35,990 respectively, placing Turkey in the lower middle income category.[3]

These figures clearly demonstrate the gap between two countries which typify the divide between developing and developed world. Other statistics such as education, health, and technology are no different. It is worth investigating some of the underpinning characteristics of development and under-development along with their effect on the viability of IT production and usage. These issues are explored in the next chapter.

Notes

1   The Janissaries were an elite military corps recruited from ethnic minorities, often Christian, across the Empire. They gradually acquired a powerful role in palace politics.
2   As the leader of all Muslims, it was only the late Ottoman Sultans who attempted to get the support of Muslims around the world when they were struggling to save the Empire from collapsing. Both attempts proved to be futile.
3   See http://www.worldbank.org

Chapter 11

Designing Development: Cultural Consonances in a Post-Cold War Era

Stephen Little with Melih Kirlidog

This chapter uses the comparison of the different development trajectories of Turkey and Japan to set a view of the path-dependence of development against the re-activation of a range of geo-economic alliances suppressed by recent history. The post-Cold War re-emergence of regional and cultural synergies, facilitated by the communication technologies underpinning globalisation, offers the possibility of development pathways based on local understandings. However, planned development policies, whether externally imposed or internally created have not always produced the anticipated results.

The preceding chapter looked at the modernisation attempts of Turkey and Japan as conscious attempts to determine a national path to parity with the pioneer industrialised nations. The notion of a simple continuum with developed countries positioned at one end and developing countries towards the other is challenged by the trajectories and outcomes of the development policies of these two nations. The different outcomes have been determined by cultural and social difference, to the extent that these impact upon the absorptive capacity of each society.

The promotion of a single pathway to development within the current global systems also seems misplaced. The cultural parameters influencing the process of modernisation are equally problematic. This chapter considers whether an individualistic culture is a precondition or a consequence of development. Does industrialisation shift societies from collectivism into individualism?

The 1990s saw the unequivocal end of the Cold War and the removal of barriers arbitrarily created at the cessation of hostilities in World War II. Subsequent political and economic re-alignments, while difficult, have allowed the re-emergence of geo-historical linkages suppressed for half a century or longer. In the Balkans these re-alignments led to the resurrection of earlier conflicts, placed in stasis by external threats. Chapter 2 described how Darrell Delamaide (1995) has identified these linkages in terms of what he describes as "super-regions" across Europe. From this perspective we are witnessing the re-emergence of older international alignments. Delamaide invokes the Hanseatic League and the Holy Roman Empire to explain the re-activation of long dormant trading relationships. The resilience of such links reflects a degree of cultural consonance which is also evident in the relationship between Turkey and the Turkic republics of the former U.S.S.R., reflecting linguistic and cultural ties which preceded the displacement of the Ottomans by the Russian Empire in the nineteenth century.

Geography is History is Geography

The Cold War concept of "Third World" identified a significant proportion of humanity primarily in terms of its exclusion from superpower confrontation. In the regions where colonialism was succeeded by national development, the end of the Cold War has meant reduced attention from the former protagonists. In some respects this has been beneficial, as major confrontations are less frequently played out over third party resources. In many instances it has reduced the flow of resources and technology, albeit often related to militarisation and its infrastructural requirements. Even now the aftermath of externally sponsored conflicts from the Cold War era are still being resolved in Southern Africa.

In many countries now seeking sustainable development, the current relative neglect means that the legacy of post-colonial infrastructures must be tackled with little outside support. Transport and communications networks may offer little synergy with current needs or potential regional development. In many cases existing resources reflect an agenda of resource exploitation, not national development. The route of the railway between the Turkish capital Ankara and Istanbul is a good example of this. Being part of the Istanbul-Baghdad line, it was constructed by a German company and completed in 1892. Its 567-kilometre length reflects the advantageous conditions that had to be granted to the company by the ailing Ottoman Empire: According to the contract, the company could search for and exploit all minerals for a distance of twenty kilometres on both sides of the railway. As a result, the railway was constructed at least 100 kilometres in excess of a direct route. This line is still being used and is the busiest line in Turkey. One could estimate the associated waste of fuel and time over more than a century. A similar situation is reported by

Nyanchama (1995) in Africa where the colonial railway lines transcend regions and lead to the sea without meaningful internal networking. Such a usage of technology manifests itself also in African telecommunications where it is usually much easier to call a European city from Africa than it is to call a neighbouring African capital or town in an adjacent region.

Comparable problems in Eastern Europe reflect the dismantling and division of structures which both pre-date and post-date nineteenth century colonialism. The economic complementarity of the Soviet Union may have served both strategic and nation building objectives, as described in relation to military production in Chapter 9. Now, however, it creates difficulties for the emerging independent states seeking economic self-sufficiency in the CIS and beyond. Elsewhere, however, the regional synergies identified by Delamaide (1994) offer an alternative view of available and potential pathways for development.

Delamaide describes a European political geography going back to the Hanseatic League and the Holy Roman Empire. Delamaide's attribution the patterns of potential development across an enlarging European Community to a range of geo-historical connections suggests that the globalising IT slogan *Geography is History* employed some years ago by British Telecom, should be reversed. Enduring cultural links, whether established through trade, migration or colonisation can be identified throughout the emergent global system. The role of ICTs in supporting diasporas and in ensuring the reliable flow of financial remittances was touched on in Part I and will be revisited in the concluding chapter.

The infrastructures which support such re-emerging links are not simply physical but include the institutional legacy of earlier relationships. For example, Nobes and Parker (1981) present a range of taxonomies of variation in accounting practice across the globe. These relate zones of influence both to the initial development of modern accounting in Scotland and England, its subsequent spread though other Anglophone cultures and the effect of alternative models on the emergence of spheres of influence. It has already been noted that the emergence of English as a global language emphasises the existence of both cultural and linguistic barriers and pathways within the world economy (Crystal, 1997).

Significantly, in India the use of English as a *lingua franca* across the southern states undoubtedly assisted in the emergence of a software industry in the Bangalore region and elsewhere. An institutional legacy which had been derived from British models also eased collaborations with British and North American companies in which key business process are supported on a real-time basis from southern India. Dhillon, Hackney and Ranchod (1998) argue that the benefits of essentially off-shore participation in the global economy are limited for the economy as a whole. However, by the late 1990s, Indian engineers had begun acquiring Asian language skills, particularly Japanese, in order to access these additional markets. The English base has served as a stepping stone and exemplar of the approach needed for participation in a globalising IT industry.

The new information infrastructure presents a number of additional challenges in the development and diffusion of technology and associated standards. Barriers to participation in the formation of a global economy in general and the enabling information technologies in particular, exist in relation to character-sets and their support. Innovations in information technology have been most successful where they were mapped on to existing cultural frameworks, whether at the level of national or business culture. Thus, as noted in Chapter 5, the first "killer application" for end-users, the spreadsheet, provided an electronic version of the twenty column analysis paper already in use in Western economies.

In East Asia computer support for numerical and scientific tasks quickly reached levels comparable with the West, but the lack of support for non-Roman text limited progress in administrative and commercial use. Shepard's (1993) description of the technical complexities of networking in an environment that must move beyond the ASCII standard was also noted in Chapter 5. Technologies that do not need to incorporate a specific character set have been more easily adopted, and Castells and Hall (1994) attribute the refinement and promotion of fax technologies by Japanese companies as evidence of their need to support logographic text. Rather than attempting to overcome cultural barriers, such users have applied available technologies to more directly relevant areas of advantage (Kaye and Little, 2000).

Communications technology includes writing systems. The unique Korean *hangul* script, specifically designed to increase literacy, has both reinforced national identity, and delivered the high levels of literacy which underpinned the rapid industrialisation of South Korea. Across the People's Republic of China the Chinese script continues to serve the purpose of providing a single written expression supporting a wide range of regional dialects and languages in a way that a more phonetic script could not. The process of script reform has produced growing variation between the forms used in mainland China, Taiwan or even Japan. Nevertheless, in applying Delamaide's geo-historical perspective to Greater China, it is obvious that this unique common basis of written language contributes to the continuing regional synergy.

Paradoxically, there ultimately may be some advantage in the different learning trajectory imposed by the delay in the emergence of effective support for non-Western characters. The current changes in business and administrative practices can be incorporated in the new systems now being deployed, and the problem of legacy systems side-stepped. The positive aspects of late adoption were discussed in Part II and this window of opportunity will be re-examined in the concluding chapters.

Societies and Synergies

Synergy is derived from the Greek word *syn-ergos* meaning to work together. In its contemporary usage it is applies to situations where the whole is larger than its parts. It was introduced to social science by Ruth Benedict who was an anthropologist. After her death in 1948 some of her works were published by Abraham Maslow with an introduction of Margaret Mead (Maslow and Honigman, 1970). Benedict's field studies on native tribes, most of which were in North America, led her to categorise them as low synergy and high synergy societies. She argued that each society had a distinct flavour and character which made them dissimilarly functional.

Low synergy societies were anxious, nasty, aggressive, hateful, and insecure. On the opposite side high synergy societies were affectionate, kind, and secure. She also classified the "primitive" societies based on distribution of wealth. In the "funnel system" the wealth created is funnelled into the richest persons of the tribe. This is often accomplished by claiming the labour of others. The rich get richer and the poor get poorer. This results in sustained insecurity for both classes. In the "siphon" system the wealth is constantly channelled away from its greatest concentration and spread to the entire community. This system provides the societies of good will, where murder and suicide are rare or actually unknown. If such societies have periods of great scarcity, all members of the community co-operate to get through these periods as best they can.

Since Benedict's study is based on "primitive" societies with extremely homogenous and small population, one has to exercise caution to apply its findings to today's complex societies of millions. Nevertheless, it is logical that the level of synergy in a society should have some implications for development.

In classical Western economics, Adam Smith's "invisible hand" represents a different form of synergy, where individuals seeking self-interest are guided in such a way that their combined efforts produce wealth for the entire society. In other words, without deliberately pursuing it, individual efforts produce more good than the sum of such efforts. Similar synergy, which is the prerequisite for development, seems to be lacking in many developing countries. Instead, one can argue that efforts of individuals in many of the developing countries usually resemble a zero-sum game where one's gain is the other's loss and little additional wealth is created in such. Moreover, part of the wealth created with dubious procedures is transferred out of the country finds its way to private accounts in Western banks. Such a practice, advantageous only to the banks and the account holders, is common in almost all developing countries including the much publicised Asian success stories in the last four decades. However, it can be argued that an important difference between the "Asian Tigers" and other developing countries is their comparatively egalitarian societies where usually lower-income holders also benefit from the wealth generated (Stiglitz, 2002).

Both Turkey and Japan retain elements of pre-industrial society in terms of the relationship between individuals, families and the state. In the case of Turkey one of the most important factors related to this fact is that individuals tend to identify themselves with their sub-groups more than with the larger society. Responsiveness to one's family, religious group, or fellows from the town of origin is usually more important than responsiveness to the general public. A clannish attitude is further nourished by mass migration from rural areas to cities where individuals must have the support of such sub-groups in order to survive in the jungle-like conditions.

In such an environment people tend to feel free to construct unlicensed homes which constitute more than half of the total dwellings in Istanbul. Most of these homes are constructed on public lands and some of them are equipped with a hook to the nearest power pole for free electricity. In this way entire neighbourhoods can appear in a matter of days. This way of life is clearly a collectivist one where people enjoy the support of their community. However, given that a burden is placed on the entire public, it is clearly a corrupt form of collectivism where synergy is created only for the sub-group to the cost of the greater society. When applied to the greater society, this example resembles Ruth Benedict's low synergy society where acts of individuals or groups are mutually opposing and counteractive. On the other side of the picture is the crucial comfort and support along with almost excellent synergy provided to the individual by his or her sub-group.

In industrial Japan, much of the social infrastructure is provided by community-based voluntary organisations (Ben-Ari, 1991). Membership of a family unit defines citizenship and acts as the basic element of society. However, the strong commitment to national identity, built around a myth of national uniqueness, and often translated into loyalty to an employing organisation, prevents the sub-optimisation evident in Turkey. Japan's industrial organisations still rely on a community sensibility, rather than an economically rational one. Learmount (2002) suggests that this sensibility is the key difference between Japanese and Western corporate governance.

The transformation from the community *(gemeinschaft)* type of social order to society *(gesellschaft)* is one of the aspects of modernisation that comes with industrialisation (Hofstede, 2001). Turkey, still in the process of modernisation, has an important portion of its population in rural areas with backward modes of agricultural production. The majority of the urban population retains strong ties with the rural areas from where they migrated only a few decades ago. Thus, although the majority of the urban population physically lives in urban areas, their behaviour is closer to rural than to urban styles of conduct.

The natural consequence of the culture shock of semi-industrialisation and frustration stemming from inability to access urban resources is the attachment to an immediate community that provides shelter against the alien rather than the greater society that has little to offer. This mechanism is not particular to Turkey, it is pertinent to other comparable developing countries as well. The concluding chapter looks at aspects of modernisation through information and communication technologies which support the retention of community and identity.

Time, Technology and Time-frames

Chapter 8 examined the influence of time-frames. on design trajectories and the determination of design outcomes. It concluded with a brief consideration of the difference in time-frames. between Western and developing contexts. Hall (1989) distinguishes societies as monochronic and polychronic depending on their usage of time and space. In monochronic societies individuals tend to perform one job at a time. Except for "birth and death" all important activities are scheduled to be carried out one after the other without interrupting an unfinished task. Northern Europeans and Northern Americans are monochronic people. Conversely, in polychronic societies such as Middle Easterners and Latin Americans tasks tend to be accomplished simultaneously. Perhaps with the exception of tasks which are prerequisite in nature, it is not necessary to finish a task to start another one. What is important is to accomplish the task, whether or not to schedule. This type of behaviour commits less emphasis to time-keeping than monochronic societies. Hall has observed that shopkeepers try to serve all their customers simultaneously in polychronic societies and the difficulty of adhering to appointments in such societies impacts on cross-cultural working.

An analogy could be made between monochronic societies where time and space are compartmentalised and von Neumann architecture which constitutes the basic principles of computers. According to this concept computers process one task at a time and they have compartmentalised sub-systems which perform different tasks. However, this analogy should not be stretched to argue that computers and information technologies can only be developed and used effectively in monochronic societies. Current massively parallel supercomputers, with their ability to perform tasks simultaneously, bear a closer resemblance to polychronic societies than monochronic ones and the virtual adjacencies created by networked relationships impact on perceptions of both time and space.

Communication and Context

Hall (1989) distinguishes messages conveyed between individuals and groups according to their level of context. According to this taxonomy a low context message or communication is one which carries the mass of the information explicitly. At the other end of the spectrum stand high context messages where the bulk of the information is either in the physical context or already internalised by the participating individuals. Low context communication is direct and explicit whereas high context communication is indirect and implicit. Hall goes on to contend that individual cultures can be positioned in the spectrum of high to low context. Germans and Scandinavians are at the low context end of the spectrum and Chinese are at the opposite end with proximity to Arabs and some Mediterranean cultures as well as to Japan.

Information and communication technologies, by their exact and extremely explicit mode of internal and external interaction, are good examples of low context communication. Although their exactness and explicitness can be used to develop applications such as fuzzy logic which is imprecise in nature, there is no room for ambiguity in the message exchange within the computer. Extreme precision and thoroughly explicit coding are the most important characteristics of a computer system. The computer, in its current form, does not need to know the background and context of a message conveyed internally and externally.

Since computers are products of the Western world, industrialised and usually low context in nature, could there be a cause-result relationship among these three concepts? Can it be argued that industrialisation led to diminishing context in the communication among individuals and this in turn provided a ground for the invention of the computer? To what extent did the industrialisation impose machine-like behaviour on humans? Or should it be argued that the Northern European societies where industrialisation flourished were already low context societies three or more centuries ago? The former is more plausible; the requirements of industrialisation influenced individuals towards more machine-like behaviour, stripping context from communication, and conveying their messages to each other in exact and direct terms. The twentieth century trajectory of scientific management described in Part I certainly fits this model.

Japan, as usual in such cultural comparisons, seems to be an exception which supports this argument. The pressures for institutional change which emanate from Western competitors and trading partners amount to a demand for a move towards a lower context culture. Following the theory, this is also true for countries like Turkey whose modernisation attempts lag Japan.

The second part of the question also awaits an answer. Has the low context behaviour of individuals had a catalysing affect on the development of computer-based information systems? Certainly the key insights into communication theory presented by Shannon and Weaver (1949) are based on a highly disembedded and technical understanding of communication. Even if the answer to this question is yes, one must not overlook the fact that the invention culture that comes with industrialisation is a whole and it affects and is affected by not only the mode of communication, but the entire spectrum of human behaviour. The immediate practical concerns of cryptography and nuclear energy were discussed as catalysts for the invention of the computer in Chapter 3.

Abstraction and Representation

Although seemingly trivial, an important difference between East and West is the employment of perspective in paintings. Quoting Ramos (1981), Sargut (2001) argues that perspective started in Western painting with the Renaissance and its importance extends far beyond art. In the middle of the second millennium Western societies have been through a transformation whereby two important developments occurred. Both of these developments are related with the usage of reason and they have been the keys for the Western societies to understand and interpret nature in such a way that the future industrial revolution and unprecedented steps in civilisation would be realised. Unlike the Eastern individual who comprehended nature "as is", the Western enlightenment facilitated the encryption and abstraction of concepts and events. Encryption reduced the amount of information to be processed and abstracting provided the information to be processed systematically.

These two concepts seem to be prerequisite not only for analysing, but also for changing the world. The first of them was to get the *real* picture of the world instead of the raw image. To this end, abstraction or encryption was used where necessary. The second was to shape nature according to human will. With perspective, this involves the introduction of some encryption that confers feeling of reality and depth to the paintings. It could be argued that it was an unconscious reflection to the art resulting from the unprecedented changes in the material world.

Apparently content with God's creation "as is" and thus having little motivation for changing the world, Eastern people of the period probably had a lower level of encryption and abstraction for events and objects. Possibly related to this, Eastern miniatures did not have perspective. Orhan Pamuk's (2001) novel *My Name is Red* vividly narrates the tension among the miniaturists of sixteenth century Istanbul, capital of the superpower of the age. Admiring the method of perspective favoured by Venetian masters, some miniaturists tend to import it while some others eagerly defend the traditional ways. Iranian miniatures and Japanese paintings also did not have perspective. It was later introduced to Japan by Dutch painters.

The higher level of encryption and abstraction, probably the most important enablers of the enlightenment, had more tangible consequences in science. The advance of Western science was realised by these two concepts which facilitated application of new methods to sophisticated theoretical and practical problems as well as tool production and usage. Chapter 7 associates the development of clock-based time with the emergence of capitalism in the West. It is striking that Ottomans, who prayed five times at strict and varying times of the day, did not produce nor extensively use clocks until the nineteenth century. In Japan the mechanical clock was probably introduced in 1551 (Morris-Suzuki, 1994). Considerable ingenuity was used to adapt it to the Japanese system in which the daylight hours were divided into six equal periods, followed by six equal periods of darkness, regardless of the season.

The lack of adoption by the Ottomans of such an important and useful tool for the practice of religion cannot go unnoticed, given the very close ties, sometimes hostile and sometimes friendly, with the West. The absence of clocks cannot be explained by the lack of trade either, because there has always been a vibrant trade with the West exchanging all kinds of raw materials and finished products. The lack of culture of technology and disinterest in technological products except for weaponry and other military needs seems to be the cause. The continued usage of caravans in highway transportation instead of animal powered carts and thereby comparably less usage of the wheel can also be placed in this context.

A lower level of abstraction, possibly deeply rooted in the collective psyche, manifests itself in the contemporary Turkish society as the preference of verbal communication as opposed to written communication. Although both speech and writing could both be regarded as abstraction mechanisms, writing clearly involves a higher degree and is a more advanced and enduring form of communication that has a binding effect for parties. According to the Human Development Report of UNDP (2002) 14.9 percent of the Turkish population of 15 years and older is still illiterate. The same report ranks Turkey first in the number of cellular mobile subscribers and fifth in telephone mainlines among eighty-four Medium Human Development countries in the year 2000 (UNDP, 2002). However, the total circulation of daily newspapers is about three million for a population of sixty-seven million and albeit the existence of a narrow but vivid intellectual milieu, a typical book edition does not exceed two thousand copies. These numbers clearly indicate an inclination towards verbal culture which is reinforced by economic difficulties.

In contemporary Turkish society the lower level of abstraction manifests itself frequently in daily life. An example is the usage of spatial direction. Although not inexistent, it is not common to use the terms such as Northern Ankara or Western Istanbul to designate a region or suburb. Instead of using these abstracted terms of direction, it is usually preferred to use the name of the suburbs or regions "as is".

An inclination towards verbal culture has not been an encouraging factor for the development and usage of the information technologies at the centre of the economic development process. By definition, developing a computer program requires an extremely high degree of abstraction that involves symbolising tangible entities and events with intangible codes and program statements.

The implementation of computer applications in an organisational setting involves some degree of substitution of face to face communication with the computer's written interaction and is little supported by the preferred verbal communication habits of some societies. However, these cultural attributes may be less significant that the resistance, open or concealed, in response to poor software and technical support generally, the substitution of computers for jobs, or technophobia as a combined effect of advanced age and computer illiteracy. On the contrary, computerisation is usually eagerly welcomed by organisational members who perceive it as a must for their career. The reverse effect of verbal culture on the diffusion of IT could better be explained by the fact that it has a slackening and retarding nature on the process, which means that usually a higher degree of effort and more time is required for IT implementation in such cultures.

Verbal versus written culture seems to be related to industrialisation and "development". In particular industrialisation, where immense memory requirements are necessary, must have profoundly affected an apparent transformation from verbal to written culture. In discussing automation and informatisation, Zuboff (1988) quotes Clanchy (1979) who has illustrated the reluctant acceptance of written documentation in place of verbal agreement in the West. This process took over three centuries of early English history.

Individualism, Collectivism and Virtual Collaboration

Part II looked at culture at the professional, organisational and institutional level. In *Culture's Consequences* Hofstede (2001) distinguished five (four in the previous edition of the book) bi-polar dimensions of national culture. Although that book drew a great deal of debate and criticism some of which are reasonably convincing, (McSweeney, 2002) it is still regarded as a classic text in inter-cultural research. According to Hofstede's model the bi-polar dimensions are the measures of individualism versus collectivism (I-C), power distance, uncertainty avoidance, masculinity versus femininity, and long versus short term orientation. In individualistic cultures, the emphasis is on individuals; everyone is regarded as responsible for their own actions and rewarded or punished for what they have done, or not done. Consequently, self-reliance and independence are seen as key values for life. In contrast, collectivist cultures emphasise collective behaviour and values. The I-C measure could be an important key to the evolution of Turkish and Japanese societies over the last one and a half centuries.

Industrialised countries usually have a higher score and non-industrialised ones usually have a lower score in the index. Thus the I-C measure may provide a rough measure of a country's position in relation to its development process. Like almost all Eastern cultures Turkish and Japanese cultures are regarded as collectivist, rather than individualistic. This is more so for Turkish culture which has a score of 37 in the index. Japan's score is 46 which is somewhere between highly collectivist and highly individualistic cultures. This is to be expected, since Japan provides an example of successful transformation from a traditional society to an industrialised one in a short span of time. Its position in the middle of the I-C measure is expressive, because it reflects both the overwhelming traditional roots which are still so alive in that country alongside its completed industrialisation process. Its middle position is an indication of its late industrialisation.

Like most types of advanced technology, diffusion of IT to developing countries creates some turbulence which results from the fact that different cultural approaches have to co-exist in the same country, same region, and even the same organisation. Some concepts of IT which are regarded so natural in individualistic cultures where information technologies are produced may not be so in some other cultures. During the consultation experience of an Enterprise Resource Planning (ERP) implementation in a multinational operating in Turkey, Kirlidog (1997) observed that the staff in headquarters kept their passwords secret. However, using passwords to log in to the system was an unnecessary nuisance for lower rank and less educated shop floor personnel who wrote their passwords on the notice board "to be used in case they are not around". Contrary to the well educated and thereby relatively individualistic HQ personnel, keeping a password to oneself was regarded as paranoia or arrogance in the collectivist environment of the shop floor personnel. This type of dichotomy, indigenous and exogenous cultures as observed by Kaye and Little (2000), is common in Turkey with deep cultural roots in the East, but a strong commitment to an orientation towards the West.

The concluding chapter moves away from an examination of the pathways of development at the level of the nation state to examine forms of bottom up engagement with the current socio-technical disposition of the global economy. These new forms of engagement suggest the emergence of forms of collaboration which offer a bridge between both locations and cultures.

Chapter 12

Through the Window or Through the Looking Glass: Prospects for Greater Equity in Development

This book has argued that information and communication technologies underpin an emerging global system of production and consumption of material and human resources (Castells, 1996; Bello, 1999). Part I argued that information and communication technologies have transformed production chains into a networks linking the complementary comparative advantage of sets of physical locations (Dicken, 1998). Choices in development paths become in a large part determined by the relationship of an economy or region to the global system, which in turn depends upon an ability to acquire or appropriate the key technologies. In the past the terms of availability have been dictated by the originators. However, the shift from wired to satellite infrastructure has disrupted the top-down hierarchical management of the distribution of resources. While the wireless technologies appear to offer access to the "information economy" to peripheral areas, to be of use the technology also must be accessible in a mature and robust form capable of appropriate adaptation to specific situations and needs.

The extent to which "windows of opportunity" can be kept open and exploited becomes central to an understanding of exclusion and inclusion. The cost of acquisition of relevant technologies is a fraction of the cost of their design and development. The marginal cost of connection becomes affordable to groups that are remote, either geographically or economically from the source of the technology. The cost advantage of wireless technologies becomes obvious when compared with the cost of alternative conventional, fixed terrestrial structures. However, there remains the need for local understanding of the technology, and appropriate styles of use. Such understanding requires experiential learning (Sproull and Kiesler, 1991). Without this the limited resources at the margins may be channelled into models that have been created in developed settings and which deliver comparatively little local benefit.

Here and Now: Time, Space and Exclusion in the New Dispensation

Part I of the book introduced the nature of the emerging global context formed in the post-Cold War period. The neo-liberal agenda which displaced Keynesian models of development offers little more benefit to the periphery than the direct colonial relationships of the past. However, the critical role of information and communication technologies does distinguish the present form of globalisation from earlier forms of internationalisation. The dynamic of the emerging global economy was characterised as a web which overthrows the traditional spatial hierarchy of colonial trade and sets core and periphery in a new form of adjacency.

Part I looked at the characteristics of an emerging global system, noting that the ability to separate production from consumption through the new electronic adjacencies led Lipietz (1992) to argue that this signals the end of the "Fordist compromise". Production workers remote from the destination market are often denied access to the products of their own labour. Their partial inclusion in the system becomes an issue of control as much as of contribution; inevitably the infrastructure created to support this status is optimised to the requirements of the core of the dominant triad of developed economies, not its periphery.

Castell's (1996) *creative milieu* and *network enterprise* were discussed in Part I as models of the new forms of connectivity and collectivity. Arguments for the acknowledgment of complementary regional associations in contrast to national boundaries from Ohmae (1995) and Delamaide (1994) were also introduced.

Part I concluded with an argument that prospective shifts in technology offer windows of opportunity for countries and regions disadvantaged by the current distribution of communication infrastructure to make up considerable ground by leapfrogging over the critical gap between the wired and unwired worlds.

An early example was the work of the Centre Mondial Informatique et Ressources Humaines in Saharan and sub-Saharan Africa discussed in Chapter 5 in which solar powered lap-top technology was deployed in Saharan Africa (Roper, 1983). Satellite linked, solar powered, hand-held technologies are now in use amongst the illiterate bushmen of South Africa (Little, Holmes and Grieco, 2001). The Cybertracker system enables the bushmen of the Kalahari to instantaneously transmit information about their environment beyond their local boundaries.

Chapter 5 described how at the end of the twentieth century there was a shift of communications from geostationary Earth orbit (GEO) to medium Earth orbit (MEO) and low Earth orbit (LEO) satellites. This technical change leapfrogged over the chronic infrastructure deficit of less developed regions (Price-Waterhouse, 1998). Existing communications infrastructure has become potentially obsolete and 3.9 billion people judged to have no telecommunications access entered the same communication space as the most affluent users of mobile communications technologies.

The development potential of this technology has yet to be exploited fully, and it remains targeted at specialist and premium users. Nevertheless, the infrastructure has been put in place and a paradigm established. Other, simpler, incremental technologies have filled the critical gap in potential networks. WiFi (wireless high fidelity) networking technology was developed to allow flexible wireless computer networking within buildings and across compact sites. It has quickly been adapted to bridge the critical last link between unwired households and communities and the fast Internet. By replacing omni-directional aerials with directional antennae, significant distances can be covered.[1] In South Africa, the same level of ingenuity has bridged this gap with a physical courier system between schools and Internet access points.[2]

Another key technology, complementary to satellite communication is the global positioning system (GPS) described in Part I. In commercial terms, this has fared better than the satellite phones which are competing with an extensive infrastructure and user-base for established technologies in the wealthiest regions. The European Union is committed to the development and deployment of the *Galileo* system, a high-resolution civil system, a contrast to the current U.S. provision of degraded military signals. Significantly China has chosen to buy into this system as a prime user (People's Daily, 2003), with a number of applications directed to the support of development in the remoter provinces.

The question of what can be achieved by marginal players in terms of influence over an emerging global "techno-economic paradigm" (Dosi, 1986) is crucial for both smaller nation states and sub-national regions. The "window of opportunity" metaphor from Part I can be used to evaluate the consequences of shifts in the definitions of centre and periphery in the global economy and shifts in the nature of exclusion from that economy. This concluding chapter re-examines physical and virtual access to resources and technology, and the ability of marginal players to adjust to changes in emphasis by mainstream players. Some characteristics of robust networking and association are derived from examples of grassroots virtual organisation and a guerrilla paradigm of access.

Frames and Paradigms: Open and Closed

Part II presented a design paradigm as a means of understanding the choices and trade-offs confronting individuals, groups and cultures wishing to define their relationship to the emergent global system. The closing chapter of Part II described the strong influence of military technology on the determination of such choices. Failures in complex military technology were used to characterise a technocratic top-down and convergent approach to design, both in development and application.

The consequences of a top-down positivist view of systems and processes is analysed by Johnson (2002). He argues that an approach to international relations driven by military superiority and capability has become self-defeating for the United States. It has created a situation of "blowback" in which interventions intended to resolve instability simply engender a further cycle of disruption in response. Once military capability is identified as a nation's unique advantage, the most complex situations appear to be amenable to solution through the threat or use of military force. Lindqvist (2001) demonstrates the persistence of a technocratic, positivist view of the efficacy of aerial warfare, in the face of all evidence to the contrary.

The approach of the military and civilian bureaucracies and technocracies described in Part II is reflected within the Bretton Woods universe of large international institutions. The potential and possibilities offered by the Internet have been framed within this mode. For example, the development gateway established by the World Bank contrasts with the peer-to-peer models of interaction emerging from the activities of non governmental organisations (NGOs), and others that share grass-roots origins. Criticism of the development portal has been in terms of its closed view and gate-keeping potential in a situation in which the diversity generated in the divergent stage of design (Jones, 1980) is needed.

National governments share a similar view of "e-government". The accessibility of the Internet has been seen as an interface between the citizen and the government, rather than a space in which negotiation and adjustment can take place. Some alternative, grassroots approaches to e-governance are described below, but there is one striking example of inclusion for a particularly remote community. As mentioned earlier, the bushmen of the Kalahari, by touching an icon on the screen of the hand-held set or by drafting of an animal form, deliver important environmental management data to a receiving agency. The same technology could be used in the provision of services and extension of political participation for remote and otherwise un-connected communities.

Interestingly, open and inclusive models of intervention and development are being created by the developers of the core information technologies themselves. The rise of the Open Software Foundation (OSF) and its co-operative approach provides a contrast to the centralised Microsoft model of commercial software development. The OSF provides a paradigm of collective decision-making at the core of the global economy's enabling technology. For the Microsoft approach Raymond (2001) uses the metaphor of the cathedral in which a multitude of skilled workers pursue an integrated vision. He contrasts this with the metaphor of the bazaar in which an open community of developers trades experience and software for mutual and separate ends over the Internet. This collaborative model of shared practice and experience echoes the non-technical communities which have also made use of the web as a space in which to share collective experience and develop collective skills with which to engage a remotely determined status quo.

Open software development (OSD) means that the products are both affordable, and amenable to adjustment and development in line with local conditions and with local resources. Such adjustments allow services to be both more closely relevant to the end users, and more robust in terms of their cultural consonance with local practices. This is in marked contrast to the dominant Microsoft model of commercial development within the United States. Minority language communities may never be provided with a version of the software (and this is only ever likely to be a direct word-for-word translation of pre-existing menus). In some cases they have also been denied access to source code to fund and provide this adaptation for themselves. Communities of software developers committed to the open development of flexible and affordable technology have appeared in both developed and developing regions.[3]

Designing Places in the World: Getting There from Here

Part III opens with a comparison of two different historical paths of development, each representing the efforts of a country which was consciously trying to emulate the established industrialised nations. The accounts, covering the nineteenth and twentieth centuries, show that no single convergent pathway to development is likely to exist in the twenty-first century.

Current shifts in technology offer a window of opportunity for countries and regions disadvantaged by the current distribution of communication infrastructure. Those excluded from the benefits of the global economy are often those paying its greatest social and economic costs. In response the excluded are utilising the very information and communication technologies that facilitates the system under criticism. If, however, they are to make up significant ground, if not to catch up with the leaders, then the removal of the barrier of physical and technical infrastructure must be followed by engagement with the problems of social and institutional infrastructures.

The interaction between social space and technical infrastructure in the globalising economy produces new adjacencies which cut across the divide between included and excluded regions. These virtual adjacencies produce patterns of both divergence and convergence. Previously separate spheres of activity, such as the white collar work of Western Europe and South India have been drawn into contact, if not direct competition. Equally the distinction between public and domestic space has been eroded.

The current Western understanding of the nature of the household is a product of the relatively recent past, reflecting the intense effort put into orderly displacement of women from paid industrial labour at the conclusion of the Second World War. In the post-war period the nuclear family became the focus of an emerging consumer ethos and the role of female household members was associated with domestic consumption rather than public production.

In the Western economies, the process of the separation of the domestic and productive spheres began with the onset of the factory system during the industrial revolution. This was never completed. The modern household as understood in the West is a recent stage in a broad process of separation of paid employment and home life. The new electronic adjacencies have been brought into the household by connection to the infrastructure of globalisation. As a result the division between public and private spheres has become more permeable.[4]

As a consequence in the West the post-industrial household is re-acquiring features of the pre-industrial household. With the post-Fordist loss of secure employment and the introduction of "portfolio" working, the home becomes once again a locus of production, distinct from the public sphere of "work" which emerged with the onset of the industrial revolution. The state has taken a hand in this process with the option of electronic tagging and home confinement to displace the task of imprisonment to the family.[5]

The industrial home was presented as a support structure for paid male employment conducted elsewhere. The gendering of activity within the household, enshrined in the U.K. housing design guides, was reinforced by a gendering of the technical artefacts themselves. "White goods" can be seen as gendered around "housework" and the female sphere, "brown goods" may be seen as associated with male recreational pursuits within the home.

This model of the industrial household has been largely adopted in the industrialising countries of East Asia. Current middle class developments around Shanghai would not look out of place in suburban California. In areas of weaker economic activity, however, the interpenetration of economic core and periphery described in Part I can be illustrated by the growth of outworking within the urban cores of cities such as London, Manchester, Melbourne and Sydney. The textile and clothing industry at the core of the first industrial revolution now relies upon outworking and home-working to compete with lower wage economies.[6]

As electronic communication becomes an increasingly effective substitute for physical movement, the use of remoter locations increases, and the level and sophistication of work now relocated to South Asia or the Caribbean from Europe or North America continues to grow.[7]

Marvin's (1988) description of the social learning curve associated with the introduction of new electrically-based technologies at the turn of the nineteenth century and the social learning identified by Sproull and Kiesler (1991) suggest that we are likely to see this practical learning process continuing for some time. What is clear is that an alternative paradigm in support of development will not emerge without input from the grass-roots.

Learning and Networking: A Vygotskiian View of the World Wide Web

In Part I the need for a process of organisational learning to move beyond the technical effects of direct substitution of information technology for manual processes was introduced (Sproull and Kiesler, 1991). Chapter 3 introduced a range of influences on design methods and understandings, including the socio-technical systems view which represented a significant change from the view that the introduction of technology was a neutral process leading to predictable outcomes.

In a global system of technical development, standards are necessary for interoperability at each level of interaction within and between organisations and locations. O'Hara-Devereaux and Johansen (1994) argue that differences between work cultures, both professional and corporate, and the national or regional culture in which an organisation is embedded can be bridged in a "thirdspace". For them the synergy between levels is a potential resource, but the tendency towards a convergence determined by a dominant culture is seen as an obstacle to cross-cultural working.

Actor-Network Theory was introduced in Part I as an example of how this view might be incorporated into a design approach that could accommodate the parameters of "wicked problems" set out by Rittel and Webber. This offers a treatment of the human and technical components of a system in a way that avoids either technical determinism or a purely socially determined explanation.

Actor-Network Theory provides an analysis of extant systems to guide the design and development progress. An alternative, Activity Theory, is based on a theory of psychology that provides a framework for assessing the interaction between humans and technical systems through time. Kutti (1991) gives an account of the potential for this approach within information systems research and development.

Activity Theory is a Vygotskian framework for assessing the interaction between humans and technical systems. Its introduction into information systems research at the end of the 1980s represents a tangible aspect of the Cold War "peace dividend", when numbers of Soviet trained psychologists brought the methodology to the West via Scandinavia.

Activity theory has had greatest influence in the areas of learning and developmental psychology (e.g. Cole, 1985). It also offers an insight into design and development. The key concept of value to the issues addressed in this book is the "zone of proximal development" that is a supportive framework for learning and development. In the case of IS design, such a framework may be provided by the technical solution to hand. In terms of "thirdspace" (O'Hara-Devereaux and Johansen, 1994) this framework can be created in a virtual space within the ICT infrastructure.

Information and communication technology introduces new social practices and social patterns. The voice of the small social and political unit can now gain volume through co-operation and communication within the institutional capabilities of the new ICTs (Little, Holmes and Grieco, 2000). Ensuring that technologies appropriate for small and remote locations emerge must be a priority. Such technologies require the engagement of other users and beneficiaries.

Developing new practices and new knowledge has required proximity or adjacency to others who hold a relevant set of skills and interests The physical adjacency necessary in the past can increasingly be supported or replaced by electronic forms of adjacency. The OSF model demonstrates this is highly effective in a technically skilled professional community. However, the paradigm has a wider relevance. Sufficient skills for effective use of the Internet in support of advocacy and communication can be acquired relatively simply and collectively. This process of skilling can draw on extensive experience with electronically supported distance education and the "e-mentoring" techniques enumerated by Salmon (2000).

The support of Internet technologies allows the maintenance of community and identity described by Miller and Slater (2000) in the case of Trinidadians. The benefits of a migrant link-up to the community net of the place of origin are many: with the establishment of an efficient micro-banking system linked to a community network funds can be readily transferred from migrants in the wealthier location back to their home site. The reliable remittance of funds through an micro-banking systems, such as the Grameen system in Bangladesh (Yunus, 1999) ensures that externally generated resources are returned to the home location for development purposes (Little, Holmes and Grieco, 2000).

In Ghana, both cultural and commercial sites maintain the contact with home and provide a family-based reliable infrastructure for access to wealthy markets by Ghanaian[8] goods for the continuing support of that identity in North America.

The Self Employed Women's Association in India makes use of the World Wide Web to promote its cause of advancing the interests and improving the situation of poor women.[9] The Grameen Bank has extended its activities to the support of communication technologies for poor village women as part of their empowerment.[10] This gives the women an ability to check on market prices and to better organise their finances and production. Elsewhere fishermen user the technology to check market prices before landing their catches.

The new electronic form of adjacency is critical to the development of new development practices and knowledge. The new technology creates the opportunity for individuals and agencies which are physically distant from one another to be in real time public contact with one another: it is a new collective form of social contact. Electronic adjacency permits instantaneous interaction between distant individuals: new forms of knowledge are generated in this new interactive practice, though social and political theorists have been slow to document and analyse this new social state (Carter and Greico, 2000). The speed and ease of new communication over distance enables the collecting together of views and opinions which were historically fragmented and disparate. Crucially, the transparency of this discourse permits the opportunity for those who were historically excluded from decision making to enter core domains. Such transparency is crucial, for example in the defence of indigenous knowledge which is increasingly under threat from Western corporations seeking to create intellectual property rights over traditional practices (Chataway et al, 2003). Traditional practices are now being archived on the World Wide Web so that they can both be shared and protected.[11]

Re-balancing Development: The Role of Information and Communication Technologies

This concluding chapter has drawn together examples and counter examples of struggles and achievements at the periphery of the globalising economy. These demonstrate the responses to the exclusion from the benefits of the global economy of those paying its greatest social and economic costs. They utilise the very information and communication technologies that facilitates the system under criticism. Examples of this access were used to challenge definitions of centre and periphery in the global economy and to identify shifts in the nature of exclusion from that economy. Physical and virtual access to resources and technology, and the vulnerability of marginal players to changes in emphasis by mainstream players were introduced in earlier chapters. Robust approaches to networking and association from extant examples of virtual organisation represent a guerrilla paradigm of activities. This is literally true in the case of the Zapatista movement, but equally applicable to the political mobilisation that has taken place around the very issues of globalisation.[12]

The grassroots response to top down prescriptions also provides an opportunity to close the loop of e-governance and to provide quality real-time feedback on the consequences of policy decisions made by governments[13] In North East England community groups have used both hand-held communication and positioning devices to log the performance of public transport and to record performance on web sites close to real-time.[14] This closes the loop of e-governance and provides clear evidence of policy failure, or success to policy makers.

Such an action-based research approach offers new prospects for both the evaluation and development of information systems themselves, and the maintenance of support from across the affected community.

In the Indian sub-continent e-governance is being approached from both top level government and local community levels. These coalesce in Pondicherry, where a hub-and-spoke model of data and communication has been established for six villages.[15] The villages can communicate with each other as well as to the Internet. Dial-up Internet connection is accessed by a variety of wired and wireless paths, utilising solar power. A major objective is ownership at the village level, with support available from the hub.

Elsewhere in India the issue of robust and affordable technical platforms suitable for such environments has been tackled through the development of the Simputer,[16] a robust low-cost hand-held solar powered device suitable for non-literate users. Even this low cost device must be shared around a village community, and commercial smart card technology has been used to provide a cheap and robust means of securely storing individual data away from the device.

Early applications for the Simputer include the field collection of information on crops under cultivation for the government of Karnataka and the support of mobile applications for micro-finance institutions.

Even deeper into the margins of the global system, SELF[17] is delivering photo-voltaic solar power and wireless communication to remote communities in the Amazon basin, following on from similar projects in East and South Asia and sub-Saharan Africa.

This concluding chapter gives some indication of the wide range of communities engaged in the design and development of new social-technical systems. These initiatives are evidence of the determination and commitment of a diverse coalition of activists to the collective design of a paradigm that eliminates the digital divide between centre and periphery in a still contested global system.

Notes

1 I am grateful to Alan Levy for drawing my attention to the wider significance of this robust and affordable technology.
   See his comments at http://www.bytesforall.org/9th/html/matching_wifi.htm
2 See http://www.wizzy.co.za for a description of the Wizzy Courier service.
3 See www.bytesforall.org for a South Asian on-line community.
4 For a fuller discussion of the "networked household" see Little (2000).

5   See Aungles (1994) for a detailed account of the impact of this responsibility upon families.
6   See for example Greig (1991) for a description of the textile, clothing and footwear industry in Australia.
7   See Sheller (2003) for a detailed account of the impact of these relationships on the Caribbean.
8   See http://www.ghaclad.org for examples.
9   See http://www.sewa.org/
10 See http://www.grameenfoundation.org/
11 See http://www.unesco.org/most/bpikreg.htm
12 See http://www.nologo.org which acts as a portal to a wide range of on-line activism.
13 See http://www.newnet.org.uk/neat/monitor/ and http://www.geocities.com/north_east_age for examples of such real-time monitoring.
14 See http://www.goneat.org
15 See http://www.mssrf.org/informationvillage/assessment.htm
16 See http://www.simputer.org
17 See http://www.self.org

Bibliography

Abbate J. (2000) 'Virtual Nation-Building in Estonia: Reshaping Space, Place, and Identity in a Newly Independent State' Paper presented at *Virtual Society? Get Real! Conference*, Ashridge House, Hertfordshire May 2000.

Aikin M. and Hage J. (1971) 'The organic organisation and innovation' *Sociology* Vol.5 pp.68-82.

Air International (1977) 'Jet Jubilee' *Air International* Vol.12, No.4, April pp.171-180.

Airliner World (2001) 'A320 – the family grows' *Airliner World Special: Airbus Jetliners – the European solution* pp.28-37.

Akin W.E. (1977) *Technocracy and the American Dream: the Technocrat Movement 1900-1941* Berkeley: University of California Press.

Aksin S. (1988) 'Siyasal Tarih' in *Turkiye Tarihi* 3. cilt Cem Yayinevi *('Political History' in 'History of Turkey' Vol 3)*.

Alexander C. (1964) *Notes on the synthesis of form* Cambridge: M.I.T. Press.

Alexander C. (1965) 'A city is not a tree' *Architectural Forum*, April-May 1965, pp.58-62.

Alexander C. (1977) *A Pattern Language* New York: Oxford University Press.

Alexander C. (1979) *The Timeless Way of Building* New York: Oxford University Press.

Argyris C. and Schön D. (1974) *Theory in practice: Increasing professional effectiveness* San Francisco: Jossey-Bass.

Armacost M.H. (1985) 'The Thor-Jupiter Controversy' in D. McKenzie and J. Wacjman *The Social Shaping of Technology* (1st edn) Milton Keynes: Open University Press.

Arnold E. and Senker S. (1982) 'Designing the future: the implications of CAD interactive graphics for employment and skills in the British engineering industry' EITB Occasional Paper 9, Guildford.

Art R.J. (1968) *The TFX Decision* New York: Little, Brown.

Attali J. (1991) *Millennium: Winners and Losers in the Coming World Order* New York: Times Books, Random House.

Augustine N.R. (1975) 'One Plane, One Tank, One Ship: Trend for the Future?' *Defense Management Journal* Vol.11, pp.34-40.

Aungles A. (1992) 'Electronic Surveillance and Organisational Boundaries: the Home as the Prison' in S. Aungles (ed) *Information Technology in Australia* Kensington: University of New South Wales Press.

Aungles A. (1994) *The Prison and the Home: A Study of the Relationship Between Domesticity and Penality,* Monograph No.5, Sydney: The Institute of Criminology.

Aungles A. (1995) 'Globalisation and Domestication in the Field of Penal Surveillance' Paper presented to Surveillance Conference, University of Wollongong, November 1995.

Avison D. E., Wood-Harper A. T., Vidgen R. T. and Wood J. R. G. (1998) 'A Further Exploration into Information Systems Development: the evolution of Multiview 2' *Information Technology and People*, Vol.11 No.2.

Bamford J. (1983) *The Puzzle Palace inside the National Security Agency, America's most secret intelligence organisation* New York: Viking Penguin.

Banham R. (1960) *Theory and Design in the First Machine Age* London: Architectural Press.

Banham R. (1969) *The Architecture of the Well-tempered Environment* London: Architectural Press.

Bastiaanssen W.G.M. (1998) *Remote Sensing in Water Resources Management: The State of the Art* Colombo: International Water Management Institute (IWMI) Publications.

Bell D. (1979) 'The social framework of the information society' in M.L. Dertouzos and J. Moses (eds) *The Computer-Age: a twenty year view* Cambridge: MIT Press.

Bello W. (1999) *Dark Victory. The United States, Structural Adjustment and Global Poverty* (2nd edn) (with S. Cunningham and W. Rau) Amsterdam/ London: TNI/Pluto Press.

Belussi F. (1989) 'Benetton: a case study of corporate strategy for innovation in traditional sectors' in M. Dodgson (ed) *Technology Strategies and the Firm: Management and Public Policy* London: Longman.

Ben-Ari E. (1991) *Changing Japanese Suburbia* London: Kegan Paul International.

Benedikt M. (ed) (1991) *Cyberspace, first steps* Cambridge: MIT Press.

Bennet N. (1997) 'ICI offers £1bn for Unilever arm' *Sunday Telegraph* 6 April.

Bijker W. and Law J. (eds) (1994) *Shaping technology/building society: studies in sociotechnical change*, Cambridge: MIT Press.

Birrell N.D. and Ould M.A. (1985) *A Practical Handbook for Software Development* Cambridge: Cambridge University Press.

Boje D.M., Fedor D.B., and Rowland K.M. (1982) 'Myth-making: a qualitative step in OD interventions' *Applied Behavioral Sciences* Vol.18 No.1 pp.17-28.

Bowcott O. and Hamilton S. (1990) *Beating the system: hackers, phreakers and electronic spies* London: Bloomsbury.

Brookes A. (2003) 'Future fighters' *Air International* June 2003, pp.18-22.

Brooks R. (1975) *The Mythical Man-month* Reading: Addison-Wesley.

Brown T. (2001) 'Skunk Works as a sign of failure' Paper presented at *The Future of Innovation Studies* Conference, Eindhoven Centre for Innovation Studies, September 2001.

Brown W. and Jaques E. (1965) *Glacier Project Papers: some essays on organisation and management from the Glacier Project Research* London: Heinemann.

Brubaker R. (1984) *The limits of rationality: an essay on the social and moral thought of Max Weber* London: George Allen and Unwin.

Brunner J. (1975) *The Shockwave Rider* London: Dent.

Bruntland G (ed) (1987). *Our Common Future: The World Commission on Environment and Development* Oxford: Oxford University Press.

Buchanan D. and Boddy D. (1983) *Organizations in the Computer Age: Technological imperatives and strategic choice* Aldershot: Gower.

Burrows W.E. (2001) *By any means necessary: America's secret air war* Farrer, New York: Straus and Giroux.

CAIB (2003) *Report of the Columbia Accident Investigation Board* Washington: U.S. Government Printing Office.

Callon M. and Latour B. (1992) 'Don't throw the baby out with the bath water: a reply to Collins and Yearley' in A. Pickering (ed) *Science as Practice and Culture* Chicago: University of Chicago Press.

Camilleri J.A. and Falk J. (1992) *The End of Sovereignty? The Politics of a Shrinking and Fragmented World* Aldershot: Edward Elgar.

Canter D. (1977) *The Psychology of Space London*: London: Architectural Press.

Carter C. and Greico M. (2000) 'New deals, no wheels: social exclusion, tele-options and electronic ontology' *Urban Studies* Vol.37 No.10 September, pp.1735-1748.

Castells M. (1989) *The Informational City: Information technology, economic restructuring and the urban-regional process* Oxford: Blackwells.

Castells M. (1996) *The Rise of the Network Society: The Information Age: Economy Society and Culture Volume I* Oxford: Blackwells.

Castells M. (1997) *The Power of Identity: Economy Society and Culture Volume II* Oxford: Blackwells.

Castells, M. (2000) *End of Millennium: The Information age: Economy Society and Culture Volume II* (2nd edn) Oxford: Blackwells.

Castells M. and Hall P. (1994) *Technopoles of the World: the making of 21st century industrial complexes* London: Routledge.

Castles S and Miller M.J. (1993) *The Age of Migration: International population movements in the modern world* London: Macmillan.

Chant C. (1980) *Modern Jetliners* London: Phoebus/BPC.

Chant C. (ed) (1983) *B-29 Superfortress* Sparkford: Winchmore.

Chataway J., Gault F., Quintas P. and Wield D. (2003) 'Dealing with the Knowledge Divide' in G. Sciadas (ed) *Monitoring Digital Divides and Beyond* Montreal: ORBICOM.

Checkland P. (1981) *Systems Thinking: Systems Practice* Chichester: Wiley.

Chemical Week (1998) 'ICI Seeks Buyer for Bulk of Crosfield' *Chemical Week* 25 February.

Clanchy M.T.T. (1979) *From Memory to Written Record: England 1066-1307* Cambridge: Harvard University Press.

Clark P.A. (1972) *Action Research* Harper and Row, London.

Clark P.A. (1982) 'A review of the theories of time and structure for organizational sociology' Working Paper 248, University of Aston Management Centre, U.K.

Clark P.A. (1997) 'The Duality of Strategic Time Reckoning and the Influence of National Predispositions on Production and Inventory Control Systems' in D. Caseby (ed) *Between Tradition and Innovation: Time in a Managerial Perspective*, Proc. ISDA-14, pp.235-265.

Clarke R. (1989) 'Information Technology and Dataveillance' *Communications of the ACM* Vol.31 No.5, May, pp.498-512.

Clegg S.R. (1987) 'The language of power and the power of language' *Organization Studies* Vol.8 No.1, January, pp.61-70.

Clegg S. (1990) *Modern Organizations: organization studies in the post-modern world* London: Sage.

Coates, J. and Kilian, M. (1986) *Heavy Losses: The Dangerous Decline of American Defense* New York: Penguin.

Cohen M.D., March J. and Olsen J.P. (1972) 'A garbage can model of organizational choice' *Administrative Science Quarterly,* Vol.17 No.1 March, pp.1-25.

Cohen W.M. and Levinthal D.A. (1990) 'Absorptive capacity: a new perspective on learning and innovation' *Administrative Science Quarterly* March 158-192.

Cole M. (1985) 'The zone of proximal development: where culture and cognition create other' in Wertsch J.V. (ed.) *Culture Communication and Cognition: Vygotskian Perspectives* Cambridge: Cambridge University Press.

Coleman A. (1985) *Utopia on Trial: visions and reality in planned housing* London: Hilary Shipman.

Collingridge D. (1980) *The Social Control of Technology* Milton Keynes: Open University Press.

Collingridge D. (1982) *Critical Decision-making* London: Frances Pinter.

Cooper J. (1976) 'Defence Production and the Soviet Economy, 1929-1941' *CREES Discussion Paper, Centre for Russian and East European Studies,* University of Birmingham, Soviet Industrial Project Series, SIPS No.3.

Cooper J. (1984) 'Technological Innovation in the USSR' in R.B. Langdon and G. Mallen (eds) *Design and Industry* London: Design Council.

Corbusier L. (1946) *Towards a new architecture* Architectural Press: London.

Couto R. (1988) 'TVA's Old and New Grass Roots: a re-examination of co-optation' *Administration and Society* Vol.19 No.4 February, pp.453-478.

Cowan R.S. (1983) *More Work for Mother: the ironies of household technology from the open hearth to the microwave* New York: Basic Books.

Coyne R. (1995) *Designing information technology in the postmodern age: from method to metaphor* Cambridge: MIT Press.

Cross M. (2002) 'Blair's £40bn gamble on IT' *The Guardian* 25 April, Online section p.1.

Cross N. (1972) (ed) *Design Participation* Academy London: Editions.

Crystal D. (1997) *English as a Global Language* Cambridge: Cambridge University Press.

Cyert R.M. and March J.G. (1963) *A Behavioural Theory of the Firm* Englewood Cliffs: Prentice-Hall.

D'Allest F. (1988) 'The Ariane Family' *Interdisciplinary Science Reviews* Vol.13 No.2 pp.706-165.

David A. and Wheelwright T. (1989) *The Third Wave: Australia and Asian Capitalism* Sydney: Left Book Club.

Dawes A. (2002) 'Nimrod MRA.4' *Air International* Vol.63 No.1 July, pp.45-51.

Dawes A. (2003) 'New weapons for a new doctrine' *Air International* Vol.64 No.5 May 2003, pp.16-19.

Damanpour F. and Evan W.M. (1984) 'Organizational innovation and performance: the problem of organizational lag' *Administrative Science Quarterly* Vol.29 pp.392-409.

Delamaide D. (1994) *The New Super-regions of Europe* New York: Penguin.

DeLamarter R.T. (1988) *Big blue: IBM's use and abuse of power* London: Pan.

Denning S. and Grieco M. (2000) 'Technology, Dialogue and the Development Process' *Urban Studies* Vol.37 No.10, September, pp.1065-1879.

Dhillon G., Hackney R. and Ranchod A. (1998) 'The Best of Times: The Worst of Times: The emergence of networked organisations in India' in P. Bannerjee, R. Hackney, G. Dhillon and R. Jain (eds) *Business Information Technology Management: Closing the international divide* New Delhi: Har Anand.

Dicken P. (1992) *Global Shift: transforming the world's economy* (2nd edn) London: Paul Chapman.

Dicken P. (1998) *Global Shift: transforming the world's economy* (3rd edn) London: Sage.

Dicken P. (2003) *Global Shift: transforming the world's economy* (4th edn) London: Sage.

Dickson P. (1976) *The Electronic Battlefield* London: Marion Boyars.

Donaldson R. (1985) 'Organizational design and the life cycle of products' *Management Studies* Vol.22 No.1 pp.25-37.

Douglas M. (1987) *How Institutions Think* London: Routledge and Kegan-Paul.

Douglas M. and Wildavsky A. (1982) *Risk and Culture* Berkeley: University of California Press.

Downs G.W. and Mohr L.B. (1976) 'Conceptual issues in the study of innovation' *Administrative Science Quarterly* Vol.21 pp.700-714.

Dosi G. (1986) 'Technology and conditions of macro-economic development: some notes on adjustment mechanisms and discontinuities in the transformation of capitalist economies' in C. Freeman (ed) *Design, Innovation and Long cycles in Economic Development* London: Frances Pinter.

Doxiados C. (1968) *Ekistics: an introduction to the science of human settlements* London: Hutchison.

Dreyfus H.L. and Dreyfus S.E. (1986) *Mind over Machine* New York: Free Press.

Dunning J.H. (1993) *Multinational Enterprises and the Global Economy* Reading: Addison-Wesley.

Earls J.A.M. (1990) 'Social integration of people with disabilities: the development of an information technology model based on personal growth and achievement' Unpublished PhD thesis, Wollongong: University of Wollongong.

EC/UNCTAD (1996) Investing in Asia's Dynamism: European Union direct investment in Asia European Commission/UNCTAD Division on Transnational Corporations and Investment, Office for Official Publications of the EC, Luxembourg.

Edwards M. (1974) 'Comparison of some expectations of a sample of housing architects with known data' in T. Lee and D. Kanter (eds) *Psychology and the Built Environment* London: Architectural Press.

Edwards P.N. (2000) 'The world in a machine: origins and impacts of early computerized global systems models' in A.C. Hughes and T.P. Hughes (eds) *Systems, experts and computers, the systems approach in management and engineering in World War II and after* Cambridge: MIT Press.

Eisenhower D.D. (1961) President Dwight D. Eisenhower Farewell Address to the Nation January 17, 1961.

Eldridge J.E.T. and Crombie A.D. (1974) *A sociology of organisations* London: Allen and Unwin.

Elwell F.W. (1999) *America: Understanding Contemporary Society through Classical Sociological Analysis* Westport: Praeger Press.

Ericson S.J. (1998) 'Importing locomotives in Meiji Japan international business and technology transfer in the railroad industry' *Osiris* Series 2 Vol.13 pp.129-153.

Ernst D., Ganiatsos T. and Mytelka L. (eds) (1998) *Technological Capabilities and Export Success – Lessons from East Asia* London: Routledge.

Esher (1981) *A Broken Wave: the rebuilding of England 1940-1980* London: Allen Lane.

Feenberg A. (1980) 'The political economy of social space' in K. Wooodward (ed) *The Myths of Information: technology and post-industrial culture* Henley-on-Thames: Routledge and Kegan Paul.

Feustel-Buechl J. (1988) 'The European Spaceplane Hermes and Future' Transportation Systems *Interdisciplinary Science Reviews* Vol.13 No.2 pp.180-187.

Forbes N. and Wield, D. (2001) *From Followers to Leaders: innovation management in newly industrializing countries* London: Routledge.

Ford, D. (1985) *The Button* London: George Allan and Unwin.

Forrester J.W. (1969) *Urban Dynamics* Cambridge: MIT Press.

Forristal P.D. and Keppel D. (2001) *The Application of Harvester-Mounted Forage Yield Sensing Devices* Oak Park: Crops Research Centre.

Foucault M. (1979) *Discipline and Punish: The Birth of the Prison* London: Penguin.

Franklin R. (1986) *The Defender: the story of General dynamics* New York: Harper and Row.

Freeman C. (1983) *Design and British Economic Performance* London: Department of Design Research, R.C.A.

Freeman C. (ed) (1986) *Design, innovation and long cycles in economic development* London: Frances Pinter.

Fries F.D. (1988) '2001 to 1994: political environment and the design of NASA's space station system' *Technology and Society* Vol.29 No.2, pp.568-593.

Fukayama F. (1992) *The End of History and the Last Man* Harmondsworth: Penguin.

Galbraith J. (1977) *Organization Design* Reading: Addison-Wesley.

Galbraith J.K. (1976) *The New Industrial State* (4th edn) New York: Mentor.

Gardiner J.P. (1986) 'Robust and lean designs with state of the art automotive and aircraft examples' in Freeman C. (ed) *Design, Innovation and Long cycles in Economic Development* London: Frances Pinter.

Gardiner J.P. and Rothwell R. (1985) 'Tough customers: good designs' *Design Studies* Vol.6 No.1 January, pp.7-17.

Gibson W. (1984) *Neuromancer* Dublin: Grafton Press.

Giddens A. (1979) *Central problems in social theory* London: Macmillan.

Giddens A. (1981) *A contemporary critique of historical materialism* London: Macmillan.

Giddens A. (1999) *Runaway World: How Globalisation is Shaping Our Lives.* London: Profile Books.

Giglavyi A. (1993) 'IT Landscape in Russia' International Conference on People and Information Technology ITAP'93, Moscow, May.

Gillespie R. (1991) *Manufacturing Knowledge: a history of the Hawthorne experiments* Cambridge: Cambridge University Press.

Glassman R.B. (1973) 'Resistance and loose coupling in living systems' *Behavioral Science* Vol.18 pp.83-98.

Gooday G.J.N. and Low M.F. 'Technology Transfer and Cultural Exchange Western scientists and engineers encounter Late Tokugawa and Meiji Japan' *Osiris* Series 2 Vol.13 pp.99-128.

Goodman R. (1972) *After the Planners* Harmondsworth: Penguin.

Goodman R. and Philips D. (2003) *Can the Japanese change their education system?* Oxford: Oxford University Press.

Gould P. and White R. (1974) *Mental Maps* Harmondsworth: Penguin.

Gouldner A.W. (1955) 'Metaphysical pathos and the theory of bureaucracy' *American Political Science Review* Vol.49 p.504.

Gouldner A.W. (1976) *The dialectic of ideology and technology* London: Macmillan.

Griffin P. (2003) 'Wiring the Union: Scottish "devolution" informatisation and metagovernance. *European Spatial Research and Policy - Special Issue on Metagovernance* Issue 2, 2003. pp.59-88

Grinspoon L. (1994) *Marijuana Reconsidered* Berkeley: Group West.

Gunston W. (1980) *Early Jetliners* London: Phoebus/BPC.

Gunston W. (1983) *Modern Fighting Aircraft: F-111* London: Salamander.

Halberstam D. (1971) 'The Programming of Robert McNamara' *Harper's Magazine* February.

Hall E.T. (1966) *The Hidden Dimension* New York: Doubleday.

Hall E.T. (1989) *Beyond Culture* New York: Anchor Books.

Hannan M.T. and Freeman J. (1984) 'Structural inertia and organisational change' *American Sociological Review* Vol.49, July, pp.149-154.

Harasim L.M. (ed) (1993) *Global Networks: Computers and International Communication* Cambridge: MIT Press.

Haresnape B. (1982a) *British Rail Fleet Survey Volume 1: Prototype Diesel-Electrics* Shepperton: Ian Allen.

Haresnape B. (1982b) *British Rail Fleet Survey Volume 2: Western Region Diesel-Hydraulics* Shepperton: Ian Allen.

Hartamis J. and Lin H. (eds) (1992) *Computing the Future: A Broader Agenda for Computer Science and Engineering* Washington D.C.: National Academy Press.

Harvey D. (1990) *The Condition of Postmodernity* Oxford: Basil Blackwell.

Hayashi F. and Prescott E.C. (2002) 'The 1990s in Japan: A Lost Decade' *Review of Economic Dynamics*, Vol.5 (1) pp.206-235.

Hayden D. (1981) *The Grand Domestic Revolution: a history of feminist designs for American homes, neighbourhoods and cities* Cambridge: MIT Press.

Hayes R. and Abernathy W. (1980) 'Managing our way to decline' *Harvard Business Review* Vol.60 No.3 pp.70-80.

Headrick D.R. (1981) *The Tools of Empire: Technology and European Imperialism in the Nineteenth Century* Oxford: Oxford University Press.

Higgins W. and Clegg S. R. (1988) 'Enterprise, Calculation and Manufacturing Decline' *Organization Studies* Vol.9 No.1 January, pp.69-89.

Hiltz S.R. and Turoff M. (1985) 'Structuring computer mediated communications systems to avoid information overload' *Communications of the ACM* Vol.28, No.7 pp.680-689.

Hirst P. and Thompson G. (1996) *Globalization in Question* Cambridge: Polity Press.

Hirsch S. (1967) *Location of Industry and Industrial Competitiveness* Oxford: Clarendon.

Hofstede G. (1980) *Culture's Consequences: International Differences in Work-Related Values* London: Sage.

Hofstede G. (2001) *Culture's Consequences: International Differences in Work-Related Values* (2nd edn) London: Sage.

Holloway E. (1983) *The Soviet Union and the Arms Race* London: Yale University Press.

Hughes A.C. and Hughes T.P. (2000) *Systems experts and computers: the systems approach in management and engineering, World War II and after* Cambridge: MIT Press.

Inoue T. (1998) 'Small businesses flourish in virtual village' *Nikkei Weekly* 26 January p.1.

Isahara S. (1991) *The Japan that Can Say No* New York: Simon and Schuster.

Ishibashi A. (1998) 'Car makers look for a highway into China' *Nikkei Weekly* 9 March pp.1 and 19.

Itakura K. and Yagi E. (1974) The Japanese Research System and the Establishment of the Institute of Physical and Chemical Research, in S. Nakayama, D. Swain and E. Yagi (eds) *Science and Society in Modern Japan* Cambridge: MIT Press.

Jackson T.J. (1985) 'Precision Guided Munitions for the U.S. Artillery' *Military Technology* Vol.11 pp.44-54.

Jacobs J. (1961) *The Death and Life of Great American Cities* New York: Vintage Books.

Jacobs J. (1982) *The Question of Separatism* London: Junction Books.

Jacques E. (1957) *The measurement of responsibility* London: Tavistock.

James A.D. and Howells J. (2001) 'Global companies and local markets: the internationalisation of product design and development' in R. Thorpe and S. Little (eds) *Global Change: the Impact of Asia in the 21st Century* London: Palgrave.

Jencks C. (1989) *What is Post-Modernism?* (3rd edn) London: Academy.

Johnson C. (1983) *MITI and the Japanese miracle: the growth of industrial policy 1925-1975* Stanford: Stanford University Press.

Johnson C. (1995) *Japan: Who Governs? The Rise of the Developmental State* New York: W.W. Norton and Company.

Johnson C. (2003) *Blowback: the costs and consequences of American Empire* London: TimeWarner.

Jones J.C. (1980) *Design Methods* (2nd edn) London: Wiley.

Kaldor M. (1981) *The Baroque Arsenal* London: Abacus.

Kanbur R. (2001) 'Economic Policy, Distribution and Poverty: The Nature of Disagreements' *World Development* June.

Kantor A. (1979) *Defense Politics* Chicago: University of Chicago Press.

Kaplinsky R. and Posthuma A. (1994) *Easternisation: the spread of Japanese management techniques to developing countries* Ilford: Frank Cass.

Karpat K. (2002) 'Osmanli Modernlesmesi' (*Ottoman Modernisation*) Istanbul: Imge Kitabevi.

Kay N.M. (1983) 'Innovation, markets and hierarchies' Paper presented at Long Waves in Economic Development Conference, Development Studies Association, Edinburgh.

Kaye G.R. and Little S.E. (1996) 'Strategies and Standards for Cultural Interoperability in Global Business Systems' *Proc HICSS-29: Hawaiian International Conference on Systems Science, Maui, January 1996 Vol.IV Information Systems* pp.465-473 Los Alamitos: IEEE Computer Society Press.

Kaye G.R. and Little S.E. (1998) 'Setting Standards: Strategies for Building Global Business Systems' in F. McDonald and R. Thorpe *Organizational Change and Strategic Adaptation to Global Change* Macmillan: London.

Kaye G.R and Little S. (2000) 'Dysfunctional Development pathways of Information and Communication Technology: Cultural Conflicts' *Journal of Global Information Management* Vol.8 No.1 pp.5-13.

Kim E.M. (1996) 'The industrial organisation and growth of the Korean Chaebol: integrating development and organizational theories' in G.G. Hamilton (ed) *Asian Business Networks* Berlin: deGruyter.

Kirlidog M. (1997) 'Executive computing in a developing country: a case study evaluation of Turkish experience' Unpublished PhD thesis, University of Wollongong, NSW.

Klein N. (2000) *No Logo: Taking aim at the brand bullies* London: HarperCollins.

Kleinegger C. (1987) 'Out of the Barns and into the Kitchens: Transformation of Farm Women's Work in the First Half of the Twentieth Century' in B.D. Wright (ed) *Women, Work and Technology: Transformations* Ann Arbor: University of Michigan Press.

Kling R. (1993) 'Computing our Future for a Social World' *Communications of the ACM* February.

Klingbeil A. (2002) 'IBM to quit making desktop computers' *Wall Street Journal* 9 January.

Kondratiev N. (1925) 'The major economic cycles' *Voprosy Koniunktury* Vol.1.

Kopp A. (1970) *Town and Revolution: Soviet Architecture and City Planning 1917-1935* London: Thames and Hudson.

Krugman P. (1996) *Pop Internationalism* Cambridge: MIT Press.

Kuhn T. (1962) *The structure of scientific revolutions* Chicago: University of Chicago Press.

Kuuti K. (1991) 'Activity theory and its application to information systems research and development' in H-E. Nissen, H.K. Klein and R. Hirschheim (eds) *Information systems research: contemporary approaches and emergent traditions* Amsterdam: North-Holland.

Lake J. (2001) 'Sukhoi Su-30MKI: India's great white hope?' *Air International*, Vol.60 No.6 June pp.367-371.

Lamberton D. (1995) 'Communications' in P. Troy (ed) *Technological Change and Urban Development* Sydney: Federation Press.

Lammers C.J. and Hickson D.J. (1979) 'A cross-national and cross-institutional typology of organisations' in C.J. Lammers and D.J. Hickson (eds) *Organisations alike and unalike: international and interinstitutional studies in the sociology of organisations* London: Routledge and Kegan Paul.

Landauer T. (1995) *The Trouble with Computers: Usefulness, Usability and Productivity* Cambridge: MIT Press.

Latour B. and Woolgar S. (1979) *Laboratory Life: The Construction of Scientific Facts* Princeton: Princeton University Press.

Laureau P. (2003) 'Greek Phantom upgrades progressing' *Air International* Vol.64 No.1 January p.4.

Lawrence, P. and Lorsch, J. (1967) *Organization and Environment* Cambridge: Harvard University Press.

Lawson B.R. (1982) 'Science, legislation and architecture' in B.N. Evans, J.A. Powell and R.J. Talbot (eds) *Changing Design* Chichester: Wiley.

Learmount S. (2002) *Corporate Governance: what can be learned from Japan?* Oxford: Oxford University Press.

Lera S.G. (1981) 'Architectural designer's values and the evaluation of their designs' *Design Studies* Vol.2 No.3 March pp.131-7.

Levine R.J. (1973) 'General Dynamics F-111 output to be ended by Pentagon; Rockwell B-1 seen benefiting' *Wall Street Journal* 7 June.

Lewis B. (2002) *What Went Wrong? Western impact and Middle Eastern response* New York: Oxford University Press.

Lewis H. and Allison D. (1982) *The Real World War: The Coming Battle for the New Global Economy and Why We Are in Danger of Losing* New York: Coward, McCann and Geoghan.

Lindqvist S. (2001) *A History of Bombing* New York: New Press.

Lipietz A. (1992) *Mirages and Miracles: Crises in Global Fordism* London: Verso.

Lipietz A. (1992) *Towards a New Economic Order: Postfordism, ecology and democracy* Cambridge: Polity Press.

Little S.E. (1988) *The Organisational Implications of Computing Technology for Professional Work* Aldershot: Avebury.

Little S.E. (1990) 'Task Environments and Institutional Environments: understanding the context of design decision-making' *Design Studies* Vol.11 No.1 January pp.29-42.

Little S.E. and Grieco M.S. (2003) 'Electronic Stepping Stones: a mosaic metaphor for the production and re-distribution of skill in electronic mode' paper presented at EGOS Conference, Copenhagen Business School, July 2003.

Little S., Holmes L. and Grieco M. (2000) 'Island histories, open cultures?: the electronic transformation of adjacency' *Southern African Business Review* Vol.4 No.2 pp.21-25.

Little S., Holmes L. and Grieco M. (2001) 'Calling up culture: information spaces and information flows as the virtual dynamics of inclusion and exclusion' *Information Technology and People* Vol.14 No.4 pp.353-367.

Livingstone S. (1992) 'The meaning of domestic technologies: a personal construct analysis of familial gender relations' in R.I. Silverstone and E. Hirsch *Consuming Technologies: media and information in domestic spaces* London: Routledge.

Logsdon J.M. (1986) 'The space shuttle program: a policy failure?' *Science* Vol.232 30th May pp.1099-1105.

Lovering J. (1988) 'Islands of Prosperity: the spatial impact of high technology defence industry in Britain' in M.J. Breheny (ed) *Defence expenditure and regional development* London: Mansell.

McClain J.L. (2002) *Japan: A Modern History* New York: W.W. Norton.

McConnell M. (1987) *Challenger 'A Major Malfunction'* London: Unwin-Hyman.

MacKenzie D. and Wajcman J. (eds) (1995) *The social shaping of technology* (2nd edn) Maidenhead: Open University Press.

McLoughlin J.B. (1969) *Urban and regional planning: a systems approach* London: Faber and Faber.

McSweeney B. (2002) 'Hofstede's Model of National Cultural Differences and Their Consequences: A Triumph of Faith; A Failure of Analysis' *Human Relations*, Vol.55, No.1.

Magnuson E. (1986a) 'A serious deficiency' *Time* 10th March pp.34-36.

Magnuson E. (1986b) 'Fixing NASA' *Time* 9th June pp.42-50.

Mannheim K. (1936) *Ideology and Utopia*, New York: Harcourt-Brace.

Marceau J. (ed) (1992) *Re-Working The World: Organisations, Technologies and Cultures in Comparative Perspective* Berlin: de Gruyter.

March J. and Simon H. (1958) *Organizations* New York: John Wiley.

Marschak, T., Glennan T.K. Jnr. and Summers R. (1967) *Strategy for RandD: Studies in the Microeconomics of Development* Berlin: Springer-Verlag.

Marvin C. (1988) *When Old Technologies were New: thinking about electric communication in the late nineteenth century* New York: Oxford University Press.

Maslow A.H. and Honigman J.J. (1970) 'Synergy: some notes of Ruth Benedict' *American Anthropologist* Vol.72 pp.320-333.

Mason R. and Caiger J. (1972) *A History of Japan* Tokyo: Charles E. Tuttle.

Mazlish B. (ed) (1965) *The Railroad and the Space Program: an exploration in historical analogy* Cambridge: MIT Press.

Meir R.L. (1959) 'Measuring social and cultural change in urban regions' *Journal of the American Institute of Planners* Vol.25 August pp.180-190.

Milgram S. (1974) *Obedience to Authority* New York: Harper and Row.

Miller D. and Slater D. (2000) *The Internet, An Ethnographic Approach* Oxford: Berg.

Miller D.M.O., Kennedy W.V., Jordan J. and Richardson D. (1981) *East vs. West: The Balance of Military Power* London: Lansdowne Press.

Mintzberg H. (1975) *The Nature of Managerial Work* New York: Harper and Row.

Mintzberg H. (1979) *The Structuring of Organizations* Engelwood Cliffs: Prentice-Hall.

Mitchell W.J. (1995) *City of Bits: Space, Place, and the Infobahn* Cambridge: MIT Press.

Mitsui (1977) *The 100 Year History of Mitsui and Co. Ltd.* Tokyo: Mitsui and Co.

Miyashita K. and Russell D. (1994) *Keiretsu: Inside the hidden Japanese conglomerates* New York: McGraw-Hill.

Mohr L.B. (1969) 'Determinants of innovation in organizations' *American Political Science Review* Vol.63 pp.111-126.

Mol A.P.J. (2000) *Globalization and Environmental Reform* Cambridge: MIT Press.

Monbiot G. (2003) 'Africa Left to Starve As Aid Flow Evaporates' *Guardian* 18th March.

Morgan G. (1986) *Images of Organisation* Newbury Park: Sage.

Morris-Suzuki T. (1994) *The Technological Transformation of Japan: from the seventeenth to the twenty-first century* Cambridge: Cambridge University Press.

Morrison P.R. (1984) 'An Absence of Malice: Computers and Armageddon' *Prometheus* Vol.2 pp.190-200.

Morrison P.R. (1986) 'Limits to Technocratic Consciousness: Information Technology and Terrorism as Example' *Science, Technology and Human Values* Vol.11 pp.4-16.

Morrison P.R. (2000) 'A pilot implementation of internet access for remote aboriginal communities in Australia's top end' *Urban Studies* Vol.37 No.10 September pp.1781-1792.

Morrison P.R. and Little S.E. (1991) 'Technological cultures of weapons design' *Science as Culture* Vol.2 No.2 (Number 11) pp.227-58.

Mosco V. (1987) 'Star Wars is Already Working' *Science as Culture* Pilot Issue May pp.12-34.

M.O.S.T. (n.d.) *Vision 2025: Korea's Long-term Plan for Science and Technology Development* Gwaecheon: Ministry of Science and Technology.

Mumford E. and Wier M. (1979) *Computer Systems in Work Design: the ETHICS method* London: Associated Business Press.

Negroponte N. (1995) *Being Digital* London: Coronet.

Nelson K. (1988) 'Labour demand, labour supply and the suburbanization of low-wage office work' in A.J. Scott and M. Storper (eds) *Production, Work, Territory: the geographical anatomy of industrial capitalism* Boston: Unwin Hyman.

Newman O. (1973) *Defensible Space* London: Architectural Press.

Newsweek (1995) 'When Words Are the Best Weapon' 27th February pp.36-40.

Nicholson B. and Sahay S. (2001) 'Some Political and Cultural Implications of the Globalisation of Software Development: Case Experience from UK and India' *Information and Organisation* Vol.11 No.1 pp.25-43.

Nobes C.W. and Parker R.H. (1981) *Comparative International Accounting* (2nd edn) Deddington: Phillip Allan.

Nobihuro Y. (1998) 'Telegraph and Total Capture of National Land/Nation-State' Paper presented at *International Conference on Science, Technology and Society: Science and Society Technological Turn*, Tokyo, Hiroshima and Kyoto, Japan, March.

Nuki T. (1998) 'Earlier and Faster – a new trend of Japan's production strategy' in P. Bannerjee, R. Hackney, G. Dhillon and R. Jain (eds) *Business Information Technology Management: Closing the international divide* New Delhi: Har Anand.

Numazaki I. (1996) 'The role of personal networks in the making of Taiwan's *guanxiqiye* (related enterprises)' in G.G. Hamilton (ed) *Asian Business Networks* Berlin: deGruyter.

Nyanchama M. (1995) 'African Telecommunications: Strengthening the Foundations for Effective Global Networking' in M. Odedra-Straub, R. Okot-Uma and G. Cyranek (eds) *Information Technology and Globalisation: Implication for Developing Countries* London: Commonwealth Secretariat.

O'Hara-Devereaux M. and Johansen R. (1994) *Globalwork: bridging distance, culture and time* San Francisco: Jossey-Bass.

Ohmae K. (1990) *The Borderless World: Power and strategy in the interlinked economy* London: Collins.

Ohmae K. (1995) *The End of the Nation State: The rise of regional economics* New York: Free Press.

Orru M., Biggart N.W. and Hamilton G. (1991) 'Organizational Isomorphism in East Asia' in W.W. Powell and P.J. DiMaggio *The New Institutionalism in Organisational Analysis* Chicago: University of Chicago Press.

Ortayli I. (2001) *Tarihin Sinirlerine Yolculuk* (*Journey to the Frontiers of the History*) (4th edn) Istanbul: Ufuk Kitaplari.

Ortayli I. (2002) *Imparatorlugun En Uzun Yuzyili* (*The Longest Century of the Empire*) (11th edn) Istanbul: Iletisim Yayinlari.

Pamuk O. (2001) *My Name is Red* New York: Knopf.

Papert S. (1980) *Mindstorms: children, computers and powerful ideas* Brighton: Harvester.

Parker Morris Committee (1961) *Homes for Today and Tomorrow* London: H.M.S.O.

Parkinson C.N. (1958) *Parkinson's Law: The Pursuit of Progress* London: John Murray.

Parnas D. (1985) 'Software Aspects of Strategic Defense Systems' *Communications of the Association for Computing Machinery* December pp.1326-35.

Park W. (1983) *Software Engineering Notes* July p.4.

Parsons T. (1960) *Structure and Process in Modern Societies* Glencoe: Free Press.

Parsons H.M. (1974) 'What happened at Hawthorne?' *Science* Vol.183 March pp.922-932.

Pavitt K. (1980) *Technical innovation and British economic performance* London: Macmillan.

People's Daily (2003) 'EU to co-operate with China on Galileo program' 28 October.

Perez C. (1985) 'Microelectronics, Long Waves and World Structural change: New Perspectives for Developing Countries' *World Development* Vol.13 No.3 pp.441-63.

Perez C. (1986) 'Structural changes and assimilation of new technologies in the social and economic system' in C. Freeman (ed) *Design innovation and long cycles in economic development* London: Frances Pinter.

Perin C. (1970) *With Man in Mind* Cambridge: MIT Press.

Perin C. (1991) 'Electronic Social Fields in Bureaucracies' *Communications of the ACM* Vol.34 No.12 pp.74-82.

Perrin N. (1982) *Keine Feuerwaffen mehr - Japans Ruckkehr zum Schwert 1543-1879* Frankfurt: Athenäum.

Perrow C. (1983) 'The organizational context of human factors design' *Administrative Science Quarterly* Vol.28 pp.521-541.

Perrow C. (1986) *Complex Organizations: a critical essay* (3rd edn) New York: Random House.

Perrow C. (1984) *Normal accidents: living with high risk technologies* New York: Basic Books.

Perry W.J. and Roberts C.A. (1982) '"Smart" Weapons' *Technology Review*.

Peter L.J. (1986) *The Peter Pyramid* London: Unwin.

Peters T.J. and Waterman R.H. Jr (1982) *In Search of Excellence* New York: Warner.

Pevsner N. (1949) *Pioneers of Modern Design from William Morris to Walter Gropius* New York: Museum of Modern Art.

Pfeffer J. and Salancik G.R. (1974) 'Organisational decision-making as a political process: the case of a university budget' *Administrative Science Quarterly* Vol.19 June pp.135-51.

Pitkin W. (2001) 'Community Informatics: Hope or Hype' Proc. *34th Annual Hawaii International Conference on System Sciences (HICSS-34)* Vol.8 January Maui, Hawaii.

Poon T. S-C. (2002) *Competition and Cooperation in Taiwan's Information Technology Industry: inter-firm networks and industrial upgrading* Westport: Quorum.

Porter M.E. (1990) *The Competitive Advantage of Nations* London: Macmillan.

Powell W.W. and DiMaggio P.J. (1990) *The New Institutionalism in Organisational Analysis* Chicago: University of Chicago Press.

Price-Waterhouse (1998) *EMC Technology Forecast* Menlo Park: Price-Waterhouse.

Pringle P. and Spigelman J. (1982) *The nuclear barons* London: Michael Joseph.

Pythian M. (2000) *The Politics of British Arms Sales Since 1964* Manchester: Manchester University Press.

Ramos A.G. (1981) *The New Science of Organizations* Toronto: University of Toronto Press.

Ravetz A. (1987) 'Housework and Domestic Technologies' in M. McNeil (ed) *Gender and Expertise* London: Free Association Books.

Ravid I. (1990) 'Military decision, game theory and intelligence: an anecdote' *Operations Research* Vol.38 No.2 March-April pp.260-264.

Raymond E.S. (2001) *The Cathedral and the Bazaar: musings on Linux and Open source by an accidental revolutionary* (revised edn) Sebastopol: O'Reilly.

Redding G. (1996) 'Weak organisations and strong linkages: managerial ideology and Chinese family business networks' in G.G. Hamilton (ed) *Asian Business Networks* Berlin: deGruyter.

Reinhardt U.E. (1973) 'Proposed changes in the organisation of health-care delivery: an overview and critique' *Millbank Memorial Fund Quarterly* Vol.51 (Spring) pp.169-222.

Report of the Presidential Commission on the Space Shuttle Challenger Accident (1986) Washington: U.S. Government Printing Office.

Rheingold H. (1991) *Virtual Reality* London: Secker and Warburg.

Rittel H. and Webber M.M. (1973) 'Dilemmas in a general theory of planning' *Policy Sciences* Vol.4 pp.155-169.

Roberts M. (1991) *Living in a Man-made World: Gender Assumptions in Modern Housing Design* London: Routledge.

Robinson, A. (1985) *Soviet Airpower* Hong Kong: Bison Books.

Robinson A. (2002) 'Sex sells' *InternetWorks* No.64 November pp.3 4-40.

Roethlisberger and Dickson (1939) *Management and the Worker* Cambridge: Harvard University Press.

Rogers E.M. (1962) *Diffusion of Innovations* (1st edn) New York: Free Press.

Rogers E.M. (1983) *Diffusion of Innovations* (3rd edn) New York: Free Press.

Rogers H.C.B. (1980) *Transition from Steam* Shepperton: Ian Allen.

Roper M. (1983) 'French Flock to Centre' *New Scientist* Vol.97 No.1344 10th February pp.358-361.

Rose M. (1991) *The post-modern and the post-industrial: a critical analysis* Cambridge: Cambridge University Press.

Rosenberg N. (1982) *Inside the black box: technology and economics* Cambridge: Cambridge University Press.

Rosenberg N. and Frischtak C. (1986) 'Technological innovation and long waves' in C. Freeman (ed) *Design, Innovation and Long cycles in Economic Development* London: Frances Pinter.

Rothwell R. and Gardniner P. (1983) 'The role of design in product process and change' *Design Studies* Vol.4 No.3 pp.161-170.

Roy R. (1984) 'Product design and innovation in a mature consumer industry' in R. Langdon (ed) *Design and Industry* London: Design Council.

Rugman A. (2001) *The End of Globalization: Why Global Strategy is a Myth and How to Profit from the Realities of Regional Markets* New York: AMACON.

Russell B. (1981) *Building systems, Industrialization and Architecture* London: Wiley.

Sabbagh K. (1995) *21st Century Jet: the making of the Boeing 777* Basingstoke: Macmillan.

Salaman G. (1979) *Work organisations: resistance and control* London: Longman.

Salmon G. (2000) *E-moderating* London: Taylor and Francis.

Sargut A.S. (2001) *Kültürlerarasi Farklilasma ve Yönetim* (*Inter-Cultural Differentiation and Management*) (2nd edn) Istanbul: Imge Kitabevi.

Saxenian A. (1994) *Regional Advantage: Culture and Competition in Silicon Valley and Route 128* Cambridge: Harvard University Press.

Sayles L.R. and Chandler M.K. (1971) *Managing Large Systems: Organizations for the Future* New York: Harper and Row.

Schonfield A. (1965) *Modern Capitalism* London: Royal Institute for International Affairs.

Schumpeter J. (1939) *Business Cycles* New York: McGraw-Hill.

Scott W.R. (1987a) *Organizations: Rational, Natural and Open Systems* (2nd edn) Engelwood Cliffs: Prentice-Hall.

Scott W.R. (1987b) 'The adolescence of institutional theory' *Administrative Science Quarterly* Vol.32 No.4 December pp.493-511.

Scott W.R. (1992) *Organizations: Rational, Natural and Open Systems* (3rd edn) Engelwood Cliffs: Prentice-Hall.

Selznick P. (1949) *TVA and the Grass Roots* Berkeley: University of California Press.

Selznick P. (1957) *Leadership in Administration* New York: Harper and Row.

Sewell G. and Wilkinson B. (1992) '"Someone to Watch over Me": surveillance, discipline and the Just-in-Time labour process' *Sociology* Vol.26 No.2 May pp.271-290.

Shannon C. and Weaver W. (1949) *The Mathematical Theory of Communication* Urbana: University of Illinois Press.

Sheller M. (2003) *Consuming the Caribbean: From Arawaks to Zombies* London: Routledge.

Shepard J. (1993) 'Islands in the (Data)Stream: Language, Character Codes, and Electronic Isolation in Japan' in L.M. Harasim *Global Networks: Computers and International Communication* Cambridge: MIT Press.

Silverstone F., Hirsch E. and Morley D. (1992) 'Information and communication technologies and the moral economy of the household' in R.I. Silverstone and E. Hirsch *Consuming Technologies: media and information in domestic spaces* London: Routledge.

Simon H. (1957) *Administrative Behavior* (2nd edn) New York: Macmillan.

Smith R.K. (1983) 'The intercontinental airliner and the essence of airplane performance' *Technology and Society* Vol.24 pp.428-449.

Soete L. (1986) 'Long cycles in the international diffusion of technology' in C. Freeman (ed) *Design, Innovation and Long cycles in Economic Development* London: Frances Pinter.

Sproull L. and Kiesler S. (1991) *Connections: new ways of working in the networked organization* Cambridge: MIT Press.

State Council of the P.R.C. (2001) *The Development-oriented poverty reduction program for rural China* Beijing: Information Office of the State Council of the People's Republic of China.

Stefik, M. (1985) 'Strategic Computing at DARPA' *Communications of the Association for Computing Machinery* July 690-704.

Stephens M. (1980) *Three Mile Island* London: Junction Books.

Sterling B. (1992) *The Hacker Crackdown* New York: Bantam.

Stiglitz J.E. (2002) *Globalization and its Discontents* New York: Norton.

Stinchcombe A. (1959) 'Bureaucratic and craft administration of production: a comparative study' *Administrative Science Quarterly* Vol.17 pp.163-177.

Stinchcombe A. (1965) 'Social structure and organisations' in J.G. March (ed) *Handbook of Organisations* Chicago: Rand-McNally.

Stoll C. (1989) *The Cuckoo's Egg* London: The Bodley Head.

Strauss A., Schatzman L., Ehrlich D., Buchner B. and Shabshin M. (1973) 'The hospital and its negotiated order' in G. Salaman and K. Thompson (eds) *People and Organisations* London: Longman.

Streetly M. (2003) 'The General Atomics Aeronautical Systems M/RQ-1 Predator' *Air International* September pp.40-45.

Suchman L. (1986) *Plans and Situated Action* Cambridge: Cambridge University Press.

Suckling C. (1984) 'Long range strategy in product planning' in R. Langdon (ed) *Design and Industry* London: Design Council.

Sudhakar S., Sadasivarao B., Suryaprakasa Rao B. and Venkateswara Rao V. (1996) 'Prioritization of landslide hazard zones in parts of Darjeeling district, West Bengal, India - An RS and GIS approach' Paper presented at Asian Conference on Remote Sensing, Sri Lanka, November.

Sweetman B. (1985) *Modern Fighting Aircraft – MiGs* Sydney: Hodder and Stoughton.

Taplin R. (2000) 'Perfect guidance for the stars' *The Times*, 3rd October p.17.

Taylor M.J.H. (1986) *Jet Warplanes: The Twenty-first Century* London: Bison.

Thompson J.D. (1967) *Organizations in Action* New York: McGraw-Hill.

Toffler A. (1970) *Future Shock* New York: Bantam.

Townsend R. (1970) *Up the Organization* New York: Coronet.

Trento J. (1987) *Prescription for Disaster* New York: Crown.

Trist E. and Bamforth W. (1951) 'Some Social and Psychological Consequences of the Long-Wall Method of Coal-Getting' *Human Relations* Vol.4 pp.3-38.

Tsai H-J. (1993) 'An Evaluation of Spatial Aspects of IT Strategies in Taiwan' MSc dissertation, Wollongong: University of Wollongong.

Turing A.M. (1936-7) 'On computable numbers with an application to the Entscheidungsproblem' *Proc. London Maths. Soc.*, Series 2, 42, pp.230-265.

Turing A.M. (1950) 'Computing Machinery and Intelligence' *Mind* Vol.49 No.236 October pp.433-460.

Turkone M. (1998) 'Tanzimat ve Batililasma Dusuncesinin Avrupa Birligi Surecinde Turkiye'nin Avrupalilasmasi Semineri' Istanbul: TC Merkez Bankasi (*'Reorganisation and the Thought of Westernisation' in The Symposium of Turkey in the Process of Becoming a European Country, Central Bank of Turkey*).

Turner B. (1971) *Exploring the industrial subculture* London: Macmillan.

Tyler P. (1986) *Running Critical: The Silent War, Rickover and General Dynamics* New York: Harper and Row.

UNDP (2002) *Human Development Report* New York: United Nations Development Program.

Unger J. Marshall (1996) *Literacy and Script reform in Occupied Japan* Oxford: Oxford University Press.

Utterback J.M. (1976) 'Innovation in industry and the diffusion of technology' *Science* Vol.183 pp.620-626.

Vallerani E. (1988) 'The Space Station' *Interdisciplinary Science Reviews* Vol.13 No.2 pp.156-165.

van Wolferen K. (1990) *The Enigma of Japanese Power: People and Politics in a Stateless Nation* Macmillan pp.492-3.

Vaughan D. (1996) *The Challenger Launch Decision: Risky Technology, Culture, and Deviance at NASA* Chicago: University of Chicago Press.

Veblen T.B. (1904) *The Theory of the Business Enterprise* New York: Scribner's.

Vitalari N.P. (1985) 'The need for longitudinal designs on the study of computing environments' in E. Mumford, R. Hirschheim, G. Fitzgerald and A.T. Wood-Harper (eds) *Research Methods in Information Systems* Amsterdam: North Holland.

von Bertalanffy L. (1950) 'The theory of open systems in physics and biology' *Science* Vol.111, pp.620-626.

Wagner W. (1982) *Lightning Bugs and other reconnaissance drones* Fallbrook: Armed Forces International/Aero Publishers.

Webber M. (1964) 'The urban place and the non-place urban realm' in M.M. Webber, J.W. Dyckman, D.L. Foley, A.Z. Gutenberg, W.L.C. Wheaton and C.B. Wurster (eds) *Explorations in Urban Structure* Philadelphia: University of Pennsylvania.

Webber M.M. (1968) 'The post-city age' *Daedalus* Vol.97 No.4 Fall pp.1091-1110.

Weber M. (1947) *From Max Weber* (eds – H.H. Gerth and C.W. Mills) London: Oxford University Press.

Weick K.E. (1976) 'Educational organizations as loosely couple systems' *Administrative Science Quarterly* Vol.21 pp.1-19.

Weizenbaum J. (1976) *Computer Power and Human Reason: from judgement to calculation* New York: W.H. Freeman.

Welford R.J. (1995) *Environmental Strategy and Sustainable Development* London: Routledge.

Wells L.T. Jnr (1972) *The product life cycle and international trade* Boston: Harvard Business School.

Whitford R. (2002) 'Fundamentals of Airliner Design Part 10 - Propulsion II' *Air International* Vol.63 No.2 August pp.144-150.

Wilentz A. (1985) 'No More Time for Sergeant York Weinberger scraps the controversial antiaircraft gun' *Time* 9th September.

Wilkinson B., Gamble J., Humphrey J. and Morris J. (2001) 'International production networks and human resources: the case of the Malaysia electronics industry' in R. Thorpe and S. Little (eds) *Global Change: The impact of Asia in the 21st Century* London: Palgrave.

Williams R. (1989) 'When was Modernism?' *New Left Review* Vol.175 pp.48-53.

Williamson O.E. (1975) *Markets and Hierarchies* New York: Free Press.

Winterbotham F.W. (1974) *The Ultra Secret* London: Weidenfeld and Nicholson.

Wong S-L. (1996) 'Chinese entrepreneurs and business trust' in G.G. Hamilton (ed) *Asian Business Networks* Berlin: deGruyter.

Woodward J. (1965) *Industrial organisation: theory and practice* Oxford: Oxford University Press.

World Bank (1998) *World Development Report, 1998/99 Knowledge for Development* Oxford: Oxford University Press.

York H. (1976) *The Advisors: Oppenheimmer, Teller and the Superbomb Decision* San Francisco: Freeman.

Yoshino K. (2001) 'India's IT firms shift focus from U.S.' *Nikkei Weekly* 11th June p.20.

Yu T.F. 'Hong Kong's Entrepreneurship: Behaviours and Determinants' *Entrepreneurship and Regional Development* Vol.12 No.3 July pp.179-194.

Yu T.F. and Robertson P.L. (2000) Technological Capabilities and the Strategies of Small Manufacturing Firms: The Case of Hong Kong' in N.J. Foss and P.L. Robertson (eds) *Resource, Strategy and Technology* London: Routledge.

Yuker H.E., Block J.R. and Campbell W.J. (1960) 'A scale to measure attitudes towards disabled persons' *Human Resources Study No 5* Albertson: Human Resources Centre.

Yunus M. (1999) 'The Grameen Bank' *Scientific American* November pp.114-119.

Zeile W. (1996) 'Industrial policy and organizational efficiency: the Korean chaebol examined' in G.G. Hamilton (ed) *Asian Business Networks* Berlin: deGruyter.

Zimmerman J. (1986) *Once Upon the Future: a woman's guide to tomorrow's technology* London: Pandora Press.

Zuboff S. (1988) *In the Age of the Smart Machine* New York: Basic Books.